ANCIENT INDIAN TRADITION AND MYTHOLOGY

Translated by

A BOARD OF SCHOLARS

Edited by

PROF. J.L. SHASTRI

VOLUME 4

ANCIENT INDIAN TRADITION AND MYTHOLOGY

Mahāpurāṇas (100 Vols. Approx.)

Translated into English

ISBN 978-81-208-0289-6

General Editor : **G.C. TRIPATHI**

Founding Eds. Late **J.L. SHASTRI** and Late **G.P. BHATT**

English translation of *Purāṇas* planned in a hundred volume series, of which 74 volumes have appeared so far. Translation of each *Purāṇa* is accompanied by a critical introduction, general index and footnotes

Size: Demy octavo (*Cloth bound with plastic cover*)

PUBLISHED VOLUMES

Vols. 1-4 ŚIVA PURĀṆA Tr. J.L. SHASTRI

Vols. 5-6 LIṄGA PURĀṆA Tr. J.L. SHASTRI

Vols. 7-11 BHĀGAVATA PURĀṆA Tr. G.V. TAGARE

Vols. 12-14 GARUḌA PURĀṆA Tr. J.L. SHASTRI

Vols. 15-19 NĀRADA PURĀṆA Tr. G.V. TAGARE

Vols. 20-21 KŪRMA PURĀṆA Tr. G.V. TAGARE

Vols. 22-26 BRAHMĀṆḌA PURĀṆA Tr. G.V. TAGARE

Vols. 27-30 AGNI PURĀṆA Tr. N. GANGADHARAN

Vols. 31-32 VARĀHA PURĀṆA Tr. S. VENKITASUBRAMANIA IYER

Vols. 33-36 BRAHMA PURĀṆA Tr. J.L. SHASTRI

Vols. 37-38 VĀYU PURĀṆA Tr. G.V. TAGARE

Vols. 39-48 PADMA PURĀṆA Tr. N.A. DESHPANDE

Vols. 49-71 SKANDA PURĀṆA Ed. G.P. BHATT, Tr. & Annot. SHRIDHAR BALOONI & PRATOSH PANDA

Vols. 72-73 VĀMANA PURĀṆA Tr. & Annot. R.S. SHIVA GANESHA MURTHY

Vols. 74-75 GANEŚA PURĀṆA Tr. & Annot. GREG BAILEY

PURANAS UNDER PREPARATION

• Viṣṇu Purāṇa • Brahma-Vaivarta Purāṇa • Bhaviṣya Purāṇa • Matsya Purāṇa • Devī Bhāgavata Purāṇa • Kālikā Purāṇa • Markaṇḍeya Purāṇa • Viṣnudharmottara Purāṇa

THE
ŚIVA-PURĀṆA

Translated and Annotated by

A BOARD OF SCHOLARS

PART IV

MOTILAL BANARSIDASS PUBLISHERS
PRIVATE LIMITED • DELHI

11th Reprint : ***Delhi, 2016***
First Edition: Delhi, 1970

ISBN:978-81-208-0339-8

Also Available at

MOTILAL BANARSIDASS

41 U.A. Bungalow Road, Jawahar Nagar, Delhi 110 007
8 Mahalaxmi Chamber, 22 Bhulabhai Desai Road, Mumbai 400 026
203 Royapettah High Road, Mylapore, Chennai 600 004
236, 9th Main III Block, Jayanagar, Bengaluru 560 011
8 Camac Street, Kolkata 700 017
Ashok Rajpath, Patna 800 004
Chowk, Varanasi 221 001

UNESCO COLLECTION OF REPRESENTATIVE WORKS—*Indian Series*
This book has been accepted in the Indian Translation Series of the UNESCO Collection of Representative Works, jointly sponsored by the United Nations Educational, Scientific and Cultural Organization (UNESCO) and the Government of India

Printed in India

by RP Jain at NAB Printing Unit,
A-44, Naraina Industrial Area, Phase I, New Delhi–110028
and published by JP Jain for Motilal Banarsidass Publishers (P) Ltd,
41 U.A. Bungalow Road, Jawahar Nagar, Delhi-110007

PUBLISHER'S NOTE

The purest gems lie hidden in the bottom of the ocean or in the depths of rocks. One has to dive into the ocean or delve into the rocks to find them out. Similarly truth lies concealed in the language that with the lapse of time has become obsolete. Man has to learn that language before he discovers that truth.

But he has neither the means nor the leisure to embark for that venture. We have therefore planned to help him acquire knowledge by the easier course. We have started the series of *Ancient Indian Tradition and Mythology in English Translation.* Our goal is to universalize knowledge through the most popular, international medium of expression. The publication of the Purāṇas in English translation is the step towards that goal.

PREFACE

The Purāṇic literature constitutes a vast source of ancient Indian tradition, mythology and culture. But it is composed in Sanskrit, an ancient Indian language that has now become obsolete even in the land of its origin. However, there has always existed a general demand for the reproduction of this literature in popular and universal medium of expression. The present interprise is intended to meet this long-felt need.

The origination of the present series on *Ancient Indian Tradition and Mythology* in fifty volumes is due to Shri Sundarlal Jain, the veteran interprizer in the field of oriental publication and the leading proprietor, Messers Motilal Banarsidas. It was at his financing the project envisaged by him that the editors could execute the plan and as a part of it, at first, could bring out Śivapurāṇa in English translation complete in four parts.

Ever since the announcement of the project, an incessant stream of inquiries has been pouring in, which is a happy and auspicious sign of the growing interest, in India and abroad, in the study of ancient Indian literature. And on our part, we are confident that the present series will bring this literature within easy reach of a large number of readers who cannot find access to it otherwise.

Among the works of the Purāṇic literature, Śivapurāṇa has always attracted a large share of interest. Since it embodies the essence of Śiva's cult that has exercised for centuries a wide influence on the multi-tribal Indian community, since it explains the mode of worship of Śiva's phallic idol installed in thousands of temples spread over the vast Indian peninsula, and since it illustrates the elaborate ritual, feasts and fasts connected with Śiva, the start of the series with this purāṇa needs no apology.

The present work, divided into four parts, comprises the complete English translation of Śivapurāṇa. The translation is based on the Sanskrit text as published by the Pandit Pustakalaya, Varanasi. This text follows, with certain emendations, the Bombay text of Kṣemarāja Śrikṛṣṇadāsa and is fairly reliable. Still the text of certain verses constituted from defective manuscripts has proved too conjectural. Naturally, the defective original would defy our efforts for accuracy in translation. But such verses are few and far between; they do not affect the quality of translation as a whole.

Still there is a general question with every translator as to whether the rendering should be close to the original or a little freer. It is a constant dilemma and obviously every translator tries to strike a balance. We believe that the original should be followed as closely as possible without sacrificing the spirit of the language in which it is so rendered. And we have tried to follow this principle as best as we could.

In the process of translation we discovered that on a variety of subjects—geographical, historical, philosophical, religious and the like—the text needed elucidation that could not be covered by a mere translation. We have, therefore, provided footnotes on these topics. The footnotes are brief but illuminative. They supply the background without which an exegesis of the text would not be possible.

A critical introduction has been prefixed to Part I of this Purāṇa. The reader will find therein some interesting and instructive information on the nomenclature, authenticity, date and general characteristics of this work.

In order to make the edition as useful as possible a general index has been appended. It includes among other words, the names of persons, places, rivers, lakes and mountains, of which the identity, already discussed in the footnotes, is marked here by introducing a letter of abbreviation put within the bracket against the name. We have taken care to avoid unnecessary repetition and therefore we have included the constantly recurring names, as those of the deities and sages, only when there is some special reason for specifying them.

Before closing, it is our pleasant duty to put on record our sincere gratitude to Dr. S. K. Chatterjee, Dr. V. Raghavan, Dr. R. N. Dandekar, Shri K. R. Kripalani and the authorities of the UNESCO for their kind encouragement and valuable help which render this work more useful to scholars than it would otherwise have been. We must also thank Shri T. V. Parameswar Iyer for his valuable spade-work which lightened our labours especially in their initial stage.

In fine, we avail of the opportunity to state that any critical suggestions and advice for improvement are welcome and will receive proper consideration from us.

Editors

ABBREVIATIONS (Text)

AGI	Ancient Geography of India : Cunningham
Agni	Agni Purāṇa
AIHT	Ancient Indian Historical Tradition : Pargiter
ASR	Archaeological Survey Report.
AV	Atharvaveda.
Āpg	Āpastamba Gṛhyasūtra
ĀŚS	Āśvalāyana Śrautasūtra
BD.	Brahmāṇḍa Purāṇa
BDH	Baudhāyana Dharmasūtra
Bha	Bhaviṣya Purāṇa
Bhāg	Bhāgavata Purāṇa
Bju	Bhasmajābālopaniṣad
Br.	Brahma Purāṇa
Brah.	Brahmāṇḍa Purāṇa
Bṛs.	Bṛhatsaṁhitā
BV	Brahmavaivarta Purāṇa
Devī Bhāg	Devī bhāgavata Purāṇa
GAMI	Studies in the Geography of Ancient and Medieval India : D. C. Sarkar
Gar.	Garuḍa Purāṇa
GD.	Geographical Dictionary of Ancient and Medieval India. : N. L. Dey
G.Dh.S.	Gautama Dharmasūtra
GEAMI	Geographical Encyclopaedia of Ancient and Medieval India : Bajpai
GP.	Geography of the Purāṇas : S. M. Ali.
H. Dh. Ś	History of Dharmaśāstra : Kane
HIL	History of Indian Literature : Winternitz
HM.	Hindu Mythology : Dowson
HS.	Hindu Saṁskāra : Pandey

JRAS	Journal of the Royal Asiatic Society (Great Britain)
Kā. S.	Kāma Sūtra : Vātsyāyana.
K.P.	Kālikā Purāṇa
KRS	Koṭirudra Saṁhitā (Śp)
KS	Kāṭhaka Saṁhitā
Kumāra	Kumārasambhava
Kūrma	Kūrma Purāṇa
Liṅga	Liṅga Purāṇa
Mahā N.	Mahānārāyaṇa Upaniṣad
Manu	Manusmṛti
Mat	Matsya Purāṇa
Mār	Mārkaṇḍeya Purāṇa
MB	Mahābhārata
MI	Medieval India : Kern
MKP	Mārkaṇḍeya Purāṇa
MMK	Mañjuśrī Mūlakalpa
MNU	Mahānārāyaṇopaniṣad
MP	Matsyapurāṇa—A Study : V. S. Agrawal
MS	Maitrāyaṇī Saṁhitā
MŚ	Mānava-Śrauta-Sūtra
N.	Nirukta
Nār	Nāradīya Purāṇa
Padma	Padma Purāṇa
Pañca	Pañcatantra
PGS	Pāraskaragṛhyasūtra
PM.	Pūrvamīmāṁsā
Raghu	Raghuvaṁśa
RS	Rudrasaṁhitā
ṚV	Ṛgveda
S.C.	Suśruta Cikitsāsthāna
Śiras U.	Śiras Upaniṣad
SK	Skanda Purāṇa
Sṛṣṭi	Sṛṣṭikhaṇḍa of Rudrasaṁhitā of Śivapurāṇa
SSP	Studies in Skandapurāṇa

ŚP	Śiva Purāṇa
ŚP. MB.	Śāntiparva of Mahābhārata
ŚRS	Śatarudra Saṁhitā
Śveta. U.	Śvetāśvatara-Upaniṣad
ŚP. VS	Śiva Purāṇa : Vidyeśvara Saṁhitā
ŚB.	Śatapatha Brāhmaṇa
ŚT.	Śakti Saṅgama Tantra
TĀ	Taittirīya Āraṇyaka
TB	Taittirīya Brāhmaṇa
TU	Taittirīya Upaniṣad
US	Umā Saṁhitā of Śivapurāṇa
Var	Varāha Purāṇa
Vā	Vāyu Purāṇa
Vām	Vāmana Purāṇa
Vāyu	Vāyu or Vāyavīya Saṁhitā of Śivapurāṇa
Vāyavīya	,, ,, ,, ,,
Viṣṇu	Viṣṇu Purāṇa
VS	Vājasaneyisaṁhitā of Śuklayajurveda
Yāj	Yājñavalkya
Yuddha	Yuddhakhaṇḍa of Rudrasaṁhitā of Śivapurāṇa

ABBREVIATIONS (Index)

c = city
f = forest
k = king
l = lake
m = mountain
r = river
t = tribe

CONTENTS

UMĀSAMHITĀ

KAILĀSASAMHITĀ

VĀYAVĪYASAṀHITĀ, SECTION I

VĀYAVĪYASAṀHITĀ, SECTION II

UMĀSAṀHITĀ

CHAPTER TWENTYNINE

(*The primeval creation*)

Śaunaka said:—

1. The great narrative of the conversation of Sanatkumāra and Vyāsa has been heard by me as narrated by you. It has bestowed the knowledge of truth.

2. Now I wish to hear about the creation of Brahmā, the manner of its origin and the way in which you heard it from Vyāsa.

Sūta said :—

3. O sage, listen to the divine story that destroys all sins; the variegated story that is being described by me; the story full of meaning and well known details.

4. He who teaches or hears this story repeatedly sustains his family and is honoured in the world of heaven.

5-6. Puruṣa is eternal and he is of the nature of Sat and Asat as Pradhāna and Puruṣa. The creator of the worlds created Pradhāna after becoming Puruṣa. He created the Creator of all living beings devoted to Nārāyaṇa. O great sage, understand him to be Brahmā of immeasurable strength and prowess.

7. O leading sage, obeisance to that Self-born being from whom the Kalpas and all beings originate.

8. After bowing to that Puruṣa, lord Hiraṇyagarbha, I shall explain the excellent mode of creation again.

9. Brahmā is the creator; Viṣṇu is the protector and Śiva is the annihilator. Even when the time passes there is no other cause of that creation.

10. Being self-born himself the lord, desirous of creating various subjects, created only the waters first. He then instilled virility into them.[1]

11. The waters are called Nāra (belonging to Nara).

1. Manu 1, 8.

The waters are the progenies of Nara. Since waters had been his abode he is called Nārāyaṇa.[2]

12. The Egg floating in the water assumed golden colour. Brahmā himself famous as the self-born was born there.[3]

13. After staying there for a year, lord Hiraṇyagarbha, dichotomised that egg and created heaven and earth.[4]

14. Fourteen worlds were created including those above and below. With the intervening space between those two pieces the lord created the ether.[5]

15. He created the earth floating in the waters and the ten quarters in the firmament. Then he created the mind, the speech, love and anger and the sexual delight.

16. The excessively brilliant creator created seven mental sons, the sages, Marīci, Atri, Aṅgiras, Pulastya, Pulaha, Kratu and Vasiṣṭha.[6]

17. They have been decisively termed the seven Brahmās in the Purāṇas. Brahmā again created the Rudras arising from anger.

18. He created the sage Sanatkumāra too, the eldest of all. They are thus seven born. The Rudras were born afterwards.

19. Sanatkumāra stays with controlled brilliance. From them seven great families originated, all being divine and worshipped by the celestial sages.

20. Endowed with sacred rites they were born along with the other Sages. The lightning, the thunderbolt, the red clouds and the rainbow were created.

21. He created water at the outset. He created the rain-bearing cloud. He created the Ṛks, the Yajus and the Sāmans for facilitating Yajñas.[7]

22. With these he worshipped the gods worthy of being adored. This is what we had heard. He created the gods

2. Ibid. 1. 10.
3. Ibid 1. 9.
4. Ibid. 1. 13-14.
5. Ibid. 1. 13-14.
6. Manu adds Pracetas, Bhṛgu and Nārada Ibid. 1. 35.
7. Manu 1. 23.

from his mouth, the manes from the chest, men through impregnation and the Asuras from his loins.

23. Living beings high and low were born of his limbs as the patriarch Āpava generated the creation of the aquatic beings.

24. When the beings created did not increase he dichotomised his body and became man and woman.[8]

25 With his greatness he persuaded the universe and created the people. Viṣṇu created the Virāṭ (the cosmic being). Thus the Puruṣa Virāṭ was created.[9]

26. Know that he was another Manu that began the age. That lord, Puruṣa, created all the subjects out of Vairāja.

27. The creations of Viṣṇu were not born of womb. They were long-lived, famous, blessed and possessed of progeny.

28. O excellent sage, thus the premeval creation has been narrated to you on knowing which one attains his cherished goal.

CHAPTER THIRTY

(*Description of Creation*)

Sūta said:—

1. When the subjects were created the patriarch Āpava as Puruṣa acquired as his wife Śatarūpā who was not born of womb.[10]

2. With his greatness Āpava enveloped the heaven and stood virtuously. He the noble soul became Śatarūpā thus.

3. She performed a penance for a hundred years and attained the Puruṣa of illumined penance as her husband.

4. The Puruṣa who was born is called Svāyambhuva Manu. His age is said to be seventyone Yugas.

8. Ibid. 1. 32; MP. 3. 31.
9. Manu 1. 32.
10. On the origin of Śatarūpā see HM. under Satarūpā and Virāj PP. 286, 359. For the mystic interpretation of the same see MP—A study P. 47.

5. The intelligent Śatarūpā bore the Vairāja Puruṣa two sons Priyavrata and Uttānapāda of heroic prowess.

6. The blessed lady Kāmyā, wife of the patriarch Kardama, gave birth to three sons Samrāṭ, Sākṣi, and Aviṭprabhu.

7. Lord Uttānapāda begot sons equal to Indra. He begot another son Dhruva of divine nature who had the excellent lustre and the inner bliss.

8. Dharma's daughter, the virtuously born beautiful woman named Sunīti was the mother of Dhruva.

9. Even as a child Dhruva performed penance for three thousand divine years wishing for an imperishable status.

10. Lord Brahmā, being delighted gave him a stable position as his own, facing the seven sages.

11-12 Two sons, Puṣṭi and Dhānya were born of Dhruva. Puṣṭi begot of Samutthā five pious sons viz Ripu, Ripuñjaya, Vipra, Vṛkala and Vṛṣatejas. The queen of Ripu gave birth to Cākṣuṣa Manu.

13-16. Cākṣuṣa Manu begot Varuṇa of Puṣkariṇī. O excellent sage, from Manu of great prowess, in Naḍalā the daughter of the patriarch Vaisyajanma (?) were born ten sons viz Puru, Māsa, Śatadyumna, Tapasvin, Satyavit, Kavi, Agniṣṭoma, Atirātra, Atimanyu and Suyaśas. To Puru, Āgneyī bore six sons of great lustre viz Aṅga, Sumanas, Khyāti, Sṛti, Aṅgiras and Gaya. Sunīthā, wife of Aṅga, bore him a son Vena.

17. Due to the misbehaviour of Vena the pious sages became very furious and killed him by very huṅkāra.[11]

18. Sārasvata Sages were requested by Sunīthā for the birth of a son. They then churned and pressed his right hand.

19. When the hand of Vena was churned Pṛthu was born. He had a bow and a coat of mail even as he was born and was equal to the sun in brilliance.

20. He was indeed an incarnation of Viṣṇu, for protecting the subjects, for the maintenance of virtue and for punishing the wicked.

11. Manu 7. 41.

21. Pṛthu, son of Vena, the ancestor of all Kṣatriyas protected the earth. He was the first lord of Earth, the first among those anointed in the Rājasūya sacrifice.

22. The two efficient persons Śūta and Māgadha were born of him. O great Sage, by him the earth in the form of cow was milked for the common welfare.

23. Performing a hundred sacrifices he as a king become the provider of livelihood to all the gods, sages and Rākṣasas and to men in particular.

24. Two virtuous princes, Vivitāsva and Haryakṣa were born to Pṛthu. They were great heroes who had become very famous.

25. Śikhaṇḍinī gave birth to a son Prācīnabarhis. While he roamed on the earth Kuśa grasses had their tips towards the East.

26. The daughter of the lord of the Ocean was duly married by him. The great lord, shone all the more when he had a wife.

27. Ten sons were born to Prācīnabarhis the great sacrificer, of his wife Samudratanayā.

28. They were Prācetas by name. They had mastered the science of archery. Together they practised virtue and performed penance.

29. They lay sunk in the waters of the ocean for ten thousand years, repeating the Japa of Rudragīta and meditating on Śiva.

30. While they were performing penance trees grew on the earth. When the Earth stood unprotecteu there was a great destruction of subjects.

31. O great king, after attaining boons when they returned they saw the trees. They were furious and wanted to burn them by the power of penance.

32. The Prācetasas created fire and wind from their mouths. The wind uprooted the trees and the fire burnt them.

33. On seeing the destruction of trees and observing that only a few trees were left, the valorous king Soma approached them and said.

Soma said :—

34. O Prācinabarhiṣas, O kings, subdue your anger. This daughter of the trees, Anubhūtā, is a woman of fair complexion.

35. O fortunate ones, she was conceived by me in my womb as I knew the future. Let her be your wife and make the race of the moon flourish.

36. The patriarch Dakṣa will be born of her. He, the ancient son of Brahmā, will become a creator of great brilliance.

37. With half your brilliance, and with half my brilliance this king full of Brahmā's brilliance will make the subjects flourish.

38. Then at the instance of Soma the Pracetasas lovingly took the fair-complexioned lady, daughter of trees, as their wife.

39. To her, through them was born the patriarch Dakṣa. O sage, that boy of great brilliance was born of the moon's parts as well.

40. After creating mentally the mobile and immobile beings, the bipeds and the quadrupeds, Dakṣa began creation though copulatory process.

41. In accordance with the Śāstric injunctions, he virtuously married the daughter of Vīraṇa the partriarch, the chaste lady Vīraṇī.

42. He begot of her ten thousand sons Haryaśvas. At the instance of Nārada they became detached from the world.

43. On hearing of it Dakṣa again begot of her a thousand sons Subalāśvas.

44. Thanks to the instructions of the same sage they too followed the footsteps of their brothers. Unattached and following the path of mendicants they never returned to their parents.

45. On hearing of it he became very furious and cursed the sage thus—O wretch, fond of quarrels, you will never stay permanently anywhere.[12]

12. Repeated. See Ch. 31. Verses 14-15.

46. Consoled by Brahmā, O great sage, he afterwards created women endowed with qualities and in the form of great flames.[13]

47-48. He gave ten daughters to Dharma and thirteen to Kaśyapa, two to Brahmaputra and two to Aṅgiras and two to the learned sage Kṛśāśva. O excellent sage, the remaining twentyseven daughters, named after the constellations lord Dakṣa gave to Soma.[14]

49. Asuras and others were born of the daughters of Dakṣa and had become famous. The universe was filled with them.

50. O great brahmin, the subjects thereafter were born of sexual union. The creation prior to this was through mental concepts, visualisation and touch.

Śaunaka said:—

51. Formerly it was said by you that Dakṣa was born of the thumb of Brahmā. How then did he of great penance become the son of Prācetasa again?

52. O Sūta, it behoves you to clear this doubt of mine. This is also surprising how he attained the status of of the father-in-law of Soma.

Sūta said:—

53. Birth and destruction happen everyday among the mortals. O sage, in every Kalpa these, Dakṣa and others are born again.

54. He who knows this mode of creation of Dakṣa of the mobile and immobile beings becomes endowed with progeny and longevity. After death he is honoured in the heavenly region.

13. The first half of this verse is repeated. See Chs. 31. 15.
14. The Verses 47, 48 are repeated. See Ch. 31. Verses 17, 18.

CHAPTER THIRTYONE

(*Description of the Creation*)

Śaunaka said:—

1. O son of Sūta, tell me quickly about the details of the creation of the gods, Dānavas, Gandharvas, serpents and Rākṣasas.

Sūta said:—

2. When the creation did not multiply, the patriarch asked the daughter of Vīraṇa, endowed with penance, for the purpose of creation.

3. He created different people by the process of copulation. O intelligent one, listen to them. I shall explain in brief.

4. Uniting with her, the powerful patriarch begot of Vīriṇī five thousand sons.

5-6. Nārada, son of Brahmā, had heard at the Satra that the creation can take place only through Kaśyapa in the daughters of Dakṣa. So, on seeing the created sons, the sage Nārada addressed them thus.

7. "You do not know any direction in the world. Without knowing that what can you create ? You are very childish. Proceed only after knowing the world."

8. Thus addressed by him they all proceeded to know the direction by means of their power. Without being able to reach their end they never returned to their father's house.

9. On knowing that he created five hundred sons, Nārada, the visualiser of all, spoke to them also.

Nārada said:—

10. How can you create without knowing the extent of the world ? All of you are childish. What creation do you propose to make ?

Sūta said:—

11. On hearing his words, Subalāśvas, sons of Dakṣa,

as did the Haryaśvas formerly, started in quest of all directions.

12. After reaching Puṣkara and attaining despair due to the endlessness of the world they do not return even now at the rivers from the ocean.

13. Ever since, O sage, if a brother goes in quest of a brother he perishes. That should not be done by any learned man.

14. Realising that his sons had perished, the patriarch Dakṣa cursed the noble soul Nārada in anger.

15. "O wretch, fond of quarrels, you will never stay anywhere permanently. Quarrel will always occur among the people where you happen to be present."

16. We have heard that Dakṣa the patriarch was consoled by Brahmā afterwards and that he begot of Vīriṇī sixty daughters.[15]

17. He gave ten of them to Dharma; thirteen to Kaśyapa; twentyseven to the moon and four to Ariṣṭanemi.

18. Two to the son of Brahmā, two to Aṅgiras and two to the learned Kṛśāśva. Now listen to their names.

19-20. O sage, the wives of Dharma are Arundhatī, Vasu, Yāmi, Lambā, Bhānu, Marutvatī, Saṅkalpā, Muhūrtā, Sādhyā and Viśvā. Now listen to their children. Viśvedevas are the sons of Viśvā, and Sādhyā gave birth to Sādhyas.

21. Marutvats were born of Marutvatī, Vasus were born of Vasu; the suns were born of Bhānu and the Muhūrtajas were born of Muhūrtā.

22. Ghoṣa was born of Lambā; Nāgavīthī was born of Yāmi and Pṛthivīviṣama was born of Arundhatī.

23. Saṅkalpa of the nature of Truth was born of Saṅkalpā. Aya and others were born of Vasu. They are eight. O Śaunaka, listen to them.

15. According to the present text Dakṣa had sixty daughters. Of these he gave 10 to Dharma, 13 to Kaśyapa, 27 to Soma, 4 to Ariṣṭanemin 2 to Brahmaputra, 2 to Aṅgiras and 2 Kṛśāsva. But the assignment is not uniform in all the Purāṇas. For instance MP (5. 13-14) assigns 15 to Kaśyapa instead of 13 and omits 2 of Brahmaputra to complete the given number.

The accomt is found also in RS. Sṛṣṭi. Ch. 16.

24. Aya, Dhruva, Soma, Dhara, Anila, Anala, Pratyūṣa and Prabhāsa are the eight Vasus by name.

25. Aya's sons are Vaitaṇḍa, Śrama, Śānta and Muni. Dhruva's son was lord Kāla influencing the worlds.

26. Soma's son was lord Varcas imparting lustre to others. Dhara's sons were Draviṇa and Hutahavyavaha.

27-28. Manoharā's sons were Śaśira, Prāṇa and Ramaṇa. Anila's wife was Śivā whose sons were Purojava and Avijñātagati. Anila had only two sons. Kumāra was the son of Agni in the grove of Śara grass surrounded by glory.

29. His sons were Śākha, Viśākha and Naigameya. The son of Kṛttikās was called Kārttikeya.[16]

30. Pratyūṣa's son was Devala a sage. Devala had two sons who too had children and who were intelligent.

31-32. Bṛhaspati's sister was a woman of excellence, well-versed in Yoga and she traversed the entire world maintaining celibacy. She became the wife of Prabhāsa the eighth of Vasus. O fortunate one, Viśvakarman the patriarch was born of him.[17]

33. He was the creator of thousands of skilled arts. He is the architect of the gods. He was maker of all sorts of ornaments. He was the foremost among artisans and craftsmen.

34. He built the aerial chariots of all gods. He is a great Ātman whose craft is emulated and made use of by men too.

35-36. According to another version his wife Sarūpā gave birth to crores of Rudras such as Raivata, Aja, Bhava, Bhīma, Vāma, Ugra, Vṛṣākapi, Ajaikapād, Ahirbudhnya, Bahurūpa, Mahat etc. Eleven of them are important. O sage, listen to their names.

16. Kumāra Kārttikeya is one of the four brothers, the other three being Sākha, Viśākha and Naigameya. He is the son of six Kṛttikā mothers and therefore named Kārttikeya and Sāṇmātura (MP. 5 27). The legend is found in all the Śaiva Purāṇas. Prof. Agrawal gives a mystical interpretation of the episode. MP—A study PP. 68-71.

17. The patriarch Viśvakarmā, son of Vasu Prabhāsa, was the craftsman of the gods and entrusted with the work of building chariots, ornaments, palaces etc. MP 5. 27-28, See P. 389 note 295.

37-38. These eleven are the Rudras, lords of the three worlds viz:—Ajaikapād, Ahirbudhnya, Tvaṣṭṛ, the powerful Rudrahara of many forms, Tryambaka, Aparājita, Vṛṣākapi, Śambhu, Kapardin and Raivata.[18]

39. Thus a hundred Rudras of immense prowess have been mentioned to you. Now listen to the names of Kaśyapa's wives, O excellent sage.

CHAPTER THIRTYTWO

(*The family of Kaśyapa*)

Sūta said :—

1-2. O brahmin, they are Aditi, Surasā, Ariṣṭelā, Danu, Surabhi, Vinatā, Ilā, Tāmrā, Krodhavaśā, Kadru and Muni. Now listen to the names of their sons. In the previous excellent Manvantara twelve excellent gods were born.

3-6. They are Tuṣitas. During the intervening period of the Vaivasvata and Cākṣuṣa Manvantaras they consulted one another for the welfare of the worlds. After meeting together they spoke—"We will enter Aditi and be born. This will happen for the welfare of the gods." After conferring they were born of Aditi daughter of Dakṣa and Kaśyapa son of Marīci. Viṣṇu and Indra were born again.

7-9. They along with Aryaman, Dhātṛ, Tvaṣṭṛ, Pūṣan, Vivasvat, Savitṛ, Mitrāvaruṇa, Aṁśa, Bhaga and Atitejas are the twelve Ādityas. Those who were born before as Tuṣitas were born again as the twelve Ādityas in the Cākṣuṣa Manvantara, O Śaunaka thus the names of Aditi's sons have been mentioned to you.

18. Sivapurāṇa proposes to recount the names of eleven Rudras but actually mentions twelve names. As a matter of fact Tvaṣṭā and Bahurūpa are identical names. Compare MP (5. 29-30) where Tvaṣṭā is replaced by its corresponding name Bahurūpa.

In regard to the names of the eleven Rudras the Purāṇas are not unanimous.

10. Dīptis of immeasurable splendour became the children of the twentyseven women of sacred rites and the wives of Soma.

11-12. The children of Ariṣṭanemi's wives were sixteen in number. "O celestial sage, the learned Kṛśāśva had many sons. Four of them are known as Devapraharaṇa. O sage, in his wife Arcis, Dhūmrakeśa too was born.

13. Two wives were Svadhā and Satī of whom Svadhā was the elder and Satī the younger. Svadhā gave birth to the Pitṛs and Satī to the Atharvāṅgirasaveda.

14. At the end of a thousand Yugas these will be born again. All the groups of the gods are thirtythree.

15. Just as the sun rises and sets every day so also the groups of gods are born in every Yuga.

16. We have heard that Hiraṇyakaśipu and Hiraṇyākṣa were born as the sons of Diti and Kaśyapa.

17. Siṁhikā their daughter became the wife of Vipracitti. The four sons of Hiraṇyakaśipu were famous for their strength and prowess.

18. They are Anuhrāda, Hrāda, Saṁhrāda and Prahlāda. The youngest Prahlāda was a devotee of Viṣṇu.

19. Pūloman and Mahiṣa were the sons of Anuhrāda born of Sūryā. Hrāda's wife Dhamani gave birth to Vātāpi and Ilvala.

20. Saṁhrāda's wife Kṛti gave birth to Pañcajana. Virocana was the son of Prahlāda. Bali was born of his queen Devī.

21-22. O great sage, Bali begot hundred sons of his wife Aśanā. He was a great devotee of Śiva. He engaged himself in the activities of devotion to Śiva. He was charitably inclined and liberal-minded. He attained meritorious fame and austerity. His son Bāṇa was foremost among the devotees of Śiva. By propititing Śiva he attained the leadership of Gaṇas.

23. The story of Bāṇa has already been heard by you. In the battle Kṛṣṇa was delighted with him.

24-25 Hiraṇyākṣa's five sons were strong and learned. They were Kukura, Śakuni, Bhūta Santāpana, Mahānāda and Kālanābha. Thus the sons of Diti have been mentioned. O sage, now listen to the names of the sons of Da

26-28. Danu's sons were hundred in number and were of severe exploits. Ayomukha, Śambara, Kapola, Vāmana, Vaiśvānara, Puloman, Vidrāvaṇa, Mahāśira, Svarbhānu, Vṛṣaparvan and the powerful Vipracitti—these were the sons of Danu begot by Kaśyapa. O sage, now listen to the names of their sons. O sinless one, incidentally I shall mention a few of them.

29-30. Prabhā was the daughter of Svarbhānu. Śacī was the daughter of Puloman. So also Upadānavī, Hayaśirā and Śarmiṣṭhā were daughters of Vṛṣaparvan. Pulomā and Pulomikā were the daughters of Vaiśvānara. They were the wives of Kaśyapa son of Marīci and had many heroic sons.

31. Kaśyapa, son of Marīci, endowed with great penance, begot of them sixty thousand sons delighting the Dānavas.

32. Kālakhañjas, the powerful sons of Pulomā, lived in Hiraṇyapura.[19] They could not be killed either by the Dānavas or by the gods.

33. Vipracitti's sons, born of Siṁhikā, were later killed by Arjuna by the grace of Brahmā.

34. Due to the intermixture of Daityas and Dānavas these sons became valorous and famous as Saiṁhikeyas. They are thirteen in number.

35-36. They were the very powerful Rāhu and Śalya, Bala, Mahābala, Vātāpi, Namuci, Ilvala, Svasṛpa, Ajika, Naraka, Kālanābha, Śaramāṇa and Śarakalpa. These increased their races.

37. Many sons and grandsons were born of them increasing the race of Danu. Being innumerable they are not mentioned in detail.

38. In the family of Saṁhrāda the Daiteyas Nivātakavacas and Maruts were born and they were purified by penance.

39-40. Ṣaṇmukha and others are glorified as the sons of Tāmrā. Kākī, Śyenī, Bhāsī, Sugrīvī, Śukī, Gṛdhṛikā, Aśvī, and

19. This city of the Paulomas and Kālakhañjas (or Kālakeyas) as mentioned in the Mahābhārata (Vana P. CLXXIII. 13) and the Kathāsaritsāgara (XLV. 135) stood on the sea-route leading to Pātāla. Its exact locus remains still unidentified.

Ulūkī were the daughters of Tāmrā. Kākī gave birth to crows and Ulūkī to owls.

41. Śyenī gave birth to vultures, Bhāsī to Bhāsas Gṛdhrī to Gṛdhrakas. Śukī gave birth to parrots and Sugrīvī to auspicious birds.

42. Tāmrā the beloved of Kaśyapa gave birth to horses, camels and donkeys. Thus the family of Tāmrā has been described to you.

43. Vinatā had two sons Aruṇa and Garuḍa. The latter was the most excellent among birds. He was terrible by virtue of his activities.

44-47. Surasā gave birth to a thousand serpents of immeasurable power. They had many hoods. They were powerful enough to traverse the sky, the important among them were the kings Śeṣa, Vāsuki and Takṣaka, Airāvata, Mahāpadma, Kambala and Aśvatara. The sons of Ailā were Padma, Karkoṭaka, Dhanañjaya, Mahānīla, Mahākarṇa, Dhṛtarāṣṭra, Balāhaka, Kuhara, Puṣpadanta, Durmukha, Sumukha, Khararoman, Kharapāṇi and many others.

48. Krodhavaśā gave birth to many who were the fanged animals and birds both of land and water. Varā's sons were animals.

49. Anāyuṣā's sons were fifty. They were very strong. The chief amongst them were Bala, Vṛtta, Vikṣara and Bṛhan.

50-51. Surabhi gave birth to rabbits and buffaloes; Ilā to trees, creepers, spreading vines and all kinds of grass; Khaśā gave birth to Yakṣa and Rākṣasas, Muni gave birth to the celestial damsels. Ariṣṭā gave birth to serpents more excellent than human beings in their power.

52. O great sages, thus the descendants of Kaśyapa have been explained to you. They had hundreds of sons and grandsons.

CHAPTER THIRTYTHREE

(*Description of the creation*)

Sūta said:—

1-5. Such is the creation as mentioned in the Manvantara, Svārociṣa, O dear. Now I shall describe the creation as evolved by Brahman while offering oblations in the elaborate Vāruṇa sacrifice in the great Vaivasvata Manvantara. All the Brahmarṣis born in the beginning, Pitāmaha made his mental sons. When a great fight ensued between the gods and the Dānavas, Diti lost all her sons. She approached Kaśyapa and propitiated him. The delighted Kaśyapa asked her to choose a boon as she pleased. She chose the boon that she be favoured with a son of immeasurable power capable of slaying Indra.

6. He granted her the boon of her choice. The sage of great penance advised her celibacy and other restraints for a hundred years.

7. The pious fair-comlexioned lady conceived. She began to observe celibacy and other restraints.

8. After impregnating Diti, Kaśyapa of noble sacred rites went away satisfied for the performance of penance.

9. Indra waited for finding out a weak point in her. He found one such when the period of hundred years was short by a year.

10. Due to the gravity of the event destined to happen, once Diti did not wash her feet. She went to sleep with head hanging down.

11. In the meantime Indra entered her belly with the thunderbolt. He cut off the foetus into seven pieces.

12. While being split into seven the foetus began to cry in seven different tones. Indra told the foetus "Do not cry, Do not cry" repeatedly. He cut them again but they did not die.[20]

13. O sage, being felled down they told him with

20. For full details of the legend see MP. Ch. 7.

Maruts are so called that when Indra split the foetus of Diti they cried and did not stop. Then Indra ordered them not to weep, hence they became known as Maruts.

palms joined in reverence. "O Indra, why do you wish to kill us? We are your brothers, the Maruts."

14. O brahmin sage, at the will of Śiva, they eschewed their Daitya nature. They were accepted by Indra with due fraternity.

15. In the name of Maruts they became gods of great prowess. Thus traversing the sky the fortynine Maruts became assistants of Indra.

16. When they flourished, Viṣṇu the patriarch, offered them kingdoms beginning with Pṛthu. Listen to that.

17. Ariṣṭa was the heroic person. Kṛṣṇa the patriarch was ever victorious. Parjanya was the presiding deity of clouds. This entire universe belongs to him.

18. O great sage, I have explained the creation of living beings to you. Listen to the division of kingdoms. I shall explain that duly now.

19. After crowning Pṛthu the son of Vena in the emperorship, Brahmā began to assign the kingdoms in due order.

20. He crowned Soma in the kingdom of birds, creepers, stars, planets, sacrifices and austerities.

21. He crowned Varuṇa in the kingdom of waters; Vaiśravaṇa as the lord of kings; Viṣṇu as the lord of Ādityas and Pāvaka as the lord of Vasus.

22. He crowned Dakṣa as the lord of patriarchs, Indra as the lord of Maruts, and Prahlāda of great strength as the lord of Daityas and Dānavas.

23. He crowned Vaivasvata Yama in the kingdom of Pitṛs, Mātṛs, Vratas, Mantras and cows.

24. He crowned the trident-bearing Śiva, in the kingdom of Yakṣas, Rākṣasas, kings, goblins and ghosts.

25. He crowned Himavat as the lord of mountains, the ocean of rivers, the tiger of deer and Bull as the lord of cows.

26. He crowned the banyan tree in the kingdom of plants and trees. Thus the kingdom was assigned everywhere by the lord of subjects.

27. The lord of the universe, the soul of all, established the son of patriarch Vairāja in the kingdom in the east.

28. Similarly, O great king, he established Sudhanvan, son of Kardama, the patriarch, in the kingdom in the south.

29. The lord directed and assigned the unfailing noble-minded son of Rajas, Ketumat as the king in the kingdom in the west.

30. He crowned the indefatigable son of Parjanya the patriarch, Hiraṇyaroman, in the kingdom in the north.

31. O Śaunaka, the details of Pṛthu the son of Vena have been narrated to you. This base is glorified as the most ancient spot of great prosperity.

CHAPTER THIRTYFOUR

(*The enumeration of Manvantaras*)

Śaunaka said:—

1. Please describe in detail all the Manvantaras. I wish to hear of all the Manus too.

Sūta said:—

2-3. O great sage, six Manus have already been mentioned to you viz. Svāyambhuva, Svārociṣa, Uttama, Tāmasa, Raivata and Cākṣuṣa. The present Manu is called Vaivasvata, O great sage.

4-6. The Manus of future are Sāvarṇi, Raucya, Brahmasāvarṇi, Dharmasāvarṇi, Rudrasāvarṇi, Devasāvarṇi and Indraāsvarṇi. All these constitute the Manus of the past, present and future. These have been enumerated by me as I have heard.

7. O sage, these fourteen Manvantaras extending over the period past, present and the future have been mentioned to you. A Kalpa consisting of a thousand Yugas is constituted by these.

8. O Saunaka, listen. I shall explain the sages, their sons and the gods; all are famous. Listen with pleasure.

9. Marīci, Atri, the holy lord Aṅgiras, Pulaha, Kratu, Pulastya and Vasiṣṭha—these seven are Brahmā's sons.

10. O sage, the seven sages are in the northern quarter. In the Svāyambhuva Manvantara there were the gods named Yāmas.

11-12. The ten noble-souled sons of Svāyambhuva Manu were—Āgnīdhra, Agnibāhu, Medhā, Medhātithi, Vasu, Jyotiṣmat, Dhṛtimat, Havya, Savana and Śubhra. O great sage, the Indra there was Yajña.

13. Thus O dear, the first divine Manvantara has been mentioned to you. I shall explain the second one. Know as it is.

14-15. In the second Svārociṣa Manvantara these must be known as the great sages, viz-Ūrjastambha, Parastambha, Ṛṣabha, Vasumat, Jyotiṣmat, Dyutimat and the seventh Rociṣmat. Then the Indra was Rocana. The gods were known as Tuṣitas.

16-17. O great sage, the ten noble-minded sons of Svārociṣa Manu, all of great heroism and exploits were Harighna, Sukṛti, Jyotis, Ayomūrti, Ayasmaya, Prathita, Manasyu, Nabha and Sūrya.

18. O sage, the second Manvantara has been mentioned by me. I shall explain the third one. Know it factually.

19-20. Vasiṣṭha's seven sons famous as Vāsiṣṭhas and Hiraṇyagarbha's sons of great splendour known as Ūrjas are mentioned as the sages. Uttama the Manu had ten sons, O great sage.

21-22. They were Iṣa, Ūrjita, Ūrja, Madhu, Mādhava Śuci, Śukravaha, Nabhasa, Nabha and Ṛṣabha. The gods were Satyavedaśruta and others. O sage, the Indra then was Satyajit. He was the ruler of the three worlds.

23. The great third Manvantara has been explained. O sage, listen. I shall mention the fourth Manvantara.

24. The seven sages were Gārgya, Pṛthu, Vāgmin, Janya, Dhātā, Kapīnaka and the seventh Kapīvat. The groups of gods were Satyas.

25-26. The Indra there was Triśikha. O sage, listen to the names of Manu's sons. The ten sons of great rites of the Manu Tāmasa were Dyutipota, Sautapasya, Tapaḥśūla, Tāpana, Taporati, Akalmāsa, Dhanvin, Khaḍgin, Mahat and Ṛṣi.

27. The fourth Manvantara of Tāmasa Manu has been mentioned to you. O dear, now listen to the great fifth Manvantara.

28-29. Devabāhu, Jaya, the sage Vedaśiras, Hiraṇyaroman, Parjanya, Ūrdhva Bāhu, Somapa—These and others constituted the seven sages. They were engaged in truth. The gods were Bhūtarajasas of the nature of performing penance.

30. Indra was named Vibhu and he was the lord of the three worlds. The name of the Manu was Raivata. He shall be known as the brother of Tāmasa.

31. O sage, Arjuna, Paṅktivindhya and others shall be known as his sons. They are endowed with great penance. They stay on the mountain Meru.

32. Raucya son of Ruci the patriarch was the Manu. His son born of the queen Bhūti was Bhautya.

33. The future Manus in this Kalpa will be seven. The future great sages will also be seven in each Manvantara in the heaven.

34. Rāma, Vyāsa, Ātreya, Dīptimat, Subahuśruta, Bharadvāja, and the lustrous Aśvatthāman son of Droṇa will be seven sages in this Manvantara.

35-37. Śaradvat son of Gautama, Gautama, Kṛpa, Kauśika, Gālava, Ruru and Kaśyapa will be future seven sages. The future gods are three in number as mentioned by Svayambhu. They are the sons of the noble-souled Kaśyapa the son of Marīci. Bali the son of Virocana will become their Indra.

38-39. O Śaunaka, the future ten sons of Sāvarṇi the Manu will be Viṣāṅga, Avanīvat, Sumanta, Dhṛtimat, Vasu, Sūri, Sura, Viṣṇu, Rājā and Sumati. Thus the eighth Manvantara has been mentioned. Now listen to the ninth Manvantara.

40-42. I shall mention Dakṣasāvarṇi Manu at the outset. Listen. Medhātithi, Paulastya, Vasu, Kaśyapa, Jyotiṣmat, Bhārgava, Dhṛtimat, Aṅgiras, Savana son of Vasiṣṭha, Havya son of Atri, and Pulaha—these seven are the sages in the Rauhita Manvantara. O great sage, the groups of gods are three.

43-44. They are the sons of the patriarch Rohita, son

of Dakṣa. These are the nine sons of great strength of the first Sāvarṇi—Dhṛṣṭaketu, Dīptaketu, Pañcahasta, Nirākṛti, Pṛthuśravas, Bhūridyumna, Ṛcīka, Bṛhata and Gaya.

45-47. In the tenth Manvantara of the second Sāvarṇi the following are the sages, viz. Haviṣmat, Pulaha, Prakṛti, Bhārgava, Āya, Mukti, Ātreya and the imperishable Vasiṣṭha along with the seven great sages viz, Paulastya, Prayati, Bhāmāra, Kaśyapa, Aṅgirā, Anenasa, and Satya. Those known as Dviṣimant are the groups of gods.

48-49. Śambhu, Maheśvara himself is as their Indra. The ten sons of the Manu are Akṣatvat, Uttamaujas, Bhūriṣeṇa the powerful, Śatānīka, Nirāmitra, Vṛṣasena, Jayadratha, Bhūridyumna, Suvarcā and Arcis.

50. In the eleventh Manvantara of the third Sāvarṇi there are seven sages. Understand them as they are glorified by me.

51-52. Haviṣmat Kaśyapa, Vapuṣmat Vāruṇa, Ātreya, Vasiṣṭha, Anaya, Aṇgiras, Cārudhṛṣya, Paulastya, Niḥsvara, Taijasa Agni. The first seven are the sages and the last three groups are of gods.

53-54. There are the sons of Brahmā known as Vaidhṛtas. The grandsons of Sāvarṇa and the sons of the third Sāvarṇi are—Sarvaga, Suśarman, Devānīka, Kṣemaka, Dṛḍheṣu, Khaṇḍaka, Darśa, Kuhu and Bāha, nine in all.

55-57. Now know the seven sages of the fourth Sāvarṇi from me—Dyuti son of Vasiṣṭha, Ātreya of good penance, Angiras an embodied form of penance, Kaśyapa the ascetic. Paulastya the sage, Pulaha interested in penance and Bhārgava the storehouse of penance. The groups of gods are known as five and they are the mental sons of Brahmā.

58-60. The Indra then is Ṛtadhāman. He is the happy ruler of the three worlds. In the future twelfth Manvantara, O, sage, the seven great sages are Dhṛtimat, Angiras, Havyavat Paulastya, Tattvadarśin Paulaha, Nirutsava Bhārgava, Niṣprapañca Ātreya, Nirdehạ, Kāśyapa and Sutapa the descendant of Vasiṣṭha.

61-62. The groups of gods are three in number as mentioned by Svayambhū. They are: Divaspati Indra, Vicitra and Citra. Naya, Dharmadhṛta, Andhra, Sunetra, Kṣatravṛddhaka, Nirbhaya, and Sutapas Droṇa are the sons of Raucya Manu.

63-65. In the fourteenth Manvantara of Satya Manu the seven sages are Āgnīdhra Kāśyapa, Māgadha, Paulastya Atibāhya Bhārgava, Śuci Aṅgirasa, Yukta Ātreya, Ajita grandson of Vasiṣṭha, and Pulaha. They are the final seven sages. The gods are the holy Cākṣuṣas. Śuci will become Indra.

66. After getting up early in the morning the repetition of the names of these sages of the past and future increases the happiness of men.

67-68. O great sage, listen. The groups of gods are five. The sons of this Manu are—Taraṅgabhīru, Budhna, Tanūgra, Anugra, Abhimānin Pravīṇa, Viṣṇu, Saṅkrandana, Tejasvin, and Sabala.

69. The earlier Kalpa is in the authority of Bhauma, Thus I have explained the Manus past and future.

70-71. These were mentioned to Vyāsa by Sanatkumāra of great splendour. When the thousand Yugas are complete they, of good penance, return to Brahmaloka when their task of protecting the people is over. Each Manvantara consists of seventy one Yugas with some period left over.

72. These fourteen Manus are glorified. In each Manvantara there is re-creation after annihilation.

73. It is difficult to explain Manvantara even in hundreds of years. The Kalpa that follows a hundred thousand Kalpas is named Niśśeṣa.

74-75. There all the living beings are burnt by the sun's rays. O sage, all of them enter Viṣṇu at the end of Kalpas along with the Ādityas. Viṣṇu then creates all living beings. This happens again and again.

76-77. Lord Rudra annihilates them I shall explain it at the end of Vaivasvata Kalpa. Thus I have mentioned all about the Manvantaras to you. It is a holy narrative condusive to wealth and increase of the family.

CHAPTER THIRTYFIVE

(*The description of Vaivasvata*)

Sūta said:—

1. Vivasvat was born of Dakṣa's daughter and Kaśyapa the great sage. His wife was Saṁjñā, daughter of Tvaṣṭṛ and also known as Sureṇukā.

2. Due to the unbearable heat of her husband she in her prime of youth was dissatisfied.

3. Being scorched and not being able to hear the brilliance of the lustrous sun, the fair-complexioned lady was excited and sorrowful.

4-5. O sage, the sun begot three offsprings of her: the patriarch Manu Śrāddhadeva, Yama and Yamunā born as twins.

6. On seeing the brilliance of the sun as unbearable as the fire at the final dissolution she created Chāyā of herself.

7. She of illusory form told Saṁjñā : "O sweet-smiled auspicious lady, what shall I do for you, please tell me".

Saṁjñā said:—

8. "Welfare unto you. I go to my father's house alone. Indeed you have to stay in this house without aberration.

9. These two well-behaved sons and this pretty girl should be happily protected if you wish to please me."

Chāyā said:—

10. "O lady, I shall brook their misdeeds even as much as pulling out my hair. I shall make no complaint to you. O goddess, you can go away happily."

Sūta said:—

11. Ashamed on being addressed thus, the lady went to her father's house but was rebuked by him. He urged her again and again to return to her husband.

12. She assumed the form of a mare. Going to Northern Kurus she wandered among the people.

13. The sun took her for Saṁjñā and begot of her a son the Manu Sāvarṇi.

14. Though requested by Saṁjñā, Chāyā did not love the elder children. She loved her own son more and fondled him always.

15. The younger brother Yama could not bear that. He did not forgive. Ever since childhood he was furious and and ill-tempered due to the gravity of what was destined to happen later.

16. When Yama, son of Vivasvat threatened Chāyā she became infuriated and cursed him angrily.

17. Due to excessive anger she cursed—"Let your leg fall off". Yama approached his father with palms joined in reverence and said.

18-20. "I was agitated due to Chāyā's words. I am sorry and frightened of the curse. I had only said that a mother shall have impartial and equal love for all her children. She has lost affection for us. She nurtures only the youngest one. Hence I raised my foot. It behoves you to forgive me. O lord of gods, O foremost among the refulgent ones, I have been cursed by my mother. O lord of rays, let not my leg fall off by your grace."

The sun said:—

21. O son, there shall be a great cause for this. That was why you too who know virtue and speak the truth had been infuriated.

22. It is not possible to make your mother's words false. Worms will take away the flesh from your leg and go to the earth.

23. Her words will come up true and you will also be saved. Have no doubt, O deer, cheer up your mind, O lord.

Sūta said:—

24. O great sage, after saying thus to his son Yama, the sun angrily spoke to Chāyā.

The sun said :—

25. O beloved wife, O evil-minded angry lady, what it is that you have done ? Why do you love one son more ? You shall tell me.

Sūta said:—

26. On hearing the words of the sun she told him the truth. Scorched by him she consoled him thus.

Chāyā said:—

27. This fierce form of yours was not pleasant to Saṁjñā. She was scorched by your excessive brilliance. She could not bear it. She now resides on the grassy plain in a forest.

28. O lord of rays, she is endowed with the power of Yoga. She has resorted to yogic practice. She is praiseworthy. O lord of gods, be favourable to her by sending the message of your opinion.

29. I shall change your form. I shall make it pleasingly brilliant.

Sūta said:—

On hearing this, the sun was appeased.

30. The sage Tvaṣṭṛ put him on the turner's lathe and sharpened him further. His blazing form was slightly reduced in brilliance.

31. When the form was made more pleasingly brilliant by Tvaṣṭṛ it shone splendidly. Then resorting to Yogic practice he saw his wife Saṁjñā.

32. He assumed the form of a horse and approached her for sexual indulgence with her who could not be overwhelmed by any living being due to her lustre and observance of restraint.

33. O sage, in the course of the sexual activity she suspected him to be another man. Hence she received the semen through the mouth into the nostril.

34. Thence were born the twin gods Aśvins, the foremost among physicians. They are known as Nāsatyas and Dasras.

35. The sun showed his pleasingly splendid form to them. On seeing her husband she was extremely delighted.

36. The chaste lady returned to the house with her husband with the face beaming with pleasure. The pair rejoiced more than before.

37. This incident distressed the mind of Yama. As pious king he gladdened the subjects virtuously.

38. Yama of great lustre attained the lordship of the names and the guardianship of the quarters.

39. Sāvarṇi Manu became the patriarch. In the Sāvarṇika Manvantara he will become the future Manu by virtue of his action.

40-42. The lord is performing penance even today on the top of Meru[21]. Their younger sister, the famous Yamī, became the most excellent river Yamunā, the sanctifier of all the worlds. He is called Sāvarṇi Manu in the world. He who listens to or retains in memory this origin of the gods attains great fame. Should he suffer from any adversity he will be rid of it.

CHAPTER THIRTYSIX

(*The description of the nine sons and the race of Manu*)

Sūta said:—

1. Nine sons all equal to him were born of Vaivasvata Manu. Later they became very lofty, bold and devoted to the virtues of Kṣatriyas.

2. They were Ikṣvāku, Śibi, Nābhāga, Dhṛṣṭa, Śaryāti, Nariṣyanta, Nabhaga, Karūṣa and Priyavrata.[22]

3-5. Desirous of sons, Manu the patriarch performed a sacrifice. O great sage, when no sons were born as a result of the sacrifice, the famous Ilā was born, wearing divine garments, bedecked in divine ornaments and with a

21. See P. 310 not and P. 623 note.

22. There is no consensus of opinion in the Purāṇas about the names. Pargiter who collated the Puranic texts on the topic suggested the following names इक्ष्वाकु, नाभाग, घृष्ट, शर्याति, नरिष्यन्त, करूष, प्रांशु, नाभानेदिष्ट and पृषध्र· ŚP agrees in respect of the first five but it substitutes. शिबि, नाभाग (·द्वितीय) and प्रियव्रत प्रांशु, for नाभानेदिष्ट and पृषध्र· Probably the second नाभाग is identical with नाभनेदिष्ट. The identification of शिबि and प्रियव्रय with प्रांशु पृषघ is douhtful.

divine body. Manu the chastiser addressed her as Ilā and said "Follow me". Ilā replied to him.

Ilā said:—

6. She spoke these words to the patriarch desirous of a son—"O foremost among the eloquent, I am born of the parts of Mitra and Varuṇa.

7-9. I am approaching them. I shall never be interested in sinful things." After saying this, the chaste lady approached Mitra and Varuṇa and spoke with palms joined in reverence "O great sages, I am born in the sacrifice of Manu through your parts. I have come to you. Please tell me. What I can do for you. O lord, create other sons so that your race may flourish."

Sūta said:—

10. When the chaste lady born in the sacrifice of Manu said, the sages Mitra and Varuṇa spoke thus respectfully.

Mitra and Varuṇa said:—

11. O virtuous beautiful lady of fair complexion, both of us are pleased with your self-control, humility and truth.

12. O blessed lady, you will attain our fame. You alone will become the son establishing the family of Manu.

13. You will be famous in the three worlds as Sudyumna, beloved of the universe, virtuous in conduct and enhancer of the race of Manu.

Sūta said:—

14. On hearing that she returned to her father's presence. On the way, getting an opportunity, Budha invited her for sexual intercourse.

15. King Purūravas was born of her out of the union with Budha. O intelligent one, this son was the handsome and intelligent man who later became the husband of Urvaśī.

16. After bearing the son Purūravas she became Sudyumna as a result of Śiva's grace.

17. Sudyumna had three very virtuous heirs Utkala, Gaya and the powerful Vinatāśva.

18. O brahmin, O great sage, Utkala was assigned the country Utkala;[23] Vinatāśva was given the territories on the West and Gaya was given Gayā and the eastern territories.

19. O dear, when Manu passed away, the earth was divided into ten regions.

20-24. Ikṣvāku the eldest son got the central territory. At the instance of Vasiṣṭha, Sudyumna gave the virtuous territory Pratiṣthāna[24] to Purūravas. O grart sages, Sudyumna had the characteristics of both man and woman. The Śakas were the sons of Nariṣyanta. Nabhaga's son Ambarīṣa got the region Bāhlaka[25] and so was known as Bāhleya. Śaryāti had a son and a daughter. The son was known as Ānarta and the daughter as Sukanyā who later became the wife of Cyavana. Ānarta's son was Raibhya known also as Raivata.

25. In the territory[26] of Ānarta he got the city Kuśasthalī which was extremely brilliant and was the seventh among seven cities.

26. He had a hundred sons of whom the eldest and the most excellent was Kakudmin. He was brilliant, strong, virtuous and a protector of brahmins.

27. A daughter Revatī was born to Kakudmin. She was endowed with great beauty, She was another Lakṣmī.

28. The king Kakudmin the lord of all went to

23. It is modern Orissa.

24. Here Pratiṣthāna is Prayāga but the Purāṇas are not agreed upon its locus. Some place it on the north and some on the east side of the Ganges. Others place it on the north bank of the Yamunā.

There is another Pratiṣṭhāna=Paiṭhan in the Aurangabad District of the former Hyderabad State.

25. Bāhlaka is identical with modern Balkh in the northern part of Afghānistan. See KM Ch. XVII.

26. It is identical with Gujrat and part of Malavā. Its chief city was Kuśasthalī also called Dvārakā.

Brahmā's region near Brahmā, accompanied by his daughter in order to ask him about a suitable bridegroom for her.

29. While dance and music was going on, he stood there waiting for a moment near Brahmā.

30. Although it was only a Muhūrta in Brahmā's region many Yugas had passed by. But O sages, the king Kakudmin did not know anything about it.

31. Then he bowed to Brahmā the great Ātman, humbly and with palms joined in reverence told him about his mission.

32. On hearing his purpose the patriarch Brahmā laughed. Addressing the great king Kakudmin, he said.

Brahmā said:—

33. Listen, O King Kakudmin, O lord of the earth, son of Raibhya, to my words with attention. I shall tell you the truth particularly.

34. All those bridegrooms you had in view have been killed by the efflux of time. Even their family is extinct. Time is the devourer of everything.

35. O king, your city too has been destroyed by Puṇyajanas, the Rākṣasas. It is now the twenty-eighth Dvāpara Yuga and the city has been rebuilt by Kṛṣṇa.

36. In the name of Dvāravatī because it has many entrances, it is very beautiful. It is protected by the Bhojas, Vṛṣṇis and Andhakas with Kṛṣṇa as their leader.

37. O king, now go there and give this daughter of yours to Baladeva the son of Vasudeva.

Sūta said:—

38. Thus commanded, the king bowed to him and went to that city. On realising that many Yugas had elapsed he was surprised along with his daughter.

39. Then he gave his daughter, the youthful maiden, Revatī to Bala the brother of Kṛṣṇa in conformity with the Śāstric rituals.

40. Then he, the great lord, went to the celestial summit of Meru and propitiated Śiva observing penance.

The sages said:—

41. Raivata stayed in Brahmā's region for many Yugas. He returned to the mortal world as a young man. This is my great doubt.

Sūta said:—

42. O sages, near Brahmā there is no old age, hunger, thirst, aberration or premature death to any one.

43. Therefore the king did not attain old age or death, nor his daughter. After consulting Brahmā about the bridegroom he returned still a young man.

44. Going to the divine city Dvāravatī[27] rebuilt by Kṛṣṇa, he got his daughter married to Bala.

45. Hundred sons were born to that virtuous great lord. Through many wives Kṛṣṇa too had innumerable sons.

46. The family of the two noble souls was very great. All the Kṣatriyas in every quarter became delighted and virtuous.

47. Thus the race of Śaryāti has been narrated to you. O brahmins, I shall succinctly mention the details of others too. Listen attentively.

48. Nābhāga had a son Dhṛṣṭa. After establishing the Kṣatriya race and performing the brahminical rites he attained brahminhood.

49. Dhṛṣṭa's race originally Kṣatriya became brahmin family on the earth. Karūṣa's descendants the Kārūṣas were Kṣatriyas, insubjugable in war.

50. Nṛga who was also a son of Manu was a liberal donor of riches to brahmins and of cows.

51. Once due to an error in his charitable gift of a cow, prompted by his own sins and crooked intellect, he became a chameleon and was redeemed by Śrīkṛṣṇa.

52. An excellent son was born to him named Prayāti, the knower of virtues. This I have heard from Vyāsa and have now briefly mentioned to you.

53. Pṛṣadhra, a son of Manu was made the keeper of

27. See P. 1229 note 90.

cows by his preceptor. During the nights, observing the posture of heroes, he diligently looked after the cows.

54. Once a tiger entered the cowshed to attack the cows. On hearing the shrieks of the cows he woke up. Strong that he was he seized a sword to kill it and started.

55. On seeing the lord armed with a sword the frightened tiger slipped away. Not knowing it and mistaking a reddish brown cow as the tiger he hit it with his sword on its head.

56. Due to rain and gust of wind in the night he was deluded. Thinking that the tiger had been killed he returned to his place.

57. When the night dawned into day he got up and went there. He saw only the cow killed and not the tiger. He felt dejected.

58. On hearing about the incident and realising that he had committed a sin unconsciously and not wilfully, the preceptor cursed him—"Become a Śūdra, not a Kṣatriya."

59. On being cursed by his preceptor, the family priest out of anger, Pṛṣadhra started from there and went to the great forest.

60. Dejected by sufferings he became detached and practised Yoga. He burnt himself in conflagration and attained the greatest goal.

61. Kavi, son of Manu, was highly intelligent due to Śiva's blessings. After enjoying divine pleasures here he attained the rare salvation hereafter.

CHAPTER THIRTYSEVEN

(*The race of Manu*)

Sūta said:—

1. Formerly Ikṣvāku was born as the son of Manu through the nose. He had a hundred sons who were liberal in bestowing gifts.

2. Before them O brahmins, there were no kings in Āryāvarta. Of them the eldest was Vikukṣi. He became the king of Ayodhyā.

3-4. Listen to one of his misdeeds. He wanted to perform Śrāddha but before performing the same he ate a rabbit and came to be known as Śaśāda. Abandoned by Ikṣvāku, he entered a forest.

5. When Ikṣvāku passed away he was installed a king at the instance of Vasiṣṭha. He had fifteen sons of whom the chief was Śakuni.

6. They all became kings and protectors of the northern country. Ayodha's son was the powerful king Kakutstha.

7. Kakutstha's son was Arinābha. His son was Pṛthu. Pṛthu's son was Viṣṭarāśva. From him was born Indra the lord of people.

8. Indra's son was Yuvanāśva, the ruler of Śrāvasta. His son was Śrāvastaka who built Śrāvasti.[28] Śrāvastaka's son was Bṛhadaśva.

9. His son was Yuvanāśva and Kuvalāśva was his son. Since he slew Dhundhu he became the excellent king Dhundhumāra.

10-11. Kuvalāśva had hundred sons who were excellent archers. He was entrusted with the kingdom by his father. After transferring the royal glory to the son the king entered the forest. But Uttaṅka prevented him.

Uttaṅka said:—

12-14. Listen. You shall protect the earth virtuously. O king, only when protected by you can the earth be relieved of excitement and sorrow. It does not behove you to go to the forest. There is a Dānava, proud of his strength near my hermitage, in the snow-covered wilderness, full of sea-sand. He is indestructible even to the gods. He has a huge body and is very strong.

15. He stays underground concealed by the sand. The terrible Rākṣasa son of the demon Madhu is Dhundhu by name.

28. This celebrated city is situated in the modern gonda district of Uttara Pradesh

16. He stays there performing a terrible penance for the destruction of the worlds. At the end of every year he exhales terribly.

17. When he exhales, the whole world including mountains, forests and wilderness, quakes. Blazing flames with pink smoke smoulder everywhere.

18. Hence, O king, I cannot stay in my hermitage. O strong one with huge arms ward him off desiring the welfare of the worlds.

19. Let the wordls become happy and peaceful after he had been killed by you. O lord of earth, you alone can slay him.

20. O sinless one, a great boon has been granted to you. Viṣṇu will heighten your splendour by his own splendour.

21. Great virtue accrues from the protection of the subjects. A similar opportunity is wanting in the forest. Let not your mind be directed that way.

22. O leading king, nowhere such a virtue exists as it does in the protection of the subjects. This has been pursued by the saintly kings of yore.

23. Thus requested the saintly king entrusted his son Kuvalāśva with the task of thwarting Dhundhu.

24. "O holy lord, O excellent brahmin, I have already laid aside my weapons. Here is my son who will surely destroy Dhundhu."

25. Having said thus and instructed his son the king proceeded with penance. Kuvalāśva accompanied by Uttaṅka went to fight with Dhundhu.

26. At the approach of Uttaṅka and for the benefit of the worlds, lord Viṣṇu entered him with his splendour.

27. When the invincible Kuvalāśva started there was a loud shout in the heaven. "This glorious prince will slay Dhundhu."

28. The gods surrounded him with garlands of flowers. They praised him saying "Be victorious, Be long-lived."

29. The most excellent among the victorious, the king went there accompanied by his sons. He caused an ocean to be dug in the midst of that vast expanse of sand.

30. O brahminical sage, heightened in strength by the splendour of Viṣṇu he became very brilliant and stronger.

31. O brahmin, the demon Dhundhu was found out, concealed beneath the sand towards the western quarter as the sons of the king dug up the place.

32. He appeared to consume all the worlds out of fury in the fire emerging from his mouth. Water too gushed out from him as from the moon-stone at the moonrise.

33. The hundred sons were scorched and burnt in the fire. O great sage, among them only three survived.

34. O leading brahmin, then the king of great splendour rushed at the very powerful Rākṣasa, the brahmin-slayer Dhundhu.

35. The king quaffed off the gushing water through fiery arrows and quelled the fire through water.

36. After killing the aquatic demon of huge body with his strength, the king requested Uttaṅka to survey his work.

37. O great sage, Uttaṅka granted him boons. He gave him never-ending wealth and invincibility to enemies.

38. He blessed him with interest in virtue, perpetual residence in the heaven and the imperishable world to his sons who were killed in the battle.

39. Three of his sons survived. The eldest of them was Dṛḍhāśva. Haṁsāśva and Kapilāśva were younger princes.

40. Haryaśva was the son of Dṛḍhāśva who was the son of Dhundhumāra. Nikumbha who was always engaged in sacred rites was the son of Haryaśva.

41. Saṁhatāśva an expert in war was the son of Nikumbha. Akṣāśva and Kṛtāśva were the sons of Saṁhatāśva.

42. He had two daughters Haimavatī and Dṛṣadvatī honoured by the good. She was famous in the three worlds. Her son was Prasenajit.

43. Prasenajit had a chaste wife Gaurī.[29] She was cursed by her husband and turned into the river Bāhudā.

44. His great son was Yuvanāśva, the lord of the earth. Māndhātā famous in the three worlds was Yuvanāśva's son.

45-46. Śaśabindu's daughter the chaste Caitrarathī was his wife. She was the eldest sister of ten thousand brothers. Māndhātā begot of her two sons, Purukutsa, the knower of sacred rites and Mucukunda the righteous.

47. Purukutsa's son was Trayyāruṇi. His son was Satyavrata.

48-50. He was evil-minded. Whenever sacred mantras were recited he put obstacles. After the marriage was celebrated he abducted the brides of others with force, out of lust, delusion, fun or arrogance. He abducted the virgins to satisfy his lust. The king Trayyāruṇi forsook him for such evil practices. Infuriated he called him a disgraceful wretch.

51. When cast-off he asked his father where to go. The king asked him to stay with the outcastes.

52. Cast off by his father the righteous king and protector, the heroic Satyavrata lived with the outcastes.

53. Becoming detached due to the activities of his son, the king Trayyāruṇi forsook everything and went to the forest in order to perform penance to propitiate Śiva.

54. O brahmin sage, due to that sinful misdeed Indra did not rain in his kingdom for twelve years.

55. Viśvāmitra of great penance abandoned his wife in that land and performed extensive penance in the marshy foreshore of the ocean.

56. His wife tied her middle son round her neck and offered him for sale in exchange for a hundred cows in order to sustain the other children.

57. On seeing her offering her own son, tied round her neck, for sale, Satyavrata released him.

58. The mighty Satyabrata sustained him just to satisfy Viśvāmitra and out of human sympathy.

29. Gaurī, wife of king Prasenjit or grandmother of Māndhatā was cursed by her husband and transformed into Bāhudā or Bāhukā or Saitavāhinī, a river of Eastern India. The hermitage of Śaṅkha and Likhita are said to have been situated on its bank (Mbh. XII. 23. 18-19.)

59. Ever since then, that son of sage Viśvāmitra came to be called Gālava because he was tied round the neck. He too performed great penance.

CHAPTER THIRTYEIGHT

(*From Satyavrata to Sagara*)

1. By his devotion to Viśvāmitra his compassionate nature and his vow, Satyavrata nurtured and looked after Viśvāmitra's wife.

2. O sage, he killed deer, boars and buffaloes of the forest and he cast off their flesh near the hermitage of Viśvāmitra.

3. In virtue of his being the priest and the teacher the sage Vasiṣṭha looked after the holy centres, cows, clans and the harem.

4. Vasiṣṭha nursed more and more grudge against Satyavrata forced by the gravity of what was destined to happen.

5. Vasiṣṭha had not prevented the father from exiling the son from the kingdom because there was sufficient cause for the same.

6. When the seventh step is taken (round the fire in the altar) the marriage becomes valid. But Satyavrata did not understand this secret.

7. Only for the satisfaction of his father did he do the same thinking that the family customs should remain unviolated.

8. When he was abandoned by his father Vasiṣṭha did not interfere on his behalf. The sage proclaimed that he would never install him in this kingdom.

9-12. During the twelve years of famine and drought Satyavrata observed his vow. When there was no meat available the prince saw the wish-yielding cow of Vasiṣṭha. O sage, the king who observed the ten tenets[30] of Dharma

30. Cp. Manu. VI. 91

धृतिः क्षमा दमोऽस्तेयं शौचमिन्द्रियनिग्रहः ।
धीर्विद्या सत्यक्रोमधो दशकं धर्मलक्षणम् ॥

killed the cow either due to anger or greed or exhaustion or hunger. The meat of the same he utilised to feed Viśvāmitra's son. On hearing of it the sage Vasiṣṭha became angry and said.

Vasiṣṭha said

13. If the two iron stakes thrust by me fail I shall fix another cruel one.

14. Your transgression is threefold. You have displeased your father, killed the cow of your preceptor and used things unsprinkled with holy water.

15-16. He called him Triśaṅku and ever since he is known as Trisaṅku. When Viśvāmitra returned he was pleased with Triśaṅku for having maintained his family during his absence. When pressed to choose a boon the prince chose it.

17. When there was drought for twelve years he had helped his family, therefore the sage anointed him in the kingdom of his father and officiated as priest in his coronation.

18. Ever as the gods and Visiṣṭha were watching, the saintly lord Viśvāmitra made him ascend heaven in his physical body.

19. His wife Satyarathā, hailing from the family of Kekayas[31] bore him a son who was named Hariścandra.

20. That king Hariścandra is known as Traiśaṇkava. He is famous as the performer of the Rājasūya sacrifice and as an Emperor.

21. Hariśchandra's son Rohita was famous. Rohita's son was Vṛka and Bāhu was born of Tṛka.

22. Haihayas and Tālajaṅghas removed that king. O brahmin, he was very virtuous.

23. Bāhu begot a son. Sagara was born with poison. Reaching the hermitage of Aurva, he was saved by Bhārgava.

24. Securing fiery missiles from Bhārgava king Sagara

31. Kekayas lived between the Jhelum and the-Beas and had their capital at Girivraja (Girijak or Jalālpur) on the Jhelum.

conquered the earth after killing Tālajaṅghas[32] and Haihayas.[33]

25. He defeated Śakas,[34] Bahūdakas, Pāradas[35] tagaṇas[36] and Khaśas.[37] He established a good religious cult and ruled over the earth virtuously.

Śaunaka Said :—

26. How was he born with poison ? How did he conquer the Kṣatriyas ? O son of sūta, please narrate this in detail.

Sūta said:—

27. O sage, listen with attention. I shall narrate what Vaiśampāyana said on being asked by Janamejaya, son of Pārīkṣita.

Pārikṣita said :—

28. O sage, how was the king born with poison ? How did he kill the kings ? Please narrate this.

Vaiśampāyana said :—

29. O dear, O lord of the subjects, the kingdom of Bāhu who indulged in vices was captured by Haihayas and Tālajaṅghas and the Śakas.

30. Five groups of Rākṣasas are mentioned, viz.—Yavanas,[38] Pāradas,[39] Kāmbojas,[40] Pahlavas[41] and Bahūdakas.[42]

32. These constituted one of the five clans of Haihayas, the other four being वीतिहोत्र, भोज, अवन्ति and तुण्डिकेर।

33. Haihayas formed a branch of the Yādavas who ruled at Māhiṣmatī (Mod. Māndhātā in the Nimar District, M.P.) on the Narmadā river.

34. The original home of the Śakas was the Valleys of the Jaxartes and Oxus. But they had settled in India after they had conquered the country.

35. Pāradas are identical with the Pārthians who lived in the Khorasam region.

36. The Tagaṇas or Taṅgaṇas had their headquarters at Taṅgaṇāpura near jyotirmaṭha in Garhwal (Ep. Ind. Vol. XXXI. P. 286).

37. According to Al-Biruni, the Khasas were a Himalayan tribe now represented by the Khakkas of Kashmir.

38. Yavanas are identical with the Indo-Greeks who settled in the northwestern part of India and adjoining lands.

39. See No. 35 above.

40. Kāmbojas lived in the land between the Rajauri Valley in Kashmir and the Hindukush mountains. Some scholars locate the tribe near Badakhshan beyond the Hindukush.

41. Pahlavas or the Pahlavis are identical with the Persians.

42. Bahūdakas remain unidentified.

31. O king, these five groups of Rākṣasas pursuing activities of exploit on behalf of the Haihayas seized the kingdom of Bāhu and gave it to the Haihayas.

32. Having lost the kingdom, Bāhu went to the forest along with his wife. Distressed that he was he abandoned his life.

33. One of his wives belonging to the house of Yadu followed him in pregnancy. Due to jealousy as a result of her expected son before her, the co-wife administered poison to her.

34. She made the funeral pyre of her husband ready and was about to enter the fire, Aurva Bhārgava mercifully prevented her.

35. The queen stayed in his hermitage for the sake of her child in the womb. She served the sage, mentally remembering Śiva.

36. Once when the Muhūrta and the Lagna were good when the five planets were ascendant the child was born along with the poison administered to the queen.

37. In that auspicious Lagna, O excellent sage, the king Sagara, of mighty arms, was born.

38. Aurva performed the postnatal rites of that prince. He taught him Vedas and Śāstras and instructed him in the use of missiles.

39. The blessed Sagara, earnestly learnt the lore of the fiery missile, in accordance with the rules of procedure, the missile that is unbearable even to the gods.

40. The infuriated Sagaras, equipped with this miraculous and other weapons and with his own natural strength, killed the Haihayas.

41. This Sagara became foremost among the famous, earned fame in all the worlds and established piety on the earth.

42. Then the Śakas, Yavanas, Kāmbojas and Pahlavas, being destroyed sought refuge in Vasiṣṭha.

43. After deceitfully compelling them to enter into an agreement, Vasiṣṭha of great brilliance offered them freedom from fear and brought them to king Sagara.

44. At the instance of his priest Sagara maintained

his vow by destroying their mode of worship and effecting alterations in their hair style.

45. He released the Śakas after shaving off half of their heads. Complete tonsure was assigned to Yavanas and Kambojas.

46. Pāradas were given close hair-cut and Pahlavas were asked to grow beard and moustache. All of them were deprived of the right of the Vedic study and the use of Vaṣaṭkāra.

47. All those Kṣatriyas who had been deprived of virtue were re-instated in piety. The entire earth was conquered by him virtuously.

48. Thus conquering the earth virtuously the king instituted a horse-sacrifice.

49. O sage, the sacrificial horse was let loose, followed by his sixty thousand sons. It reached the shore of the ocean in the south-eastern region.

50. It was stealthily removed by Indra, king of the gods, for his selfish ends near the sea-shore and taken underground.

51. In order to search out the horse, king Sagara caused the country around dug up through his sons.

52. While it was being dug near the ocean, they met the sage Kapila, the primordial Puruṣa of cosmic form.

53. As he woke up from trance all but four of the sixty thousand sons were burnt by the fire from his eyes.

54. The four who were spared were Harṣaketu, Suketu, Dharmaratha and Pañcajana. They became the kings establishing his line.

55. Lord Viṣṇu granted him five boons, viz. flourishing family, intelligence, fame, the ocean as son and wealth.

56. By that virtue he attained the fatherhood of ocean. He regained the sacrificial horse from the ocean.

57. He performed a hundred horse-sacrifices and became famous. He acquired wealth bestowed by Śiva. He propitiated the deities by performing the sacred rites.

CHAPTER THIRTYNINE

(*Kings of the solar race*)

Śaunaka said:—

1. How were the heroic sons of Sagara born? By what means did the sixty thousand of them become valorous?

Sūta said:—

2. Sagara had two wives. They had wiped off their sins by penance. When Aurva the sage was propitiated by them he granted them a boon.

3. One of them chose the boon of sixty thousand sons. The other chose one son who would maintain the line of succession in the race.

4. Having received the boon of heroic sons she gave birth to a big gourd of seeds which were separated.

5. They were put in jars of ghee and nurtured by nursing maidens. They became princes and enhanced the delight of all.

6. When they were burnt by Kapila one Pañcajana became king.

7. Pañcajana begot a son Aṁśumat whose son was Dilīpa. Dilīpa's son was Bhagīratha.

8. It was this Bhagīratha who brought Gaṅgā to the sea and made her his daughter.

9. Bhagīratha's son was Śrutasena. His son was the virtuous king Nābhāga.

10. Ambarīṣa was the son of Nābhāga. Sindhudvīpa was his son. Ayutājit was the heir and successor to Sindhudvīpa.

11. His son was king Ṛtuparṇa, who knew the secret of the dice and was a friend of king Nala.

12. Ṛtuparṇa's son was Anuparṇa. His son was Mitrasaha who was known as Kalmāṣapāda also.

13. Kalmāṣapāda's son was Sarvakarman. Anaraṇya was the son of Sarvakarman.

14. Anaraṇya's son was king Muṇḍidruha. His sons were Niṣadha, Rati and Khaṭvāṅga.

15. Khaṭvāṅga returned from the heaven, lived for a

Muhūrta and attained all the three worlds, O sinless one, through his intellect and truthfulness.

16. Dīrghabāhu was his son. Raghu was his son. Aja was his son and Daśaratha was born of him.

17. Rāma was born of Daśaratha. He was very pious and famous, a part of Viṣṇu and a devotee of Śiva. Rāvaṇa was killed by him.

18. His story has been described in the Purāṇas. It is famous in the Rāmāyaṇa. It has not been mentioned here in detail.

19. Rāma's son Kuśa was very famous. Atithi was born of Kuśa. His son was Niṣadha.

20. Nala was the son of Niṣadha. Nabhas was the son of Nala. Puṇḍarīka was the son of Nabhas. Kṣemadhanvan was his successor.

21. The powerful Devānīka was the son of Kṣemadhanvan. Devānīka's son was the king Ahīnagu.

22. Ahīnagu's heir was the powerful king Sahasvat. Vīrasena was his son, a scion of the family of Ikṣvāku.

23. Vīrasenā's heir was Pāriyātra. From him a son Bala was born. Sthala was his son.

24. His son was the valorous Yakṣa born of a part of the sun. His son was Aguṇa and from him was born Vidhṛti.

25. His son Hiraṇyanābha was a great preceptor of Yogic science. He was the disciple of the sage Jaimini and an expert in the spiritual science.

26. It was from this great king that Kauśalya Yājñavalkya studied the spiritual science of Yoga that unrevels the knotty mesh of the heart.

27. His son was Puṣyanāman. His son was Dhruva. Agnivarṇa was his son. His son was Śīghra.

28. His son was Marut. He became a Siddha by means of Yoga. This king is alive even now in a village Kalāpa.[43]

43. Kalāpagrāma is in the eastern land on the Himalāyas, having hundreds and thousands of the hermitages of the sages. See Geo. of the Purāṇas P. 57.

The verse suggests the probable date of ŚP. in the reign of King Marut, son of Agnivarṇa of the solar race.

29. At the end of Kali he will revive the extinct solar race along with the contemporary sages.

30. Pṛthuśruta was his son. Sandhi was his son. Amarṣaṇa was his son and Marutvat was his son.

31. Viśvasa was his son. His son was Prasenajit. Takṣaka was his son and his son was Bṛhadbala.

32. These are the kings of Ikṣvāku family who had gone before. Now listen to the future kings of this family, the most excellent of those who know sacred virtue.

33. Bṛhadbala's son will be Bṛhadraṇa. Urukriya will be his son.

34. His son will be Vatsavṛddha. His son will be Prativyoman. Bhānu will be his son whose son will be Divārka, lord of a vast army.

35. His son will be a great hero, Sahadeva. His son will be Bṛhadaśva. The powerful Bhānumat will be his son.

36. The powerful Pratīkāśva will be the son of Bhānumat. King Supratīka will be his son.

37-41. Marudeva born of an auspicious star will be his son; his son will be Puṣkara; his son Antarikṣa; his son Sutapas; his son the heroic Mitrajit; his son Bṛhadbhāja and his son Barhināman; his son Kṛtañjaya; his son Raṇañjaya; his son Sañjaya; Śākya his son, Śuddhoda his son, Lāngala his son; his son Prasenajit; his son will be Śūdraka; Ruṇaka his son; Suratha his son and Sumitra his son. Thereafter the family becomes extinct.

42. The family of the Ikṣvākus will end with Sumitra, the family with kings of variegated exploits, sacred rites and virtuous practice.

43. Reaching upto Sumitra the king in the Kali age that auspicious race will become merged in outside families. It will flourish again in the Kṛta age.

44. These are the kings in the solar race who made profuse monetary gifts. Those mainly mentioned belong to Ikṣvāku's family.

45. This is the auspicious creation of the sun Vivasvat, who is glorified as Śrāddhadeva, the bestower of nourishment to all living beings.

46. Reading and listening to this creation of Vivasvat,

man attains Sāyujya after enjoying happiness here. He will be blessed with progeny.

CHAPTER FORTY

(*The power of the Manes*)

Vyāsa said:—

1. On hearing about the excellent solar race of Śrāddhadeva, the sage Śaunaka respectfully asked Sūta.

Śaunaka said

2. O Sūta, disciple of Vyāsa, of long life, obeisance be to you. A divine and pious story has been narrated to us.

3. It has been mentioned by you that Śrāddhadeva is the progenitor of the solar race. I have a doubt therein which I shall mention before you.

4. How did the sun become Śrāddhadeva? I wish to hear this. Please clear this doubt with pleasure.

5. O holy lord, please mention the glory and the benefit of Śrāddha rite whereby the manes are pleased and bless the performer with prosperity.

6. I wish to hear this too, namely the creation par excellence of the manes. O intelligent one, please mention this particularly. Have mercy on me.

Sūta said:—

7-9. O Śaunaka, I shall mention everything concerning the creation of the manes. This was narrated to the intelligent Mārkaṇḍeya by Sanatkumāra. I shall mention it to you. It bestows the benefit of all cherished desires. Bhīṣma the foremost of the virtuous lying on the bed of arrows was requested by Yudhiṣṭhira to whom he spoke thus.

Yudhiṣṭhira said:—

10. How is nourishment achieved by a man desirous of nourishment? I wish to hear this. What is it that makes a man free from distress?

Sūta said:—

11. On hearing the question of Yudhiṣṭhira, Bhīṣma the knower of Dharma spoke with pleasure even as every one was listening.

Bhīṣma said:—

12. O Yudhiṣṭhira, those who perform Śrāddha rites with pleasure delight everyone through them as a result of the favour of the manes.

13-15. Men desirous of benefits perform Śrāddhas, keeping in view, the father, the grandfather and the great-grandfather in three balls of rice. O Yudhiṣṭhira, the manes bless the man desirous of piety with piety, desirous of progeny with progeny and desirous of nourishment with nourishment.

Yudhiṣṭhira said:—

16: Some manes are in the heaven and some are in the hell. The fruit accruing to the living beings is determined by their activity.

17. How do the Śrāddhas go to the manes? How those in the hell can derive the benefit?

18. I have heard that even the gods worship the manes. I wish to hear this. Please mention this in detail.

Bhīṣma said:—

19. O suppressor of enemies, in this context, I shall narrate an event as I have heard from my father who had left this world.

20. At the time of Śrāddha, the ball of rice for my father was kept ready by me. My father split the ground and requested me to offer the same into his hand.

21. Thinking that it was not the procedure enjoined in the Kalpa texts I placed the Piṇḍa on the Kuśa grass without further thought.

22. "O sinless one, O most excellent of the descendants of Bharata, gladdened by me my father spoke in sweet words.

23. O most excellent of men, I only tested you. I have been redeemed by you the knower of sacred rites and a good scholar. I have been blessed with a real heir in you.

24. What the king does by virtuous or authoritative rites, the subjects too emulate, taking them to be backed by precedent.

25. O most excellent of the descendants of Bharata, listen to the eternal virtues of the Vedas. Proof of the Vedic rite has been shown by you.

26. Being delighted I shall grant you excellent boons lovingly. Accept them. They are difficult to obtain in the three worlds.

27. Death will have no hold on you as long as you wish to live. With your permission it may be effective again.

28. What is it that you wish for ? I shall grant you an excellent boon. O foremost among the descendants of Bharata, what is in your mind ? Mention it".

29. When he had said this, I saluted him with palms joined in reverence and said—"O bestower of honour, if you are pleased, I am content. I ask you a question. Please answer it.

30. He said to me—"Tell me. If you wish I shall grant it to you". When I asked him again the king told me.

Śantanu said :—

31. O dear, listen. I shall explain your question factually. The entire "Pitṛkalpa" has been heard by me from Mārkaṇḍeya.

32. O dear, what you ask me now I had asked the sage Mārkaṇḍeya. He, the knower of sacred rites, replied to me.

33. O king listen. Once as I looked up into the sky, I saw a great aerial chariot coming over the mountain.

34-35. I saw in the aerial chariot a great blazing mass of splendour as brilliant as glowing coal and very pleasing to the mind having nothing to excel it. I saw a man of the size of a thumb lying therein. He was very brilliant as if fire had been placed over fire.

36. I bowed to him. With my head bent down, I asked the holy lord. "O holy lord, how may we know you ?"

37. The pious soul told me "you have not that penance

and austerity, O sage, whereby you may know me, the son of Brahmā.

38. I am Sanatkumāra. What can I do for you ? The other sons of Brahmā are younger to me.

39. My seven brothers are invincible and their families are established. But we pursue the rites of ascetics restraining the Ātman in the Ātman.

40. Even as I was born I became famous as Kumāra. O sage, hence I am called Sanatkumāra (the eternal bachelor).

41. Since you have piously performed penance with a desire for my vision I have appeared before you. Welfare be to you. What wish of yours shall I carry out ?"

42. When he said this I told him—"O holy lord, listen. Please narrate factually the original creation of the Pitṛs.

43. When requested thus he said to me. Listen to everything factually. O dear one, I shall explain to you the auspicious creation of the Pitṛs truthfully.

Sanatkumāra said :—

44. Formerly Brahmā created the gods and said to them, "Worship me". But they who sought benefits eschewed him and worshipped the Ātman.

45-46. They were cursed by Brahmā thus. You will be deluded and become senseless". Hence unable to know any thing and being insensible they bowed to Pitāmaha and said "Please bless us." Being requested thus he said to them for the sake of expiation.

47. "Ask your sons. You will then attain perfect knowledge". Urged thus the senseless ones asked their sons boldly.

48-50. They were asked to perform expiatory rites. O sinless one, the gods were thus addressed by the sons. "Let the sons be approached." The gods who had been cursed by Brahmā told him that the sons had gone away. Then Brahmā told the gods thus "O gods, listen, You are not Brahmavādins, the believers in Brahmā's cult.

51. Hence what has been mentioned by the sons, the

most excellent of the perfectly wise shall be followed without hesitation and not otherwise.

52. O dwellers of heaven, let the gods and the Pitṛs worship one another with great delight. This will confer the cherished desires."

53. Sanatkumāra said :—O great sage, then their doubts were cleared. With delight they became the mutual bestowers of happiness at the instance of Brahmā.

54. Then the gods said "Since you addressed us as sons you will undoubtedly become Pitṛs.

55. In the Śrāddha of the Pitṛs, undoubtedly the performer will propitiate Soma who being delighted and enhanced by the offering shall gladden the worlds.

56-58. They will delight the ocean, the mountain and the forest, all consisting of the mobile and immobile beings. Those who desire nourishment and perform Śrāddha rites are given nourishment by the Pitṛs who are propitiated. Those who give three Piṇḍas in the Śrāddha mentioning the names and Gotras delight the Pitṛs wherever they be and are looked after by them.

59-60. Let these words be truthful. Whether gods or Pitṛs we are father and sons successively. Thus the Pitṛs who became sons virtuously were famous in the world as mutual beneficiaries.

CHAPTER FORTYONE

(The attainment of the seven hunters)

Sanatkumā said:—

1. O foremost among the performers of penance, the Pitṛs in the heaven are seven in number. Four of them are embodied and three bodiless.

2. The primordial groups of gods, brahmins and others worship them. With the power of their Yoga they strengthen and gladden Soma.

3-6. Hence people shall offer Śrāddhas especially to the Yogins. A silver vessel or a vessel with silver when offered with Svadhā, delights the Pitṛs. When the sun is in the northern transit he shall make offerings in the fire or in its absence in water. He shall propitiate fire-god, Soma or Yama. Those who delight the Pitṛs with devotion are delighted by Pitṛs. The Pitṛs bestow nourishment, offspring, heaven, health and other desired objects.

7. O sage, the rites of Pitṛs are better than the rites of the gods. O brahmin sage, since you are a devotee of the Pitṛs you shall be free from old age and death.

8. O sage, the goal attained by devotion to the Pitṛs is not attained by the practices of Yoga. O great sage, so devotion to the Pitṛs shall be pursued with care.

Mārkaṇḍeya said :—

9. After saying thus and immediately bestowing the vision of perfect knowledge the lord of the gods disappeared.

10. O Bhīṣma, listen again. Formerly, even after learning the code of Yoga, the brahmin sons of Bhāradvāja were degraded due to their evil course.

11. Their names which indicate their activities are Vāgduṣta (defiled in speech), Krodhana (angry), Hiṁsra (violent), Piśuna (backbiter), Kavi (poet), Svasṛṣa (self-creating) and Pitṛvartin (worshipping the pitṛs)

12. O dear, the sons of Kauśika became the disciples of Garga. When their father had expired they went in exile.

13. At the instance of their preceptor they looked after his cow and her calf. All of them were unjust in their actions.

14. O descendant of Bharata, once in their course of wandering in the forest, they were oppressed by hunger. They had the cruel intention of injuring the cow then.

15. Kavi and Svasṛṣa forbade them do so. But they could not be prevented from that act.

16. The brahmin Pitṛvartin who performed Śrāddha everyday with devotion to the Pitṛs spoke to them angrily.

17. If it is not possible to stop this do it with the Pitṛs in view. Perform the Śrāddha, ye all cautiously.

18. If performed thus, the cow will attain piety undoubtedly. By worshipping Pitṛs we shall not be affected by sin.

19. O descendant of Bharata, on being advised thus, they all sprinkled the cow with sacred water, dedicated it to the Pitṛs and used it as their food.

20. After eating the cow they said to the preceptor saying—"The cow is killed by a tiger. Let the calf be accepted."

21. The sage accepted the calf with great distress. The killers of the cow became sinful by their false reverence and service.

22. O dear, in due course, when their term of life expired the seven brothers passed away.

23-24. They were reborn as the sons of a hunter as a result of their cruelty, violence, being ignoble towards the preceptor and their over-indulgence in fierce violence. They were reborn in the country of Daśārṇas.[44] They were strong, intelligent and experts in piety.

25. They were engaged in the practice of sacred rites. They were free from the delusion of hunting animals. On the beautiful mountain Kālañjara they passed their time with distress.

26. Recollecting the event of their death the forest-roamers became forbearers, free from Dvandvas and averse to taking gifts.

27. The hunters performed auspicious rites, and holy deeds, disassociating themselves from the wicked. They had the power of the memory of the previous birth.

28. Whatever sacred rites they had heard in the preceptor's hermitage in the previous births were retained in their minds. So also the goal of non-return to this world.

29-30. They performed their penance, had their food and finally cast off their lives on that mountain. O descendant of Bharata, O king, the different places where they fell dead are still seen in the same manner on the mount Kālañjara.[45] Thanks to their activities neither auspi-

44. The Western Daśārṇa comprised the Eastern Mālwa including the kingdom of Bhopal with its capital at Vidiśā while the eastern Daśārṇa formed a part of Chattisgarh district in the Madhya Pradesh (B.H.D. Sec. III).

45. See P. 1273 note 128.

cious nor inauspicious, they were reborn in a life neither auspicious nor inauspicious.

31. On an island in an auspicious spot the seven became aquatic birds. They were reborn as Cakravāka birds in a life that is neither auspicious nor inauspicious.

32. They abandoned the contact with their mates. They were like sages practising sacred rites, free from associations and Egotistic feelings. They remained calm. They did not accept gifts. They were free from Dvandvas.

33. They were birds only in name. They were holy bachelors delighted in renunciation. They were birds practising sacred rites.

34. They could remember their previous births. They grew old even as they were bachelors. They remained together free from aberrations and performed good rites.

35. When they were born as brahmins they acted falsely to their preceptor. Still in their birth as birds they attained knowledge as a result of the Śrāddha they had performed.

36. They had performed the Śrāddha for the Pitṛs with due rituals. They retained memory of previous noble birth.

37. The knowledge of Brahma practised by the ancients or found in the preceptors' families stands as of yore even today. One shall practise that knowledge therefore.

38. They were of noble birth and were named Svatantra. Suyajña, Sumanas, Suvākśuddha and the fifth one Chidradarśaka.

39. While they were practising sacred rites an auspicious event happened there. O great sage, please listen to that.

40. The prosperous king of Nīpas,[46] endowed with strength, and accompanied by his harem entered that forest.

41. The Cakravaka Svatantra yearned much, on seeing the happy king endowed with the glory of the kingdom pass along.

46. Nīpa signifies a land lying at the foot of a mountain. Whether a particular locus is meant to be conveyed by this word is not clear.

42-43. I have become weary with the observance of fasts and steady penance. If there is a merit accruing from penance or the observance of checks and restraints let me become like him the abode of fortune and bliss.

Mārkaṇḍeya said:—

44. Then two of his comrades said. "We shall be your ministers, your delighters and well-wishers."

45. After saying "So be it", the Yogic soul attained his goal. The two Cakravākas replied to him.

46. After renouncing action by the Yogic practices why do you long for such a boon? Hence hear my statement.

47. O dear, you will become a king in the excellent city of Kāmpilya.[47] These too will be your ministers who will not go astray.

48. The three did not speak about the kingdom to their four comrades. Being delighted Sumanas said again.

49. When the curse is over you will attain Yoga. Sarvasattva, Suyajña and Svatantra too will attain yogic powers.

50. Due to their favour you will attain merit. You have sprinkled the cow and offered it to the Pitṛs.

51. We shall acquire knowledge which shall work as the means of Yoga for all. This statement is bold and spirited and is quoted as a verse.

52. After attaining human life you will attain "Yoga". After saying this the learned bird Sumanas became silent.

Mārkaṇḍeya said :—

53. Thus I have menioned their story to you. What more do you wish to hear?

47. Kāmpilya was the capital of South Pāñcāla identical with modern Kāmpil in the Farrukhabad District to the south of the Ganges.

CHAPTER FORTYTWO

(*Power of the Pitṛs*)

Bhīṣma said :—

1. Mārkaṇḍeya of great intellect, O foremost among the devotees of the Pitṛs what happened after that? O excellent sage, please tell me.

Mārkaṇḍeya said :—

2. Those seven traversers of the lake Mānasa engaged in sacred rites and Yoga got their bodies withered up taking in only air and water.

3. After sporting about for a long time there, like Indra in Nandana,[48] the king, accompanied by his wives and the members of his harem returned to his city.

4. A son Anūha was born to him. He was highly virtuous. King Vaibhrāja established his son in the kingdom and went to forest.

5. Without taking in any food, breathing in only air he began to perform a great penance in the spot where those comrades were present.

6. Then that forest Vibhrāja shone splendidly. It became very famous as the bestower of Yogic Siddhi.

7. It was there itself that the four birds of Yogic rites and the three that fell from Yoga cast off their bodies.

8. They were reborn in Kāmpilya as seven noble souls Brahmadatta and others. All of them were free from sins.

9. Four of them had the memory of their previous births but three of them were deluded. That Svatantra of great Yogic power was now called Brahmadatta.

10. Chidradarśin and Sunetra were the masters of the Vedas and Vedāṅgas. They were born as sons of brahmins well-versed in the Vedas. They had the memory of the previous births.

11. Pañcāla was conversant with many Ṛk mantras. He became a preceptor. Puṇḍarīka became the master of

48. It is a grove of Indra lying to the north of Meru.

two Vedas. He was a Chandoga (master of prosody) and an Adhvaryu (priest of sacrifice).

12 On seeing his son Brahmadatta free from sin, the king crowned him in kingdom and attained the supreme goal.

13. Pañcāla and Puṇḍarīka established their sons in the house and went to forest. There they attained the great goal.

14. O descendant of Bharata, Brahmadatta's wife Sannati sported with her husband with single-minded devotion.

15. The other three Cakravāka comrades were born as brahmin sons in the family of a poor man, O king.

16. The four sons of Chidradarśin were endowed with Vedic study. They were Dhṛtimat Sumahātman, Tattvadarśin and Nirutsuka.

17. They were engaged in Yogic practice. They took leave of one another, bowed at the lotus-like feet of Śiva and set out.

18. The enthusiasts desiring freedom from rebirth resort to Śiva's feet. May those feet of Siva destroy sins.

19. O great sage, if any physical, mental or verbal sin is committed, one shall read this narrative with full devotion.

20-22. By repeating the names of Śiva, one gets rid of all sins soon. As soon as the name Śiva, the lord of the gods, is uttered sins are quelled like an unbaked pot in water, O great sage. In proportion to the sins committed and in order to quell them the Japa of Śiva's names shall be performed by the faithful. In order to achieve the fruits of all desires too, this Japa shall be performed accordingly.

23. He who reads or hears this for prosperity is liberated from sins and attains salvation. There is no doubt in this.

CHAPTER FORTYTHREE

(*The mode of worshipping Vyāsa*)

Śaunaka said:—

1. O Sūta having Vyāsa as preceptor, please tell me now the mode of worshipping the preceptor. What shall be done at the end of listening to the holy book ? Please mention that also.

Sūta said:—

2. After hearing the story the devotee shall worship the preceptor duly with devotion. Delighted in mind he shall make liberal gifts duly to the preceptor at the conclusion of the holy book.

3. The intelligent devotee shall bow to the propounder and worship him duly. Gifts of ornaments for hands and ears and fine garments shall be made.

4-5. After the worship of Śiva he shall present to the preceptor a cow and its calf. He shall make a book-seat with gold, a Pala in weight and cover it with a good cloth. The manuscript of the holy book written in beautiful hand shall be placed on it and given to the preceptor. The intelligent devotee will be liberated from worldly bondage.

6. O sage, a village, an elephant or a horse or other things shall be given as possible to the noble preceptor who reads and propounds the story.

7. O sage Śaunaka, Purāṇa is efficacious if it is listened to in accordance with the rules. I speak truth to you.

8. O sage, the Purāṇa full of the meanings of the Vedas, the heart of the Vedas, the meritorious holy book shall be listened to with devotion and in accordance with the rules.

CHAPTER FORTYFOUR

(*The birth of Vyasa*)

The sages said:—

1-3. O Sūta of great intellect, O store-house of mercy, please narrate the birth of Vyāsa. O holy lord, please satisfy our curiosity. Vyāsa's mother is known as Satyavatī. She was married to king Śantanu. How was Vyāsa the great Yogin born of her from Parāsara? There is a great doubt in regard to that. It behoves you to remove that doubt.

Suta said:—

4. Once, while he was making his pilgrimage, Parāśara the yogin casually came to the auspicious and beautiful banks of the Yamunā.

5. The righteous soul spoke to the ferryman who was taking his meals "Take me across the Yamunā quickly in your boat".

6. When the ferryman was thus urged by the sage he spoke to his daughter Matsyagandhā :—"Girl, quickly take this sage to the other bank in the boat.

7. This sage, O fortunate girl, is born of the womb of Dṛśyantī. He is the ocean of sacred rites. He has mastered the four Vedas. Now he desires to cross this river.

8. Thus directed by her father, Matsyagandhā began to take the great sage of solar splendour seated in the boat across the river.

9. That great Yogin who had never been fascinated even on seeing the beauty of the celestial damsels became overwhelmed by lust towards her, in the circumstances.

10. Desirous of clasping the beautiful daughter of the fisherman, the sage touched her in the right hand with his right hand.

11. The wide-eyed lass spoke to him smilingly—"O sage of controlled speech, why do you intend to perpetrate this despicable deed ?

12. O most intelligent one, you are born of the beautiful family of Vasiṣṭha. O brahmin, I am the daughter of a Niṣāda. How can our union be proper ?

13. O excellent sage, birth as a man is very difficult to obtain; especially that as a brahmin. Even there the state of an ascetic is very rarely achieved.

14. It is extremely surprising that you endowed with learning, good physique, speech, noble birth and good conduct have become subservient to the arrows of Kāma!"

15. Then she thought within: "If this Yogin engages himself in the vicious act there is none in the world to prevent him due to his power of inflicting curse."

16. After thinking in the mind thus she said to the great sage—"O holy lord, please forbear till I take you to the other bank."

17. On hearing her words the king of Yogins Parāśara left off her hand. He reached the other shore.

18. Afflicted with lust the sage caught hold of the lass. Tremblingly the lass spoke to the merciful sage.

19. "O great sage, I have foul smell and black complexion. I am the daughter of a Niṣāda. You are the most excellent of Yogins of extremely liberal thoughts.

20. The union between us is not proper as of a piece of worthless glass with gold. The sexual union of two persons of the same class and features may be conducive to bliss."

21. As the girl addressed the sage thus, the damsel was instantly converted into Yojanagandhā, (one whose fragrant odours spread to a Yojana), one of fine features and beauty.

22. Afflicted by lust the sage caught hold of her again. On seeing him bent upon seizing her she said again.

23. "It is mentioned in the Vedas that sexual intercourse shall be indulged in at night; not during the day. There is great harm in having sexual intercourse during the daytime. It is censured.

24. Hence please wait till the night falls. Now all the men will see us and so shall my father who stands at the other bank."

25. On hearing the words uttered by her, the leading sage immediately created a screen of snow, thanks to the strength of his merit.

26. When the sheet of mist spread and it looked just

as night, the girl, afraid of submitting herself to sexual intercourse, spoke to the sage again.

27. "O Yogin, your semen never fails. You may enjoy me and go away. O holy lord, I shall become pregnant, what will be my fate then?

28. O intelligent sage, my virginity will be ruined, People will laugh at me. What will I tell my father?"

Parāśara said:—

29. O maiden, O beloved girl, sport with me freely with loving emotion. You tell me what you desire. I shall fulfil it.

30. By making my advances fruitful you will be known as Satyavatī. You will deserve the respect of all Yogins and even the gods.

Satyavatī said:—

31-32. If neither my father nor mother nor anyother person on the earth comes to know of this, if my virginity is not affected, O lord, if the son born of me attains wonderful power like you, if there be sweet odour in my body for ever and if there be fresh youth in me, accept me then.

Parāśara said:—

33. Listen to me O beloved girl, all your desires will be fulfilled. A son of great fame of Viṣṇu's part will be born to you.

34. Know that there is a reason that I have become lustful. Even on seeing the beauty of celestial damsels my mind was never deluded anywhere before.

35. On seeing you of fish odour I was enamoured. O lass, lines drawn by Brahmā on the forehead cannot prove untrue.

36. O comely lady, your son will be the author of the Purāṇas, the classifier of the Vedas and renowned in the three worlds.

37. O great sage, after saying this and enjoying the beautiful lass, the sage, an expert in Yoga, took his bath in the Yamunā and went away quickly.

38. She conceived and immediately gave birth in an island on the Yamuna[49] to a son with the lustre of the sun and resembling Kamadeva.

39. In his left hand he was holding the water pot and in his right he had an excellent staff. He had matted hair of tawny colour and shone like a mass of splendour.

40. Immediately after birth the brilliant sage spoke to his mother "O mother, go as you please and I also go at my will

41. O mother, whenever you have some work, whenever you desire in your mind, please remember me. Immediately I shall come to you to fulfil your desire."

42. After saying this and worshipping his mother's feet the sage, a storehouse of penance, went away to perform penance to holy centres quelling sins.

43. She too returned to her father. The chaste lady was overwhelmed by her love for her son. She recollected his activities and described the event as her great fortune.

44. As the boy was born in an island he was known as Dvaipayana. Since he classified the various branches of the Vedas he is glorified as Vedavyāsa.

45-49. He went to these holy centres :—Tīrtharāja[50] at the outset, which bestows virtue, love, wealth and salvation, Naimiṣa,[51] Kurukṣetra,[52] Gaṅgadvara,[53] Avantika,[54] Ayodhya,[55] Mathurā,[56] Dvaraka,[57] Amarāvatī,[58] Sarasvatī,[59] Sindhusaṅga,[60]

49. The river Yamunā is personified as the daughter of the sun by his wife Saṁjna.

50. It is a famous place of pilgrimage on the northern bank of the Gaṅgā in Uttara Pradesh. See P. 35 note 27.

51. P. 76 note, P. 432 note.

52. It lies south of Thanesar, not far from Panipat in Haryana province.

53. P. 1082 note.

54. p. 1314 note.

55. It is situated on the Sarayu river in Audh near Faizabad, U.P.

56. It is situated on the right bank of the Yamunā river. Originally it was called Madhuvana from the demon Madhu who ruled there.

57. P. 1229 note.

58. It is situated on the bank of the Krsnā river in the Madras State.

59. P. 47 note. It may also refer to Mallikā Sarasvatī, KRS Ch. 1. V. 41.

60. It is the place where the Indus joins the Western Sea.

the confluence of the Gaṅgā with the ocean,[61] Kāñcī,[62] Tryambaka,[63] the seven holy banks of the Godāvarī,[64] Kālañjara, Prabhāsa,[65] Badarikāśrama,[66] Mahālaya,[67] Oṁkārakṣetra,[68] Paurusottama,[69] Gokarṇa,[70] Bhṛgukaccha,[71] Bhṛgutuṅga,[72] Puṣkara,[73] Śrīparvata[74] and Dhārātīrtha He took ablutions duly at these places and performed penance.

50-51. Wandering thus over the various, holy centres situated in different countries, the son of Kālikā reached the city of Vārāṇasī[75] where Viśveśvara himself and Annapūrṇā the great goddess, the storehouses of mercy shine in order to give salvation to the devotees.

52. After reaching the holy centre of Vārāṇasī and visiting Maṇikarṇikā the great sage discarded the sin accumulated in crores of birth.

53-57. After seeing Viśveśa and other Liṅgas, taking bath in puddles, tanks, wells and lakes, after bowing to all the Vināyakas, after kneeling before all Gaurīs, after worshipping Kālarāja and Bhairava the devourer of all sins, after strenuously eulogising Daṇḍanāyaka and other important Gaṇas, after propitiating Ādikeśava and other important Keśavas, after repeatedly bowing to Lolārka and other important suns and after offering balls of rice in all the holy spots alertly, the meritorious soul installed the Liṅga Vyāseśvara on seeing

61. The upper part of the Bay of Bengal is known as Gaṅgā-Sāgara for here the Gaṅgā joins the sea.

62. Identical with the modern Conjeevaram. See P. 1365 note.

63. It is a sacred mount, source of the Godā river.

64. The Godā rises in the Western Ghats, flows through the Deccan into the Bay of Bengal. ŚP omits to mention the seven sacred places on its bank.

65. P. 1084 note 19; P. 1310 note 141.

66. P. 1327 note.

67. This peak of the Himālayas has not been identified so far.

68. P. 1254 note.

69. P. 1264 note 125.

70. P. 1083 note 12; 1285 note 133.

71. P. 1262 note 116.

72. P. 1081 note.

73. A sacred place near Ajmer famous for the lake Puṣkara.

74. P. 1254 note

75. P. 266 note.

whom, O brahmins, man becomes a master of all lores like Bṛhaspati.

58-59. After worshipping devoutly Viśveśa and other Liṅgas he began to think frequently—"What is that Liṅga that bestows Siddhi instantaneously and worshipping whom the great god, we shall be able to attain all lores and by whose blessings I may have the power to compose the Purāṇas.

60-73. There are crores of Liṅgas; from the midst of these what shall I instal, what shall I resort so ? Can it be Oṅkāranātha, or Kṛttivāseśvara or Kedāreśa, or Kāmeśa, or Candreśa, or Trilocana, or Kāleśa, or Vṛddhakāleśa, or Kalaśeśvara, or Jyeṣṭheśa, or Jambukeśa, or Jaigīṣavyeśvara, or Daśāśvamedhesana, or Drumacaṇdesa, or Dṛkkeśa or Garuḍeśa or Gaṇeśvara, or Prasannavadaneśa, or Dharmeśa, or Tārakeśvara or Nandikeśa or Nivāseśa, or Patrīśa, or Prītikeśvara, or Parvateśa, or Pasupati, or Hāṭakeśvara or Bṛhaspatīśvara, or Tilabhāṇḍeśa or Bhārabhūteśvara, or Mahālakṣmīśvara or Maruteśa, or Mokṣeśa, or Gaṅgeśa, or Narmadeśvara, or Kṛṣṇeśa, or Parameśāna, or Ratnesvara, or Yāmuneśa, or Lāṅgalīṣa, or Viśveśvara or Avimukteśvara, or or Viśālākṣīśa, or Vyāghreśvara, or Varāheśa, or Vidyeśvara or Varuṇeśa, or Vidhīśa, or Harikeśeśvara, or Bhavānīśa, or Kapardīśa, or Kandukeśa or Ajeśvara or Viśvakarmeśvara, or Vīreśvara, or Nādeśa, or Kapileśa, or Bhuvaneśvara, or Vāṣkulīśa or Mahādeva, or Siddhīśvara or Viśvedeveśvara or Vīrabhadreśa or Bhairaveśvara, or Amṛteśa; or Satīśa or Pārvatīśvara or Siddheśvara, Mataṅgeśa or Bhūtīśvara, or Āṣāḍhīsa, Prakāśeśa, or Koṭirudreśvara, or Madālaseśvara, or Tilaparṇesvara, Hiranyagarbheśa or shall it be Madhyameśvara ?"

74. Pondering thus, Vyāsa, devoted to Śiva with his mind steady in meditation, thought for a short while.

75-77. "O I remember it now. I had forgotten it before. My desire has been realised. There is a Liṅga which is worshipped by the Siddhas. It bestows virtue, love, wealth and salvation. Its sight and touch purifies the mind. It opens the door to heaven. It is in the great holy centre, the holy centre of the Siddhas, in Avimukta. There is the great Liṅga Madhyameśvara by name.

78. There is no other Liṅga at Kāśī than Madhyameśvara for the sight of which the gods come here on every festive occasion.

79. Hence lord Madhyameśvara shall be resorted to. Many brahmins have attained Siddhis by propitiating Him.

80. Śiva is called Madhyameśvara since he is stationed mainly in the centre of Kāśī for bestowing happiness on the people.

81. It is by worshipping this deity that the Gandharva Tumburu and the celestial sage Nārada became proficient in the art of music.

82. It is by propitiating Him that Viṣṇu acquired the art of bestowing salvation; and Brahmā, Viṣṇu and Rudra became the creator, sustainer and the annihilator respectively.

83. Kubera became the lord of wealth; Vāmadeva the head of the devotees of Siva; the childless Khaṭvāṅga was blessed with children.

84. The celestial damsel Candrabhāmā of cuckoo-like sweet voice was merged into the Liṅga even as she was dancing emotionally.

85. Śrīkara, son of the cowherdess, resorted to Madhyameśvara and attained the chieftainship of the Gaṇas of the benevolent Śiva.

86. Thanks to the favour of Madhyameśvara the two gods Śukra and Bṛhaspati honoured and respected by the Asuras and gods became the master of all lore.

87. I too shall worship lord Madhyameśvara and attain the power to compose the Purāṇas immediately.

88. After resolving thus the sage Vyāsa, son of Satyavatī, took his bath in the waters of the Gaṅgā and performed the sacred rites and observances.

89. Sometimes he took in only leaves, sometimes he lived on fruit and vegetable diet, sometimes on wind or water and sometimes he observed complete fast and performed the sacred rites.

90. Thus by these observances of restraints the holy

sage worshipped Madhyameśvara thrice a day with flowers of various trees.

91. A long time elasped thus. One day early in the morning the sage was returning after his bath in the waters of the Gaṅgā.

92. The holy sage saw lord Madhyameśvara, the bestower of desires of the devotees, in the midst of the Liṅga.

93. His left side was adorned by Umā. He was wearing the hide of a tiger as his upper cloth. His body appeared beautiful with the surging waves of the Gaṅgā amidst his matted hair.

94. The moonlight of the autumnal crescent moon was forming bright patches in his forelocks. Bhasma was smeared all over his body. His body was as white as camphor or the Arjuna tree.

95. He had assumed the form of a five-year-old boy with eyes extending upto his ears. His lips were as red as the coral. He was wearing ornaments befitting a boy.

96. The lustre of his body subdued the arrogance of a crore Cupids. He was naked. His lotus-face was beaming with smiles. He was sportively singing Sāman hymns.

97-98. On seeing Śiva, the lord of Umā, the shoreless ocean of mercy, known for his fondness of devotees and easily propitiated with delighted pleasing face, inaccessible even to the Yogins, the kinsman of the distressed and the Cit-formed lord, the sage sang the song of prayer with words choked with devotion.

Vyāsa said:—

99. "O lord of gods, O fortunate one who are favourably disposed to the refugees, O lord inaccessible to words, mind and activities, and the one that are invisible even to the Yogins.

100. O lord of Umā, the Vedas too do not realise your greatness. You alone are the creator of the universe, the sustainer and the annihilator too.

101. You are the first and foremost of all gods. You

are the existence, knowledge and bliss. You have no name or family lineage. O Sadāśiva you are omniscient.

102. You alone are the great Brahman; the untier of the knot of Māyā, unsullied by the three attributes as the leaf of the lotus unaffected by water.

103. You have neither birth nor conduct of life. You have neither a native land nor a family. Even so you are the lord of the three worlds. You fulfil the desires of the three worlds.

104. Neither Brahmā nor Viṣṇu nor the gods including Indra nor the leading Yogins know your reality. We worship you of such features.

105. Everything originates from you. You are all—the lord of Gaurī, the slayer of the Tripuras, a boy, a youth, an aged man. I unite you with my heart.

106. Obeisance to lord Śiva, who deserves the worship of devotees, Obeisance to the Ancient Being; to Śiva the great Ātman,"

107. After eulogising thus when the sage Vyāsa prostrated on the ground the delighted boy spoke to him.

108. O Yogin, choose your boon, whatever be in your mind. There is nothing which cannot be granted to you since I am subservient to my devotees.

109. Then the delighted sage Vyāsa of great penance stood up and replied—"O lord what is hidden from you the omniscient?"

110. You are the immanent Soul and bestower of everything. Why does the lord force me for begging which is the cause of misery?

111. On hearing these words of Vyāsa of pious mind, lord Śiva who had assumed the form of boy smiled and said:—

The boy said:—

112. O most excellent of those who know brahman, the desire you have cherished in your heart will undoubtedly be realised ere long.

113. I the immanent lord shall station myself in your throat, O brahmin, and shall make you compose the Itihāsa and the Purāṇas efficiently.

114. The holy hymn "Abhilāṣāṣṭaka" (Eight Verses

of Desire) that you uttered now shall fulfil the desires of men who read or recite it in Śiva's temple thrice a day for a year.

115. The recital of this hymn is conducive to the increase of learning and intellect. It is the cause of all riches and the bestower of virtue and salvation to men.

116. Even a fool, getting up early in the morning taking his bath, worshipping the liṅga of Śiva and reciting this hymn for a year shall attain the status of Bṛhaspati (preceptor of the gods.)

117. This hymn repeatedly recited for a year in the presence of the Liṅga whether by a woman or a man, duly observing restraints, shall increase the intellect and learning.

118. After saying this the boy Śiva merged himself into the Liṅga. Shedding tears of love, Vyāsa was overcome with emotions.

119. Vyāsa who thus secured the boon from the great lord Madhyameśvara composed the eighteen Purāṇas sportively.

120-122. The eighteen Purāṇas Brāhma, Pādma. Vaiṣṇava, Śaiva, Bhāgavata, Bhaviṣya, Nāradīya, Mārkaṇḍeya, Āgneya, Brahmavaivarta, Laiṅga, Vārāha, Vāmana Kaurma, Mātsya, Gāruḍa, Skānda and Brahmāṇḍa are conducive to fame and merit to those who listen to the glory of Śiva.

Sūta said:—

123. You have enumerated the eighteen Purāṇas. O foremost among the knowers of the Vedas please define them now.

Vyāsa said:—

124. This selfsame question was put to Nandikeśvara by Taṇḍi the Brahminical Yogin. I shall tell you what he had said.

Nandikeśvara said:—

125. O Taṇḍi, Brahmā the four-faced deity is the main speaker. Hence, O sage, the first Purāṇa is called Brāhma.

126. The second Purāṇa is called Padma. It is so called because it mentions the greatness of the Padmakalpa.

127. Another Purāṇa composed by Parāśara and enlightening the details of Viṣṇu is called Vaiṣṇava Purāṇa. It is said to be composed by Vyāsa since there is no difference between father and son.

128. Those who know the Purāṇas speak that purāṇa as Śiva Purāṇa wherein there are many stories of Śiva in its earlier and later forms.

129. Where the stories of the goddess Durgā are mentioned, it is said to be Bhāgavata Purāṇa as well as Devīpurāṇa.[76]

130-131. The Purāṇa narrated by Nārada is called Nāradīya. The seventh Purāṇa is called, O Taṇḍi, Mārkaṇḍeya because the great sage Mārkaṇḍeya is the speaker therein. Since it is related to the fire-god, the Purāṇa is called Āgneya. Since it recounts future events the Purāṇa is called the Bhaviṣya Purāṇa.

132. Since the transformation of Brahman is narrated the Purāṇa is called Brahmavaivarta. Since the story of Liṅga is mentioned it is called Liṅga Purāṇa.

133-135. O sage, the twelfth Purāṇa Varāha is so called because it contains the story of Varāha, the great Boar. In the Skanda Purāṇa the speaker is lord Śiva himself and the listener is Skanda. In the Vāmana Puraṇa the story of Vāmana (the Dwarf-god) is mentioned. The Kūrma Purāṇa contains the story of Kūrma (the tortoise-god). The Matsya Purāṇa is so called because it is expounded by Matsya. The Garuḍa Purāṇa is so called because the speaker is Garuḍa himself. Since the story of the entire cosmic egg is mentioned, the last Purāṇa is called Brahmāṇḍa Purāṇa.

Sūta said :—

136. This question was put by me to the intelligent Vyāsa. From him the definitions of the Purāṇas were heard by me.

137. Thus was Vyāsa born of Satyavatī and Parāśara.

76. According to ŚP., the Śaivite Purāṇa Devībhāgavata, and not the Viṣṇuite Purāṇa 'Mahābhāgavata' belongs to the eighteen Purāṇas. See Winternitz H.I.L. Vol I Pt. II PP. 486-87.

He composed the excellent Mahābhārata and the Purāṇa Saṁhitās.

138. O brahmin, you shall not entertain a doubt as to why Satyavatī had sexual intercourse with Parāśara and Śantanu.

139. This wondrous birth has sufficient reasons behind it. In the story of great men the good qualities shall be grasped by the intelligent people.

140. He who reads or listens to this great secret is rid of all sins and is honoured in the world of sages.

CHAPTER FORTYFIVE[77]

(*The incarnation of Mahākālikā*)

The sages said:—

1. The beautiful episode of Śiva with various incidental anecdotes and narratives of various incarnations, is heard. It yields both worldly pleasures and salvation to men.

2. O foremost among those who know Brahman, we wish to hear from you the beautiful story of the mother of the universe, the goddess.

3. The first primordial Śakti of Siva the great Brahman, who is called Umā, is the great mother of the three worlds.

4. Her two incarnations—Satī and Haimavatī, have been heard, O intelligent Sūta. Please mention her other incarnations too.

5. Which intelligent man will be reluctant to hear the good attributes of the glorious mother? Wise men never abandon them.

Sūta said:—

6. You are all blessed and contented noble souls in as

77. For the close similarity of the form and contents of the present and succeeding chapters ending with Umāsaṁhitā compare Mār. P: the narrative of Durgā.

much as you inquire about the great story of Umā, the great mother.

7. Sages consider the dust-particles of the feet of those who listen, narrate and inquire about it, on a par with holy centres.

8. Blessed and contented are they, their parents and their family, whose mind is merged in the goddess, the great Knowledge.

9. Those who do not eulogise the goddess of the gods, the cause of all causes are deluded by the attributes of Māyā. They are unfortunate. There is no doubt in this.

10. Those who do not worship the great goddess, the ocean of the juice of mercy, fall in the blind well in the form of the cruel worldly existence.

11. Abandoning the goddess and resorting to another deity is as bad as abandoning the Gaṅgā and resorting to water in the desert for the sake of satisfaction.

12. Which excellent man will abandon her whose very remembrance bestows all the four aims of life without any strain?

13. This same question was put to Medhas by the noble Suratha. Please listen. I shall narrate what was mentioned by Medhas.

14. Formerly in the Svārociṣa Manvantara there was a king Virathā. Suratha his son was of great strength and exploit.

15. He was very munificent, truthful, efficient in duties, a devotee of the goddess, an ocean of kindness and the protector of his subjects.

16. While he was thus ruling over the earth, with the brilliance of Indra, nine other kings became desirous of seizing his land.

17. They laid siege to his capital Kolā.[78] The king had a terrible war with them.

18. That king was defeated by his powerful enemies in the war. His kingdom was seized and he was banished from his city Kolā.

78. Kolā is identical with the modern Kolhāpur in the Mahārāṣtra State.

19. The king went to another city of his along with his ministers. There too he was defeated by his enemies who had a large following.

20. His ministers and officers became inimical to him due to adverse fate. They took away all the wealth from the treasury.

21. The king left his city pretending to go out for hunting. Alone he got up on a horse and went to the dense forest.

22-23. Going about here and there, the king saw the hermitage of a great sage. It was shining all round with flower gardens. Everywhere the sound of Vedic hymns was heard. All the animals there were quiet and peaceful. The disciples and the disciples of their disciples moved here and there.

24. O intelligent one, tigers and other ferocious and powerful animals did not harass the animals of less strength in that hermitage, thanks to the power of the leading brahmin.

25. The king who was very kind and learned was welcomed and honoured by the leading sage with pleasing words, accommodation and food and stayed there.

26-27. Once the king began to think anxiously—"Alas, my kingdom has been seized by my haughty enemies. I am unfortunate. My intellect is confounded. I have lost my splendour. The kingdom which had been well guarded by my ancestors is now enjoyed by my enemies.

28. There was no king in this family as weak as I. What shall I do? Where shall I go? How shall I get the kingdom back?

29. My hereditary ministers and counsellors have left me. I do not know which king they serve now.

30-32. I do not know what plight they are in, after the ruination of the kingdom. My heroic soldiers, very enthusiastic in the battle, slayers of enemies, now serve another king. Huge elephants like mountains, horses fast as wind have gone away. Is the traditional treasury accumulated by my ancestors well guarded or not? Thus the very virtuous king became much deluded.

33-35. In the meantime a certain Vaiśya came there. The king asked him—"Sir, who are you? Why have you come here? Why do you appear to be very morose and dejected? Please tell me this, now."

On hearing the sweet words of the king, the leading Vaiśya Samādhi shed tears. He spoke to the king in words full of humility and friendship.

The Vaiśya said:—

36-38. "O king, I am a Vaiśya Samādhi, born of a rich family. Out of greed for my wealth I have been abandoned by my wife, sons and others. I am depressed by my past Karman. O king, I have come here to the forest. I am worried about my sons, grandsons, wife, brothers, their sons and friends. O lord, ocean of mercy, I am in dark about their welfare.

The king said:—

39. How is it that you love, even as senseless animals do, those sons and others who are of evil conduct and covetous for wealth and by whom you have been ousted?

The Vaiśya said:—

40. O king, words pregnant with substantial sense have been uttered by you. Still my mind is deluded by the tie of love.

41. O excellent sage, the king and the Vaiśya, both of them equally deluded then approached the sage Medhas.

42. The valorous king accompanied by the chief of the Vaiśyas bowed his head to the leading Yogin.

43. With palms joined in reverence the king spoke to the sage:—"O holy lord, it behoves you now to dispel our delusion.

44. Abandoned by the royal glory I have resorted to this dense forest. Still I am not content and happy since my kingdom has been taken away.

45. This Vaiśya has been expelled from his house by his people, wife and others. Still his sense of affinity and kinship with them does not go off.

46. What is the reason hereof? Please say. Wise though we are, our minds are afflicted and agitated by delusion. This is great foolishness.

The sage said:—

47. The great Māyā in the form of the eternal Śakti is the material cause of the universe. It is this that drags the minds of all and makes them deluded.

48. O lord, Brahmā and other gods deluded by this Māyā do not realise the truth. What then is the story of men?

49. That alone, Parameśvarī of three attributes, creates the universe; she alone sustains it and she alone destroys it at the proper time.

50. O excellent king, only he surmounts this delusion on whom the favourite goddess who assumes forms as she pleases becomes delighted.

The king said:—

51. O sage, who is that Goddess? Who is that great Māyā who fascinates all? How was that goddess born? Please tell me.

The sage said:—

52-53. When the whole universe had been one great expanse of water,[79] a vast sea, when Keśava, the king of Yogins, resorted to Yogic slumber and was sleeping on Śeṣa, two Asuras were born of the dirt in the ears of Viṣṇu. They became notorious on the surface of the world in the names of Madhu and Kaiṭabha.

54. They were terrible with huge bodies. They had the dazzling brilliance of the sun at the time of dissolution They had huge jaw bones. Their faces were hideous with curved fangs. They seemed to devour all the worlds.

79. P. 1071 note. For details see Agrawal. MP—A Study PP. 9. 266, 321. We find a rock-cut image of Ekārnava at Udayagiri (c 400 A.D.) The idea is often repeated in the Purāṇas Cf. Viṣṇu P. 1. 3,24.

एकार्णवे तु त्रैलोक्ये ब्रह्मा नारायणात्मकः ।
भोगिशय्यागतः शेते त्रैलोक्यग्रासबृंहितः ॥

55. On seeing the lotus-seated deity in the umbilical lotus[80] of the lord, the two Asuras[81] shouted "Hey, who are you?" and attempted to kill him.

56. On seeing the two Daityas and observing that Viṣṇu was still lying in the vast milky ocean,[82] Brahmā eulogised Parameśvarī.

Brahmā said:—

57. O Mahāmāyā, save me, save me, O goddess favourably disposed to those who seek refuge in you, O mother of the universe, save me from these Daityas of hideous features.

58-59. I bow to the great Māyā, the Yogic slumber, Umā, Satī, Kālarātri, Mahārātri, Moharātri, greater than the greatest, the mother of the three deities, the eternal, the bestower of the fruits of the cherished desires of the devotees, the protectress of the gods and the ocean of mercy.

60. It is by your power that Brahmā creates the world, Viṣṇu protects it and Śiva destroys it at the opportune time.

61. O Mother, you are Svāhā, Svadhā, Hrī, the unalloyed intellect, Tuṣṭi (satisfaction), Puṣṭi nourishment), Śānti (peace), Kṣānti (forbearance), Kṣudhā (hunger) and mercy itself.

62. O mother, you are the Māyā of Viṣṇu, the very consciousness, the great Śakti, Lajjā (bashfulness) and Tṛṣṇā (thirst).

63. You are Bhrānti (Illusion). You appear in the form of Smṛti (Memory): you stay assuming the form of mother. You are Lakṣmī in the house of those who engage themselves in meritorious activities.

80. The idea is often repeated in the Purāṇas. Cp M. 168. 15.

'पद्मं नाभ्युद्भवं चैतत्समुत्पादितवांस्तदा ।

सहस्रपर्णं विरजं भास्कराभं हिरण्मयम् ॥

81. Sprung from the ears of Viṣṇu while he was asleep at the end of a Kalpa, Madhu and Kaiṭabha were about to kill Brahmā but were killed by Viṣṇu. Prof. Agrawal however offers a symbolical interpretation of Madhu and Kaiṭabha as Rajas and Tamas.

82. See P. 224 note.

64. You are Jāti (Birth), Vṛtti (cause of activity) and Vyāpti (pervasiveness.) You pervade everything in the form of intelligence.

65. O Mother, please delude these unthwartable Asuras. O origin of the universe, please waken Viṣṇu the unborn lord."

The sage said:—

66-67. O king, on being requested by Brahmā for the destruction of Madhu and Kaiṭabha, the mother of the universe, the great Vidyā, the presiding deity of all Vidyās, Śakti the enchantress of the three worlds manifested herself as Mahākālī on the twelfth Tithi of the bright half of the month of Phālguna.

68. Then a celestial voice arose:—"O lotus-seated one, do not be afraid. I shall remove the thorn after killing Madhu and Kaiṭabha in the battle."

69. After saying this and coming out of the eyes, mouth etc. of Viṣṇu, the great Māyā stood before Brahmā of unmanifested birth.

70. Viṣṇu, the lord of gods stood up and saw in front of him the Daityas Madhu and Kaiṭabha.

71. A battle ensued between Viṣṇu of unequalled splendour and the two Daityas lasting for five thousand years. Then there ensued a hand-to-hand fight.

72. Deluded by the powerful great Māyā, the excellent Dānava spoke to the lord Viṣṇu—"Ask for whatever boon you desire to choose."

Nārāyaṇa said:—

73. If you are pleased with me grant me this boon that I may kill you. I do not request for any other boon.

The sage said:—

74. On seeing the earth covered by a great expanse of ocean they spoke to Keśava:—"Kill us in a spot where the earth is not covered with water."

75. After giving his consent the lord lifted up his dazzling discus, placed their heads on his loins and cut them off.

76. O king, thus I have told you about the origin of Kālikā. O intelligent one, listen to the origin of Mahālakṣmī now.

77. Although free from aberrations, and devoid of forms and features, goddess Umā manifested herself in different Yugas for the destruction of the distress of the gods, after assuming different forms and features.

78. Thus I have described to you her manifestation in bodily form whose wish alone manifests as everything efficaciously. Thus she conducts her sports in that way and thereby gives chance to her devotees to describe her attributes.

CHAPTER FORTYSIX

(*Incarnation of Mahālakṣmī*)

The sage said:—

1. There was a demon Rambha who was the crest-jewel of the race of Daityas. From him was born Mahiṣa[83] the Dānava of great splendour.

2. That king of Dānavas defeated all the gods in battle and ruled over the kingdom of heaven seated on the throne of lord Indra.

3. The defeated gods sought refuge in Brahmā. With them Brahmā went to the place where Viṣṇu and Śiva[84] were present.

4. After reaching there and bowing to Śivā and Viṣṇu the gods narrated all their woeful tale in the proper order.

5. O lords, we are harassed by the wicked Mahiṣa. We have been ousted from heaven after our defeat in the battle-field.

6. We are wandering in this world of mortals with-

83. According to MB. the Asura Mahiṣa was killed by Kārttikeya. ŚP. mentions his death at the hands of Caṇḍī.

84. The word 'Vṛṣākapī' in the dual form signifies Viṣṇu and Śiva.

out peace or happiness anywhere. O what pitiable plights we—Indra and others—have been led to !

7-8. The sinful Asura who has offered freedom from fear to the partisans of the Daityas, himself performs the ordained task of these—viz, the sun, the moon, Varuṇa, Kubera, Yama, Indra, Agni, wind, the Gandharvas, Vidyādharas and the good Cāraṇas and others as well.

9. Hence it behoves you to save us the gods who have sought refuge in you. O lords, please think of the means of killing him immediately.

10. On hearing the gods, Viṣṇu and Siva were very angry. Their eyes rolled through anger.

11. Then a great splendour issued forth from the mouths of the infuriated Viṣṇu and Śiva and from the bodies of other gods.

12. The gods who were devoted to meditation on Durgā saw the mass of splendour blazing in all the ten directions.

13. That highly terrible splendour issuing forth from the bodies of the gods joined together and became a woman Mahiṣamardinī herself.

14. Her dazzlingly brilliant face constituted the splendour of Śiva, the hairs the splendour of Yama and the arms the splendour of Viṣṇu.

15-18. Her breasts were formulated by the splendour of the moon; the waist by that of Indra; the calves and thighs by that of Varuṇa; the hips by that of the earth; the feet by that of Brahmā ; the toes by that of the sun; the fingers by that of Indra; the nose by that of Kubera; the teeth by that of the patriarch; the eyes by that of fire; the eyebrows by that of the dusk; the ears by that of the wind, her other limbs by that of other heaven-dwellers. Thus the goddess manifested herself on the lotus-seat.

19. On seeing her thus formulated by the mass of splendour of the gods, they attained great delight.

20. Observing that she had no weapons, Brahmā and other gods decided to make her fully equipped with weapons.

21. Then lord Śiva offered her a spear; Lord Kṛṣṇa gave her a discus; Varuṇa conch and noose.

22-23. The fire-god gave her Śakti; the wind-god a bow and a quiver full of arrows; Indra the thunderbolt and a bell; Yama a big staff; Prajāpati a garland of beads; Brahmā a water-pot and the sun the lustrous hair.

24-27. Kāla gave her a sword and a shining shield, the milk ocean a beautiful necklace, two fresh pieces of cloth, the crest-jewel, ear-rings, bangles, crescent-shaped ornaments, beautiful anklets, shoulder-pieces, a necklace and finger-rings. Visvakarman gave her a beautiful axe and the ocean various weapons, an impenetrable armour, a beautiful garland and a lotus.

28-29. Himavat gave her a lion and gems of various sorts. Kubera a vessel filled with wine. Śeṣa a Nāgahāra of wonderful workmanship, studded with various precious gems.

30. Thus honoured, the goddesss with these and other similar objects, ornaments, weapons etc. shouted loudly again and again.

31. The sky was filled with her terrible noise that echoed tremendously and made the three worlds agitated.

32. The four oceans shook and rolled. The earth quaked. Cries of victory were shouted by the gods harassed by Mahiṣa.

33. Then the gods eulogised the great Śakti, Ambikā in the form of Mahālakṣmī with words choked with devotion.

34. On seeing the world agitated, the enemies of the gods got up with uplifted arms and with their armies ready for war.

35. The infuriated Mahiṣa rushed at the direction of the sound and saw the goddess who had pervaded the three worlds with her beautiful lustre.

36. In the meantime, crores of great heroes led by Mahiṣāsura came there with weapons.

37-38. Cikṣura, Cāmara, Udagra, Karāla, Uddhaṭa, Bāṣkala; Tāmra, Ugrāsya, Ugravīrya, Biḍāla, Andhaka, Durdhara, Durmukha, Trinetra Mahāhanu—these and many others, heroic and efficient in battle, came there.

39. As they, the masters of weapons and missiles,

fought with the goddess in the battle a terribly long time elapsed.

40. Different weapons and missiles hurled by the hosts of enemies were rendered futile instantaneously by the power of the goddess.

41. Then the goddess hit and struck the hosts of enemies Cikṣura and others with her club, arrows, spear, Śakti and axe.

42. When his armies fell the demon Mahiṣa struggled with the hosts of soldiers that issued from the breath of the goddess.

43. He kicked some with the hoofs, hit some with the horns and others with his tail and snout.

44. After slaying the Gaṇas the chief of Asuras rushed at the lion of the goddess in order to kill it. Then she became wrathful.

45. He of great virility thrashed the ground with his hoofs, uprooted a mountain with his horns, hurled it and shouted.

46. O excellent king, heavy mountains hurled by him as he rushed all round fell in the battle-ground from the sky.

47. Clouds split by his horns were shattered to pieces. The ocean struck at with his tail throbbed and splashed water beyond the shores all round.

48. On seeing the demon Mahiṣa thus infuriated, Ambikā, the protectress of the gods, became ready to kill him.

49. She took up a noose and hurled it at him. She bound the Asura Mahiṣa. Then the demon abandoned his assumed guise.

50. Wielding Māyā, he became a lion. Soon as Ambikā tried to cut off his head he became armed with a sword.

51. She then struck him with the arrows, as he stood there with the sword and shield. He then became an elephant and struck at the lion with his trunk.

52. The goddess cut off his hand with her sword. The demon then assumed his original form.

53. He then agitated three worlds including the mobile and immobile beings. Then, Caṇḍikā of great honour and exploit became infuriated.

54. She drank the beverage again and again. With eyes rolliug she laughed aloud. The haughty Asura too, proud of his strength and exploit, roared.

55. He uprooted the mountains and hurled them at her. She too reduced them to powder and struck them with arrows.

56. With her face reddened as a result of the inebriation after drinking wine, and with her senses excited, she spoke in a tone as majestic as the rumbling of the clouds.

The goddess said:—

57. "O stupid fellow, O demon of ruined intellect, why are you stubborn in vain ? None of the Asuras in the three worlds can stand before me".

The sage said :—

58. Thus saying the goddess pounced on him, stamped on his neck and pierced him with her fierce spear.

59. Pressed with her foot and overwhelmed by her might the Asura seemed as good as half dead.

60. Still he continued to fight. His head was cut off with the sword and he was felled down on the ground.

61. Crying "Alas ! Alas" loudly, his followers, afraid of the battle fled from the scene shouting "Save us, O save us".

62. The god Indra and others, eulogised the goddess. The Gandharvas sang songs; the celestial damsels danced.

63. O king, thus the origin of Mahālakṣmī has been narrated to you. Now listen to the origin of Sarasvatī with a calm mind.

CHAPTER FORTYSEVEN

(Dhūmralocana, Caṇḍa, Muṇḍa and Raktabīja are slain)

The sage said :—

1. There was a Daitya Śumbha and another equally powerful Niśumbha. The three worlds including mobile and immobile beings were attacked by the two brothers.

2. The gods afflicted and harassed by them went to Himālaya and saluted the mother of all living beings, the bestower of all desires.

The gods said :—

3. O goddess Durgā, Victory be to you. O, beloved of your kinsmen, be victorious. Obeisance to you, the cause of the protection of the three worlds.

4. Obeisance to you, the bestower of salvation, obeisance to the great mother, the cause of the creation, sustenance and annihilation of the world.

5. O goddess of the form of Kālikā, Tārā. Chinnamastā, Śrīvidyā, Obeisance to you.

6. O goddess of the worlds, of the form of Bhairava, obeisance to you. Obeisance to Bagalāmukhī (stork-faced). Obeisance, to Dhūmāvatī.

7. Obeisance to Tripurasundarī, to Mātaṅgī, to Ajitā (the unconquered) and to Vijayā.

8. Obeisance to Jayā, Maṅgalā Vilāsinī, to you of the form of milking maid and of terrible form.

9. Obeisance to you, O goddess, of the form of the unconquered, of permanent form, the protectress of those who seek refuge in you.

10. Obeisance to the one knowable through Vedānta; obeisance to you the great soul, the heroine of infinite worlds of this universe.

11. Eulogised thus by the gods the delighted goddess the bestower of boons, spoke, to the gods—"Who is being eulogised by you here ?"

12. Then a virgin came out of the body of the goddess. Even as they were winking she spoke to the goddess with great reverence.

13. "O mother, this eulogy is addressed to me by the heaven-dwellers harassed by the powerful Daityas Śumbha and Niśumbha."

14. Since she emerged out of the inner vestures of her body she is called Kauśikī. The destroyer of the Asura Śumbha is being sung in that name.

15. She alone is said to be Ugratārikā and great Ugratārikā. She is called Mātaṅgī after the source from which she manifested herself.

16. She addressed the gods—"All of you stay here fearlessly. I shall carry out your task without any strain. I am independent".

17. After saying this, the goddess vanished. Canda and Muṇḍa—the attendants of Śumbha and Niśumba saw the goddess.

18. On seeing her beautiful form pleasing to the eyes they were fascinated. They lost their consciousness and fell on the ground.

19. Returning to their king they narrated the details to him "O king, a certain beautiful lady hitherto unseen has been seen by us.

20. Seated on a lion, on the beautiful peak of the Himavat she was served by the virgins of the gods with palms joined in reverence.

21. They massaged her feet and hands, decorated her tresses, and applied collyrium to her eyes.

22. A certain damsel held out the mirror to her face. Another handed over the betel-leaf along with cloves and cardamom.

23. Some picked up the fallen dice and stood in front of her. Some bedecked her body with ornaments and clothes.

24. Her calves and thighs are like the stem of the plantain tree. Her nose is like that of a parrot. Her arms are like serpents and creepers. She wears a beautiful girdle. The anklets round her feet are jingling.

25. Pearl necklaces heave over her breasts rendered fragrant with the musk. Necklaces shine round her neck. She was sporting about bedecked in chaplets.

26. She has semi-circular marks on her forehead. She wears ear-rings set with gems. Her plaited hair are pretty. The wide three eyes bedeck her face.

27. She is imperishable, possessed of garlands. Bangles shine in her hands. There are gold rings round her fingers. Shining bracelets make her hands dazzle.

28. She is clad in white garments. She shines in her lotus-pose with the marks of saffron on her forehead which is also bedecked with the moon.

29. She has the brilliance of lightning. She wears precious garments. Her breasts are elevated within her bodice. She holds excellent weapons with her eight uplifted arms.

30. There is no lady among the Asuras, Nāgas, Gandharvas or Dānavas in the three worlds as beautiful as she.

31. Hence the fitness for sexual indulgence with her rests only in you since she is a gem among ladies and O lord, you are a gem among men.

32. On hearing the words of Caṇḍa and Muṇḍa that great demon Śumbha sent a messenger Sugrīva to her.

33. "O messenger, there is a certain beautiful lady on the snow-capped mountain. Mentioning these words of mine she shall be strenuously brought here".

34. Thus urged by him, the excellant Dānava Sugrīva went to Himācala and spoke to the great goddess, the mother of the universe.

The messenger said:—

35. O gentle lady, the Daitya Śumbha and his brother Niśumbha are very strong and valorous. They are famous in the three worlds.

36. O goddess, I am a messenger of Śumbha. I have come with his message to which you will listen please.

37. "I have defeated Indra aud others in the battle and taken away their jewels. I enjoy the share of the gods offered to them in the sacrifices.

38. You are a jewel among women, more precious than other jewels. Resort to me or to my younger brother, exhibiting your loving emotion.

39. On hearing the message of Śumbha conveyed by the messenger the Mahāmāyā, the beloved consort of Śiva, spoke.

The goddess said:—

40-41. O messenger, you speak the truth, not the lie. But I have taken a vow that I shall endeavour to make one alone as my husband who can shake off my pride, who can conquer me in the battle. None else.

42. Hence you convey my words to Śumbha and Niśumbha. Let either do whatever is proper in this matter.

43. On hearing these words of the goddess the Asura Sugrīva returned to his king and acquainted him with every detail.

44. On hearing the report of the messenger Śumbha of stern rule angrily said to Dhūmrākṣa, the foremost of his generals.

45-46. O Dhūmrākṣa, there is a beautiful lady on the snow-capped Himālaya mountain. Go quickly and fetch her here. O excellent Asura, do not be afraid of this expedition. If she wishes to fight, you shall fight strenuously.

47. Thus directed the Daitya Dhūmrākṣa went to Himālaya and spoke to the goddess who was a part of Umā.

48. "O lady, approach my lord. Otherwise I shall kill you. I am accompanied by sixtythousand Asuras"

The goddess said:—

49. "O hero, you are commissioned by the king of Daityas. If you kill me what can I do for you ? But I consider it impossible to go without a fight."

50. Thus addressed, the Dānava Dhūmrākṣa rushed at her but was burnt with a mere Huṅkāra uttered by her.

51. Since then, that goddess is called Dhūmāvatī in the world. When propitiated she destroys hosts of enemies of her devotees.

52. After Dhūmrākṣa was killed, his army was crunched and munched by the infuriated lion. Those who were spared fled away.

53. On hearing that the Daitya was killed by the goddess, the valorous Śumbha was angry and bit his lips.

54. He sent the Asuras-Caṇḍa, Munda and Raktabīja in order. The Daityas, thus ordered, went to the spot where Ambikā was stationed.

55. On seeing the goddess seated on a lion, possessed of Aṇimā[85] and other Siddhis and dazzling the quarters with her brilliance, the leading Dānavas said.

56. "O lady, hasten to approach Śumbha and Niśumbha. Otherwise we shall kill you along with your Gaṇas and your lion.

57. O lady, choose him as your husband. He is eulogised by the guardians of the quarters and others. You will attain a great bliss rare to attain by the gods."

58. On hearing these words the goddess Ambā smiled and spoke interesting and truthful words.

59. Lord Śiva, the great Brahman, the eternal god is without a second. Even the Vedas do not understand his reality. What then of Viṣṇu and others?

60. I am His subtle Prakṛti. How can I choose another as my husband? Even if she is overwhelmed by love does a lioness choose a jackal as her mate?

61. A female elephant does not take an ass nor does a leopardess take a hare. O Daityas, overcome by the Serpent of Death you speak in vain.

62. Descend to Pātāla[86] all of you. If you have the power, fight." On hearing her provocative words the Asuras said to one another.

63. "We do not kill you as you are a woman. But if you desire for battle be ready with your lion."

64. While they spoke thus the fight ensued. The arrows rained in the battle, sharp arrows from either side.

65. Thus fighting with them sportively the goddess slew the Asura along with Caṇḍa and Muṇḍa.

66. Though they had an inimical feeling these enemies of the gods attained in the end that world which her followers go to.

85. See P. 235 note.

86. According to the Purānic Mythology it is the seventh region escending from the earth below.

CHAPTER FORTYEIGHT

(*The manifestation of Sarasvatī*)

The king said:—

1-2. O holy lord, O brahmin, what did Śumbha, the suppressor of the gods, do on hearing that Dhūmrākṣa, Caṇḍa and Raktabīja were killed by the goddess? Please tell me this now. I desire to hear the purifying tale of the goddess, the cause of the universe.

The sage said:—

3. O king, on hearing that the leading Daityas had been killed, the great Asura of commendable valour ordered his invincible followers who were thrilled at the very mention of the war.

4. At my behest the Daityas born of the race of Kālaka[87] have all assembled here with their armies and along with Kālakeyas,[88] Mauryas,[89] Daurhṛdas[90] and others. Let them march on with hopes of victory.

5. After ordering the demons, Śumbha and Niśumbha mounted on their chariots and set out. Their armies too followed them like swarms of moths rising up from a mountain definitely for their destruction.

6. Mṛdaṅgas, Mardalas, Bherikās Diṇḍimas, Jharjharas and Ānakas were sounded. The warmongers rejoiced in the battle-ground. Those who were afraid fled away for their life.

7. Clad in their martial dress the soldiers came in their healthy spirits to the battleground. Holding various weapons and missiles they teased one another each eager for his victory.

8. Soldiers on elephants, looked at the enemy with

87. In respect of this House no details are available either from the MB. or the Purāṇas.

88. Kālakeyas, descendants of Kālakā wife of Kaśyapa, are often mentioned as powerful demons in the MB. and the Purāṇas.

89. Mauryas are the descendants of the Asura Mura who is generally mentioned in connection with Prāgjyotiṣa.

90. Daurhṛdas are the descendants of the Asura Durhṛda.

indifference. In the company of the lord of Asuras they rejoiced in the battle.

9. The sound arising from the guns rose up repeatedly making the gods tremble. A great darkness enveloped the sky. Even the chariot of the sun was not visible.

10. Foot-soldiers set out in excessive numbers desirous of victory. Soldiers in chariots, on horsebacks, elephants and others set out joyously in crores and crores.

11. The rutting elephants like massive black mountains spread their trumpeting sound in the battle-field. Camels resembling small hills produced hoarse sounds from their throats.

12. Neighing horses hailing from exalted lands, with big ornaments round their necks, expert in the knowledge of their gaits planted their legs on the heads of elephants and flew like birds.

13. On seeing the army of the enemy advancing thus, Ambikā kept her bow well-strung. She sounded her bell that distressed the enemy. The lion too shook his manes and roared.

14. Seeing her bedecked in fine ornaments, holding weapons and stationed on the Himālaya mountain Niśumbha spoke words full of sentiments like a man clever in understanding the emotions of beautiful women.

15. "Even a petal of the Mālatī (Jasmine) flower thrown on the beautiful body of women like you may distress you. O goddess, how will you carry on a terrible war with the self-same handsome body of yours ?"

16. After saying thus the great Asura became silent. Caṇḍikā spoke to him—"O foolish Asura, why do you prattle in vain? Either fight or else return to Pātāla.[91]

17. The heroic demon, becoming infuriated, made a wonderful shower of arrows on the battle-field just as masses of clouds shower water during rains.

18. Along with his arrogant followers the demon fought with sharp weapons as spears, axes, iron clubs,

91. It is the lowermost of the nether regions where Vāsuki reigns over the Nāgas.

parighas, bows, Bhuśuṇḍikās, javelins, horseshoe-edged arrows and great swords.

19. In that war great elephants looking like black mountains with foreheads pierced ran here and there. The banners of Śumbha and Niśumbha white like flying cranes fluttered here and there.

20. The demons were shattered by Kālikā like fishes. The dreadful horses were beheaded and killed in the battle. The other demons were devoured by the lion.

21. In the battlefield streams of blood flowed. The dead soldiers floated. Their tresses of hair resembled the moss. Their upper cloths resembled the white foam.

22. A great fight ensued where soldiers of equal rank fought with one another. The cavalrymen fought their counterpart; the elephant-riders with those on elephants: the charioteers with those on chariots and the footsoldiers with footsoldiers.

23. Then Niśumbha thought to himself—"A terrible period has set in now. Even a poor man may become rich and rich man poor if the time is adverse.

24. A senseless fellow may become intelligent and an intelligent man dull. A wicked man may be praised by the noble. The great and the powerful may be vanquished. The weak may come out victorious in the war.

25. Victory or defeat come naturally at the stance of the lord. Neither Śiva nor Brahmā nor Viṣṇu has been able to transgress his law.

26. Heroes do not come to the battlefield for turning back. But how can I attain victory in a battle with this lady who has destroyed my entire host?

27. Indeed this lady is the ancient Prakṛti, the great Śivā come here to achieve the task of the gods and harass the army of the Daityas. She can never be an ordinary woman

28. It is inglorious to be killed by a woman or to kill a woman for those who desire to taste the pleasures of war. Still how shall we show our faces to the king of Asuras without fighting?

29. After thinking thus and sitting in a great chariot

driven by a charioteer he hastened to the spot where the lady consort of Śiva was present; the goddess whose youth was sought after by the celestial damsels.

30. He addressed her thus—"O goddess, of what avail is it if the mercenary soldiers are killed ? If you desire to fight, let both of us clad in martial dress fight with each other.

31. The goddess addressed Kālī then—"See the foolish ambition of the two Asuras. Time the instigator of good and bad actions renders the mind work in a different way when adversity is imminent."

32. Then Niśumbha attacked Caṇḍikā as well as Kālī with thousands of arrows. With the volleys of her arrows Śivā split into a thousand pieces the arrows discharged by the Asura.

33. He then lifted up his lustrous sword along with the shield and struck the lion on its head. With her great sword she split it too as the woodcutters do to a tree with the axe.

34. When the sword was split he thrust an arrow into her chest. The arrow too was cut. He then hurled the trident which powdered it with her fist.

35. Prepared to die the heroic Asura seized a mace and rushed at her. She reduced the mace into powder with the edge of her trident. The demon shattered the trident with another mace.

36. Then she struck Niśumbha with her sharp, terrible serpentine poisonous arrows that were accustomed to drink the blood of Asuras and brought him down to the earth.

37. When his younger brother of great honour and strength fell Śumbha was furious. The eight-armed demon seated himself in a chariot and came to the place where Sivā was present.

38. She blew the conch Arindama, produced unbearable bow-twang; the lion shaking its manes roared. The whole sky reverberated with the threefold round.

39. Then the mother of the universe laughed boisterously making all the demons tremble with fear. The gods shouted cries of "Victory" when she challenged the Asuras in the battle.

40. The king of Daityas hurled a spear of shining flames which was struck down by a meteor. Śivā shattered the arrows discharged by Śumbha. He too split the arrows discharged by Śivā into a thousand pieces.

41. She lifted up her trident and struck the great Asura. He fell down unconscious shaking heaven and earth along with the ocean like a mountain whose wings had been chopped off by Indra.[92]

42. Suffering the pain arising from the trident, the powerful demon, the suppressor of the gods, created ten thousand hands and struck Kālī and Caṇḍikā along with the lion, by means of his discus.

43. Splitting sportively the discus hurled by him, she hurt and struck the Asura with the trident. Thus both of them met their death at the lotus-hands of Śivā that sanctify the universe and attained the great region.

44. When the powerful Niśumbha, and Śumbha of terrible exploit were killed the Daityas entered Pātāla.[93]

45. Others were devoured by Kālī's lion. The remaining Asuras being excessively frightened fled in the quarters.

46. The rivers with clear water flowed along their paths; the winds blew very gentle to the touch: the sky became clear.

47. Sacrifices were revived by the gods and the sages, Lord Indra and the gods felt blissful again.

48-49. O lord, this story of Umā is holy and meritorious. It describes the destruction of the king of Daityas. He who regularly reads this with faith enjoys all worldly pleasures inaccessible even to the gods and attains the abode of Umā hereafter by the very grace of the goddess.

50. Thus was the goddess, slayer of Śumbha born. She is said to be Sarasvatī. O king, she has manifested herself as a part of Umā.

92. See P. 645 note.

93. Pātāla is called Balisadman—the abode of Bali. According to a legend God Viṣṇu in the form of a Brahmin dwarf craved from Bali the boon of three steps of ground and having obtained it stepped over heaven and earth in two strides but then out of respect to Bali's devotion and his grandson Prahlāda's virtues, he stopped short and left to him Pātāla, the nether region. See P. 955 note 271; P. 750 note 147.

CHAPTER FORTYNINE

(The manifestation of Umā)

The sages said:—

1. O Sūta, the most excellent among the omniscients please mention the incarnation of Umā, the goddess of all the worlds and the mother of Sarasvatī.

2. She is sung as the primordial Prakṛti of the supreme Brahman. She is both possessed and devoid of forms. She is of the form of eternal bliss. She is Satī.

Sūta said:—

3. O sages, listen lovingly to the great story, the perfect knowledge of which alone helps man to attain the great goal.

4. Once there was a clash between the gods and the Asuras. Thanks to the power of the goddess the gods became victorious.

5. Then the gods were proud and haughty. They boasted—"We are blessed. What can the Asuras do to us ?"

6. Of our unbearable prowess, the Asuras are afraid. They have gone to Pātāla saying, "Run, run".

7. Then all of them proclaimed thus: "Wonderful is the strength, splendour and good luck of the gods that has reduced the race of the Daityas.

8. Then a mass of splendour appeared, at the unprecedented sight of which the gods were surprised.

9. Ignorant of the real glory and the intention of the goddess to quell their arrogance, the Asuras said with choking throats "What is this ? What is this ?"

10. Then the lord Indra ordered the gods—"Go ye all and examine it and ascertain what it is."

11. Urged by Indra, the wind-god approached splendour and addressed it, "Who are you ?" The splendour too put the same question to him.

12. Thus asked by the big mass of splendour the wind-god replied arrogantly.—"I am Vāyu the vital breath of the universe."

13. Everything in the universe, mobile or immobile, is woven like warp and woof into me. I am the support of everything. I move the entire universe."

14. Then the great splendour said:—"If you are competent to move, O wind-god, please move this blade of grass I have set before you. Move it as you please."

15. Then wind-god put forth all his efforts. But the blade of grass did not stir from its position. Then he was put to shame.

16. The wind-god went silently to the assembly of Indra. There he narrated the details of his discomfiture.

17. "False is our pride that we are the lords. In fact we are helpless, insignificant creatures."

18. Then Indra sent all the gods. When they could not realise anything Indra himself went there.

19. On seeing Indra come, the unbearable splendour vanished immediately. Indra was surprised.

20. Then Indra thought to himself again and again—"I seek refuge in him alone whose conduct is such as this."

21-22. In the meantime, in order to bless them and remove their arrogance, Śivā, the embodied form of undeceitful mercy, existence, knowledge and bliss, manifested herself on the ninth day of the bright half of the month Caitra when the sun was in the middle of the day.

23. Shining among the mass of splendour she brightened the quarters with her brilliance. She enlightened the gods, saying "I alone am Brahman."

24. In her four hands she held boons, noose, goad and the mystic gesture of protection. She was served by the Vedas and looked beautiful and proud of her blooming youth.

25. She wore red garments and red garlands. Red sandal paste was smeared over her body. She was as dazzling as a crore of cupids. Her lustre was that of a crore moons.

26. The great Māyā, in the form of the immanent soul of all, the cosmic witness of all living beings, and the great Brahman, spoke.

Umā said:—

27. Neither Brahmā nor Viṣṇu nor Śiva the slayer of

the Tripura demon can bluff before me. What about the other gods ?

28. The great Brahman, the great light in the form of the two Praṇavas, I alone am. I am all. There is none other beside me.

29. Though devoid of form I possess forms. I constitute all principles. I am eternal and my attributes cannot be disputed. I am both the cause and the effect.

30. Sometimes I have the form of a woman, sometimes of a man. Sometimes both. I am goddess assuming all forms.

31. I am the creator, the protector and the destroyer of the world. I am the enchantress of the universe.

32. All the Śaktis—Kālī, Lakṣmī and Sarasvatī as well as others are born of my parts. So also the arts originate from me.

38. Due to my power alone the demons are conquered by you. Without knowing me of this nature you bluff as the lords of all.

34. Just as a magician makes the wooden doll of a woman dance so also I the goddess make all living beings dance.

35. Being afraid of me the wind blows, the fire-god burns and the guardians of the quarters carry on their duties.

36. Independent that I am, I sportively bestow victory on the gods sometimes and on the Daityas sometimes.

37. It is my form that is described in the Vedas as indestructible, the great abode, the one beyond Māyā and that which is greater than the greatest.

38. My form is two-fold—Saguṇa and Nirguṇa. One is mixed with Māyā and the other is free from it.

39. O gods, endowed with devotion, realise this and eschew your arrogance, worship me, the eternal Prakṛti.

40. On hearing the merciful words of the goddess, the gods eulogised her, with their shoulders drooping with devotion.

41. O goddess of the universe, forgive us. O goddess, be pleased. O mother, let us not be arrogant again. Please be merciful.

42. Since then the gods began to propitiate her as

before. They eschewed their arrogance and became pure in mind.

43. O Brahmins, thus I have narrated to you the menifestation of Umā. By only hearing this men attain the great region.

CHAPTER FIFTY

(*The incarnation of Śatākṣī etc.*)

The sages said:—

1. O intelligent one, all of us are anxious to hear the episode of Durgā every day. Please tell us another wonderful tale of the goddess.

2. O Sūta, the most excellent of the story-tellers, we are not satiated even as we hear different nectarine stories narrated by you.

Sūta said:—

3. The most powerful son of Ruru, famous as Durgama secured the four Vedas as a result of the boon granted by Brahmā.

4. Securing this strength that cannot be thwarted even by the gods he wrought havoc on the earth, making the gods tremble in heaven.

5. When the Vedas were destroyed the sacred rites were ruined. Brahmins and the gods fe.. off from their right conduct.

6. None offered charitable gifts; none performed penances; there was neither worship nor sacrifice. Then a great drought befell the earth extending to a period of a hundred years.

7. There was a great hue and cry in all the three worlds. The people felt miserable being afflicted by hunger and thirst.

8. Rivers, oceans, tanks, wells and lakes dried. Trees and plants withered.

9. On seeing the misery of the distressed subjects the gods sought refuge in the Yogic Māyā, Maheśvarī.

The gods said—

10. O Mahāmāyā, save all your people. Check your fury or the worlds will be ruined.

11-12. O ocean of mercy, O supportress of the distressed, kill this demon too just as you have killed Śumbha, Niśumbha. Dhūmrākṣa, Caṇḍa, Muṇḍa, Raktabīja, Madhu, Kaiṭabha and Mahiṣa.

13. Boys are guilty of offence at every step but who on earth brooks it except the mother ?

14. When miseries afflict the gods and the brahmins you incarnate for the welfare of the people.

15. On hearing the distress of the gods the merciful goddess revealed to them her form possessed of many eyes.

16. The goddess with her lotus-face beaming with delight held in her four hands the bow, the arrows, the lotus and different fruits and roots.

17. On seeing her people scorched and distressed, the goddess was dejected. With her eyes full of mercy she cried for nine days and nights.

18. The tears took the forms of thousands of water-currents released from her eyes. The worlds, the plants and medicinal herbs were delighted by them.

19. They turned into the rivers and oceans of deep waters. Vegetables, roots and fruits grew on the earth.

20. To the learned and the gods she distributed the fruits in her hands. To the cows she gave the tender blades of grass and to others the things they deserved.

21. All including the gods, brahmins and men were satisfied. Then the goddess said—"What else shall I do for you ?"

22. The gods then gathered together and said, "The people have been rendered happy and satisfied. O goddess, be pleased and redeem the Vedas taken by Durgama."

23. After saying "So be it" she said. "Go ye all to your abodes. Ere long I shall give you the Vedas."

24. Then the joyous gods returned to their abodes after

bowing to the goddess the cause of the universe with her eyes that resembled full-blown blue lotus.

25. Then a great bustle arose in the three regions heaven, earth and sky. On hearing it the son of Ruru besieged the city immediately.

26. Then after creating a big circle of splendour all round for the protection of the gods, Śivā herself came out of it.

27. A great battle ensued between the goddess and the Daitya. Both showered arrows in the battle, piercing the armour of each other.

28-29. In the meantime ten beautiful forms came out of Kālī Viz Tārā, Chinnamastā, Śrīvidyā, Bhuvaneśvarī, Bhairavī, Bagalā, Dhūmrā, Śrīmattripurasundarī, Mātaṅgī and Mahāvidyā with weapons in their hands.

30. Then appeared innumerable mothers of divine forms, wearing the digit of the moon and with a lustre resembling the splendour of lightning.

31. Then a terrible combat ensued between the Asuras and the mothers. The army of the son of Ruru, consisting of a hundred Akṣauhiṇīs was killed in the battle.

32. Then the goddess struck Durgama with the edge of her trident. He fell on the earth like an uprooted tree.

33. Thus after killing him the goddess redeemed the four Vedas and gave them to the gods.

The gods said:—

34. O Ambikā, for our welfare that form of infinite eyes was assumed by you. Hence sages will glorify you as Śatākṣī.

35. Since the worlds were sustained by you with vegetables sprouting from your body, you will be famous as Śākambharī.

36. O Śivā, since you killed the Daitya Durgama you will be known as Durgā.

37. O Yogic slumber, O Mahābalā, O bestower of knowledge, O the mother of the universe, Obeisance be to you.

38. Obeisance to the heroine of infinite universes known as the supreme goddess in the Mahāvākyas as Tattvamasi.

39. O Mother, we who are unaware of your power and greatness, cannot adequately eulogise you who are inaccessible through words, mind or body and whose eyes are the sun and the moon.

40. Who else will bestow mercy on seeing us the gods except the great goddess Śatākṣī the mother?

41. Effort shall be made by you so that the three worlds will not be pestered continuously with obstacles and our enemies shall be destroyed.

The goddess said:—

42. Just as the cows run about in excitement quickly on seeing their calves in distress, so also I, Satī, am excited on seeing you in distress and run about.

43. Even a moment appears to be a Yuga if I do not see you since I look at you as my own children for whom I am ready even to lay down my life.

44. No worry or anxious thought need be entertained by you endowed with devotion as long as I stand by you destroying your distress.

45. In the manner I have killed the Daityas I shall kill the Asuras. You need not entertain any doubt in this regard. Truth, I am speaking the truth.

46-47. I shall be born of the womb in the family of cowherds as the daughter of Yaśodā wife of Nandā, when Śumbha and Niśumbha will be born as Daityas. I shall kill the demons and become famous. Men will therefore call me Nandajā.

48. Since I shall be taking the form of a bee and killing the demon Aruṇa, men will glorify me as Bhrāmarī

49. Again I shall take a terrible form and devour the Rākṣasas. I shall then be famous as Bhīmā Devī.

50. Whenever there is harassment caused by the Asuras I shall surely incarnate and work for your welfare.

51. The goddess Śatākṣī, Śākambharī and Durgā are identical. In all the three the individual is the same.

52. There is no deity so compassionate as Śatākṣī the great goddess who cried for nine days on seeing her people scorched and distressed.

CHAPTER FIFTYONE

(Review of holy rites)

The sages said :—

1. O blessed disciple of Vyāsa, O Sūta the most excellent among the knowers of the Purāṇas, we wish to hear some other story of the lord.

2. We wish to hear the most excellent sacred rites of Umā, the mother of the universe, those which were narrated to Vyāsa the great Ātman by Sanatkumāra

Sūta said :—

3. All of you are blessed great souls ; steady in your devotional rites to the goddess. Now listen devotedly to the well-guarded secret of the great Śakti.

Vyāsa said :—

4. O omniscient Sanatkumāra, O intelligent son of Brahmā, I wish to hear the wonderful holy rites of Umā.

5. Please tell me what is pleasing to the great mother. What are its characteristics and on doing what can it be efficacious ?

Sanatkumāra said :—

6. O Dvaipāyana of great intellect, listen to the full description I am going to give of the secret that you ask.

7. Three paths of the glorious mother have been narrated which yield both worldly pleasures and salvation. They are paths of knowledge, holy rites and devotion

8. Jñānayoga is the union of the mind with the Ātman. The union with the external objects is called Kriyāyoga.

9. Bhaktiyoga is the concept of the unity of the Ātman with the goddess. Of the three I mention Kriyāyoga in detail.

10. It is concluded in the sacred scriptures that devotion is generated by activities, knowledge is born of devotion, liberation is the result of knowledge.

11. O excellent sage, the chief reason of liberation is the Yoga. Kriyāyoga is the greatest means of liberation.

12. One shall know the Māyā as Prakṛti and the wielder of Māyā as the eternal Brahman. After realising the identity of the two one is released from the world by bondage.

13-14. O Vyāsa, listen to the merit of the person who builds a temple to the goddess either of stone or of wood or of mud. He who builds a temple to the goddess attains the benefit which a person who worships every day through Yoga attains in plenty. That virtuous soul who builds the temple for the glorious mother enables a thousand past and a thousand future members of his family to attain liberation.

15. The sins committed by a person in a crore of births, whether they be small or big, are quelled at the very moment when the foundation for temple of the glorions mother is laid.

16-17. The glorious great Ambā is the most excellent among all the deities just as Gaṅgā and Śoṇa among the rivers, the earth in forbearance, the ocean in majesty and the sun among the planets.

18. She is the most important among all the deities. He who causes her temple to be built attains established power in every birth.

19-21. One who makes the temple for the mother in any of these holy centres becomes free from bondage—viz. Vārāṇasī, Kurukṣetra, Prayāga, Puṣkara, the banks of the Gaṅgā or the shores of the ocean, Naimiṣa, amarakaṇṭaka, the highly meritorious Śrīparvata, Gokarṇa, Jñānaparvata,[94] Mathurā, Ayodhyā, Dvāravatī etc.

22. He is honoured in the Maṇidvīpa for as many thousand years as the number of years the brickwork holds good.

94. Not identified.

23. He who makes idols with the full complement of characteristics fearlessly attains indeed the great region of Umā.

24. After installing the image of the goddess, in the auspicious stars, planets and the season, man becomes contented and blessed by the favour of the Yogamāyā.

25. After installing an auspicious image of the goddess one can redeem the men of one's family both of the past and the future.

26. O leading sage, by installing the goddess the merit derived is a crore times more than that derived by establishing the three worlds.

27. The merit cannot be calculated of the man who instals the Pañcāyatana[95] deities with Ambikā in the centre and the other four in the four quarters.

28-31. One attains great merit by repeating the names of Viṣṇu a crore times during the solar and lunar eclipses, a hundred crore times by repeating the names of Śiva, a crore times by repeating the names of Śrīdevī, a crore times by building the palace for the goddess. To the man who instals the image of the goddess, mother of the universe, identical with the three Vedas there is nothing inaccessible, thanks to the merit of the glorious mother. His sons, grandsons and others flourish. All his sins perish.

32. Even those who desire mentally the installation of the excellent image attain the great region of Umā inaccessible even to the sages.

33-34. If a man, on seeing the image being made or the temple being built thinks mentally : "If I get sufficient wealth I too will make", his family attains heaven undoubtedly. What is there in the three worlds which cannot be secured by the power of Mahāmāyā ?

35. Those who have resorted only to the goddess the cause of the universe, are not ordinary men. They are the Gaṇas of the Goddess herself.

36. Those who repeat the two syllables "U-mā" day and night, sitting, sleeping or moving become Śivā's Gaṇas.

95. The five deities referred to here are : Sun Gaṇesa, Durgā, Rudra and Viṣṇu. See p 168 note 174.

37. Those who worship the goddess Śivā, with flowers, incense and lamps whether as daily routine or on special occasions due to certain reasons will attain Umā's abode.

38. Those who clean, scrub and smear the altar of the goddess with cowdung or clay will attain Umā's abode.

39. The goddess mother bestows her blessings on the family of the person who builds a beautiful temple for the goddess.

40. The glorious mother repeats day and night: "May my devotees live for a hundred years. Let them not be the victims of adversities."

41. Ten thousand people of the person who has caused the image of the goddess Umā to be made, are honoured in the Maṇidvīpa.[96]

42. Whatever an aspirant solicits after installing and worshipping the image of the goddess he attains that.

43. Who can calculate the merit of a person who performs the ablution of the installed image of the glorious mother, with clarified butter after smearing it with honey ?

44. The devotee shall perform the ablution of the goddess either with water scented with sandal, aguru, camphor māṁsī, mustā etc. or with the milk of single-coloured cows.

45. The excellent offering shall be made with the incense of eighteen ingredients. The waving of the light for the goddess shall consist of wicks soaked in ghee or camphor.

46. On the fifth, eighth, ninth and tenth days of the dark lunar half and on new moon days the devotee shall worship the mother of the worlds with fragrant flowers.

47. Jananīsūkta, Srīsūkta or Devīsūkta shall be recited or Mūlamantra shall be chanted.

48. All flowers except Viṣṇukrāntā and Tulasī are pleasing to the goddess particularly the lotus.

49. He who offers golden or silver flowers to the goddess goes to the greatest abode where crores of Siddhas live.

50-51. After the worship the rite of forgiveness shall be

96. Not identified. Whether it has a link with the city of Maṇipura in Assam or with Maṇiparvata in the south Arcot is not clear.

performed by the devotees for the sins committed :—"O goddess, O bestower of happiness and bliss be pleased." He shall eulogise her with these words and meditate on the goddess as seated on a lion with boons and the majestic gesture of protection.

52. After meditating on the goddess, the bestower of desires on the devotees he shall offer various ripe fruits as Naivedya.

53. The man who partakes of Naivedya of Śiva Śakti shakes off all dirt and becomes pure.

54. He who performs the rite of the goddess on the third day of the bright half of Caitra is liberated from the bondage of worldly existence and attains the supreme goal.

55-56. The learned devotee shall perform the festival of the swing on the very day. He shall worship the mother of the worlds Umā and Śiva with flowers, vermilion, garments, camphor, aguru, sandal, incense, lights, naivedyas, garlands, scents and other things.

57. He shall then serve the goddess Ambā, the cause of all welfare along with Śiva.

58. Śivā bestows all desires on him who performs the rites with due observances and the festival of swinging to the goddess every year.

59-61. The third day of the bright half of the month of Vaiśākha is called Akṣayatṛtīyā. The devotee shall observe the holy rites of the mother of the universe on that day without lassitude. He shall worship Gaurī and Śiva with the flowers of Mallikā, Mālatī Campā, Japā, Bandhūka and lotus. He will be quelling the sins perpetrated in a crore of births mentally, verbally and physically. He will enjoy the four aims of life in an unmitigated manner.

62. There is nothing which cannot be achieved by a person who worships the goddess with great devotion after observing all the rites on the third day of the bright half of the month of Jyeṣṭha.

63. In accordance with the wealth that one has, one shall perform the festival of chariot which is extremely pleasing to the goddess, on the third day of the bright half of the month of Āṣādha.

64-65. The chariot is the earth. The two wheels are

the sun and the moon. The horses are the Vedas and the charioteer is the lotus-born Brahmā. The chariot shall be studded with the jewels of different types. It shall be decorated with the garlands of flowers. After making the chariot thus the devotee shall instal Śivā in it.

66. The intelligent man shall imagine that the glorious Ambikā is seated in the middle of the chariot surveying the world for protecting it.

67-69. When the chariot moves the devotee shall shout cries of "Victory" with the words "O goddess, favourably disposed to the distressed, protect us who have resorted to you". The devotee shall propitiate the goddess with the playing of musical instruments. The chariot shall be taken up to the boundary of village and the deity worshipped in the chariot itself. After eulogising with various hymns the deity shall be brought home. After prostrating a hundred times the devotee shall pray to the mother of the universe.

70-72. The intelligent man who performs the worship, holy rites, the festival of the chariot, the worship of the Mother, on the third day of the bright half of the Śrāvana and Bhādrapada, rejoices with his family. In the end he goes to the region of Umā at the highest upper worlds.

73. The devotee shall observe the holy rites of Navarātra in the bright half of Āśvina and realise his desires undoubtedly.

74. Neither Brahmā nor Śiva nor Kārttikeya nor any one else can describe the efficacy of the rite of Navarātra.

75-77. O excellent sages, by performing the Navarātra rite, king Suratha, son of Viratha, regained his lost kingdom. The intelligent king of Ayodhyā, Sudarśana, son of Dhruvasandhi secured the lost kingdom. Performing this great rite and propitiating the goddess the Vaiśya Samādhi being liberated from worldly bondage attained salvation.

78-79. Śivā fulfils the mental desires of the person who performs the rites duly in the bright half of Āśvina on the third, fifth, seventh, eighth, ninth, or the fourteenth day.

80-81. He who performs the holy rite on the third day in the bright half of Kārttika, Mārgaśīrṣa, Pauṣa, Māgha and Phālguna and worships the auspicious goddess with red flowers,

Karavīra and the like, with incense, scents etc. attains all auspicious desires.

82. For acquiring blissful conjugal life this great Vrata shall be performed by women. It shall be performed by men also for the acquisition of learning, wealth and sons.

83. Rites such as Umāmaheśvara and others are alsc pleasing to the goddess. They shall be performed devotedly by those who are desirous of salvation.

84. This compendium is highly meritorious, enhances devotion to Śiva. It is auspicious. It contains several anecdotes. It yields worldly pleasures and salvation.

85. He who listens to this with devotion or narrates it piously or reads it himself or causes it to be read attains the supreme god.

86. He who keeps this in his abode in the manuscript form written in beautiful hand and duly worships it attains all desires.

87. There will be no fear from goblins, ghosts and other evil spirits at any place. Undoubtedly he will attain sons, grandsons aud riches.

88. Hence this charming and meritorious compendium Umāsaṁhitā shall always be heard and read by those who seek for devotion to Śiva.

KAILASĀSAMHITĀ

CHAPTER ONE

(The discussion among Vyāsa, Śaunaka and others)

1. Obeisance to Śiva accompanied by Ambā, his sons and the Gaṇas, obeisance to the lord of Pradhāna and Puruṣa, obeisance to him who is the cause of creation, sustenance and dissolution.

The sages said:—

2. The beautiful Umāsaṁhitā full of various anecdotes we have heard. Now narrate the Kailāsasaṁhitā that propagates Śiva's tenets.

Vyāsa said:—

3. O dear, now listen with pleasure. Out of affection for you I shall narrate the divine Saṁhitā Kailāsa expounding Śiva's tenets.

4. Formerly the sages of great power and splendour performing penances on the summit of Himavat[97] desired to go to Vārāṇasī[98] and decided accordingly.

5. They started from the mountain and reached Kāśī. They decided to bathe there and saw Maṇikarṇikā.[99]

6-8. The lordly sages bathed there and performed the Tarpaṇa rites to the gods and others and to Gaṅgā. They visited Viśveśa the lord of the gods, bowed and worshipked him with devotion The sages, the masters of the Vedas eulogised him with Śatarudra and other mantras and thought "O, we are blessed. We are content." Due to Śiva's pleasure they realised everything. They remained ever engaged in devotion to Śiva.

97. This celebrated mountain extends from the Eastern to the Western Sea, is formed after the shape of a bow-string and forms the northern bounds of Bhāratavarṣa.

98. It is named after Varaṇā and Asī, the tributaries of the Ganges on which the city is situated.

99. It is a sacred pool in Vārāṇasī.

9. In the meantime Sūta who had left his hermitage to visit Pañcakrośa[100] reached there. On seeing him the joyous sages paid obeisance to him.

10. After bowing to Viśveśvara, the lord of gods, the consort of Umā, Sūta entered the Muktimaṇḍapa[101] along with them.

11. When Sūta the great soul, the excellent of the Paurāṇikas took his seat, the sages paid respects to him with Arghya and other ingredients of worship.

12. The delighted Sūta saw the sages of auspicious rites and enquired after their health and welfare. They replied suitably.

13. On seeing him pleased at heart the sages spoke in relevance to the context, in order to know the meaning of Praṇava.

The sages said:—

14. O blessed disciple of Vyāsa, O Sūta the best among the Paurāṇikas, you are a great devotee of Śiva, the ocean of perfect knowledge.

15. Lord Vyāsa, the preceptor of the universe has crowned you as the chief of the Paurāṇikas and made you the propounder of the Purāṇas.

16. The Purāṇic lore is firmly set in your heart. Indeed the Purāṇas explain the meaning of the Vedas.

17. Vedas arise from the Praṇava. The Praṇava is lord Śiva. Hence you are the permanent abode of lord Śiva's stay.

18. We shall be free from illness after we have drunk the nectar of Praṇava which is as sweet and pleasing as the honey oozing out of your lotus-mouth.

19. O intelligent one, you alone are our preceptor, none else. Out of compassion please narrate the nature of lord Śiva.

20-21. On hearing their words, the intelligent Sūta, the beloved disciple of Vyāsa, made obeisance to Gaṇeśa,

100. The region upto the distance of five Krośas round Vārāṇasī is called Pañcakrośī. It is sacred to Śiva.

101. It is identical with the Avimukta Tīrtha in Vārāṇasī.

six-faced Kārttika, Maheśvarī, lord Nandīśa-son of Śilāda and husband of Suyaśā, Sanatkumāra and Vyāsa and said.

Sūta said :—

22. Well done, well done, O blessed sages, your sins have been quelled. Your minds are steadied. It is rare in persons of evil deeds.

23-24. O leading sages, I shall narrate to you what was mentioned by my preceptor Vyāsa to the sages in the Naimiṣa forest. On hearing this alone men are blessed with devotion to Śiva. You shall listen with attention and joy.

25-27. Formerly in the Svārociṣa Manvantara, sages of steady rites performed penance in the Naimiṣa[102] forest where all the Siddhas live. They conducted a sacrifice of long duration, propitiated Rudra the leader of sacrifices. They desired to know the supreme nature of the lord. They waited for Vyāsa. They were engaged in devotion to Śiva and wore Rudrākṣa after smearing their bodies with the ashes.

28. Observing their eagerness, lord Bādarāyaṇa, the soul of all, the fruit of the penance of Parāśara appeared before them.

29. On seeing him the sages were delighted with beaming eyes and faces. They stood up and welcomed him with reverence.

30. With due hospitality they offered him a golden seat. Seated cosily on the golden seat the sage Vyāsa spoke majestically.

Vyāsa said :—

31. Hope you are quite well. Please say. Has the leader of the sacrifices been worshipped well by you in this sacrifice ?

32. Why lord Śiva accompanied by Ambā, the lord who releases from worldly bondage has been worshipped with due devotion by you all in this sacrifice.

33. Your activity seems to me to be the outcome of

102. See P. 76 note; P. 432 note.

your desire to hear more of the great nature of lord Śiva, the cause of salvation.

34-35. Thus urged by the sage Vyāsa of great brilliance the great sages of the Naimiṣa forest bowed to him, the noble soul whose mind was delighted by his devotion to Śiva.

The sages said:—

36-37. O holy lord, O leading sage, born of Nārāyaṇa's part, O storehouse of mercy, O intelligent one, O holy lord of all lores, you are the storehouse of the favours of Mahādeva, lord of the universe, accompanied by Ambā and the Gaṇas.

38. Our minds have been yearning for the sight of your lotus feet even as the bees yearn for the touch of lotus flowers. We are now satisfied by the vision of your lotus feet.

39. Inaccessible indeed is the sight of your lotus feet to the sinners. Since now we have obtained it we are really fortunate.

40-42. O blessed one, we are performing this long sacrifice in this Naimiṣāraṇya. We wanted to know the meaning of the Praṇava. We are discussing the greatness of lord Śiva and wish to hear all about him. But we cannot understand the same. Now it behoves you to clear off our doubts. O holy lord, we are only small-minded.

43-44. There is none else in the three worlds to clear our doubts. We are immersed in the ocean of delusion, vast and shoreless. O storehouse of mercy, take us across this ocean in the raft of Śiva's knowledge. We are truly eager to know the principle of Śiva's devotion.

45-46. Requested by the sages, the master of the Vedas, the great sage, father of Śuka, chief of the Vedic scholars, meditated within the pericarp of his heart, on lord Śiva who releases from worldly existence and who is Praṇava, the essential substance of Vedānta. Being delighted in his mind, the great sage spoke.

CHAPTER TWO

(The dialogue between the god and the goddess)

Vyāsa said :—

1-3. O blessed brahmins, the question has been well put by you. The knowledge of Śiva's principle that illuminates the meaning of Praṇava is incomprehensible. It can be obtained surely by those with whom the trident-bearing lord is pleased and not by others who are undoubtedly devoid of Śiva's devotion. This is true.

4. Lord Śiva, consort of Ambā, has been adored by you by long sacrifices. This I see actually.

5. O devotees, I shall narrate to you an ancient story containing a wonderful dialogue between Umā and Śiva.

6-8. Formerly Satī, daughter of Dakṣa, the mother of the universe abandoned her body in the sacrifice of her father in view of the insult offered to Śiva. As a result of the penance the goddess became the daughter of the Himavat. On the advice of Nārada she performed a penance for Śiva on that mountain. When lord Śiva married her with Svayaṁvara rites Pārvatī attained happiness.

9. Once she was cosily seated with lord Śiva on that great mountain. She spoke to the lord.

10-11. O omniscient lord who hath ordained to himself the five-fold duties,[103] O lord easily accessible through devotion, O lord of nectarine body, I was the daughter of Dakṣa in my former birth. I abandoned my body because of the insult offered to you. I have now become the daughter of the mountain Himavat.

12. O lord, please make me merged in the principle of pure Ātman by duly initiating me in the Mantras.

13. Thus requested by the goddess the moon-crested lord replied to the goddess with a delighted mind.

103. Vidyeśvarasaṁhitā (i7.95) recounts the five actions by which the supreme power manifests. These are सृष्टि, स्थिति, संहार, तिरोभाव and अनुग्रह ।

Lord Śiva said :—

14. If your mind is thus diverted, O goddess, you are blessed indeed. I shall initiate you so after going to the summit of Kailāsa.

15. Then after leaving Himavat and reaching Kailāsa, the lord of mountains, Śiva, recited mantras Praṇava and others in the proper order after duly initiating her.

16. Then making the goddess merged in the pure Ātman, lord Śiva went to his garden accompanied by the goddess.

17-18. Śiva bedecked the goddess with the full-blown kalpa tree[104] flowers brought by the dearest friends of the goddess the chief of whom was Sumālinī. He made her sit on his lap. Looking at her face he sat there with his face beaming with delight.

19. Then ensued the delightful discourse conformable to the Vedas between Pārvatī and lord Śiva. It was meant for the welfare of the world.

20. O ascetics, then the mother of the universe seated on the lap of her husband looked at the lord's face and said.

The goddess said :—

21. O lord, you have discoursed on the Mantras including the Praṇava. There at the outset I wish to know the meaning of the Praṇava.

22. How did Praṇava originate ? How is Praṇava mentioned ? How many Mātrās have been mentioned ? How is it that it is called the initial mantra of the Vedas ?

23. How many deities are mentioned ? What is the concept of the Vedas thereto ? What types of rites are mentioned ? What is their cause and what is their result?

24. How do the five Brahmans stay in this mantra in their proper order ? How many Kalās are enumerated ? How is it the Ātman of the universe ?

25. O Śiva, what is the link between the syllables and their meaning ? What are the places of their articulation ? Who is authorised in this ? What is the theme ?

104. It is a mythical wish-filling tree of Indra's Paradise.

26. What is the link between the knower and the known and what is the purpose? What shall be the nature of the practising devotee ? What shall be the place for the practice of meditation ?

27. Of what form is the object of devotion ? What is the benefit derived from this ? What is the procedure ? What is the place of worship ?

28. What is the mystic diagram of the worship ? O Śiva, what are the sages and the rules regarding Nyāsa, Japa etc. What is the order of procedure in this worship?

29. O lord Śiva, please mention these all particularly, if you have mercy on me. I wish to hear everything factually.

30. Thus implored, the moon-crested lord praised the goddess and began to explain.

CHAPTER THREE

(The way of Sannyāsa)

Lord Śiva said :—

1. O goddess, listen. I shall explain what you have asked for. Merely by hearing this the individual soul becomes Śiva himself.

2. To understand the meaning of Praṇava is to understand me. Praṇava is the seed of all the lores.

3. It shall be understood as very subtle but possessed of great meaning even as the seed of the Banyan tree though very small contains a huge tree. It is the initial mantra and the essence of the Vedas. Particularly it has me for its form.

4. I am the lord far beyond the attributes, the omniscient and the omnipotent. I am Śiva pervading all but stationed in the single-syllabled mantra Om.

5. They say that whatever object there is whether thesised into one or analysed in pieces is the meaning of

Praṇava, thanks to the combination and importance of the attributes.

6. It is the imperishable Brahman, the means of attaining all objects. Śiva creates universe at the outset saying "Om".

7. Since there is not much difference between the sense and the sound Om, this is explained thus. Śiva is Praṇava or Praṇava is Śiva.

8. The brahminical sages, the scholars who realize the identity between the sense and the sound know me as the single-syllabled Om.

9. Hence he who aspires for salvation and is free from aberration shall understand Praṇava as the cause of all and me as the Nirguṇa Parameśvara.

10. O goddess, I shall give this crest-jewel of mantras at Kāśī for the liberation of all Individual souls.

11. O Ambā, there at the outset I shall explain Praṇavoddhāra, the knowledge of which imparts the greatest achievement.

12. Firstly the devotee shall extricate Nivṛtti, then the the fuel, time, s aff, and the lord.

13. Thus the Praṇava of five syllables is explained by extricating the three Mātrās, Bindu and Nāda. It yields liberation to those who perform the Japa in this manner.

14. Praṇava is the vital breath of all living beings from Brahmā to immobile beings. Being the Prāṇa thus, it is called Praṇava.

15. It consists of A, U and M in the middle, Bindu and Nāda at the end. That is Om.

16. O excellent sage, the first letter (A) is like water in the south, the second letter (U) is in the north ; the letter M is like fire in the middle, before Nāda and Bindu.

17. The three Mātrās are thus mentioned in order : A. U. M. Half a mātrā is beyond it.

18. O goddess, this half mātrā is in the form of Bindu and Nāda. This cannot be described directly. It is known only by the wise.

19. O beloved, the Vedic texts beginning with "Īśānaḥ Sarvavidyānām"[105] issue from me. The Vedas indeed speak the truth.

20. I am the source of the Vedas. Praṇava expresses me. Since it expresses me the Praṇava too is mentioned as Vedādi.

21. 'A' is the great Bīja, Rajas, the four-faced creator. 'U' is the Prakṛti, source, Sattva, the protector Viṣṇu.

22. 'M' is the Puruṣa, the Bījin, Tamas, the annihilator Śiva. Bindu is Maheśvara the lord, the disappearance.

23. Nāda is Sadāśiva the bestower of blessings on all. On the top of Nāda there is Śiva who is greater than the greatest.

24. He is omniscient, the creator, the lord, free from dirt, the imperishable, the inexpressible, the great Brahman, beyond the existent and the nonexistent.

25. In the letters 'A' etc. the later one is pervasive of the earlier. The earlier one is the pervaded.

26. The five Brahmans[106] beginning with Sadya and ending with Īśāna are stationed in the five letters 'A' etc. They are my very forms in order.

27. O Śivā, in the syllable 'A' eight Kalās of the form of Sadya exist. "In 'U' thirteen Kalās of the form of Vāma exist.

28. The eight Kalās of the form of Aghora are stationed in 'M'. In Bindu four Kalās of the form of Puruṣa exist.

29. In Nāda five Kalās born of Īśāna are present. Thus their state of being the soul of the universe is due to the recognition of their sixfold identity.

30. The sixfold objects constitute Mantra, Yantra, deity, universe, the preceptor and the disciple. O beloved, listen to the meaning of these objects.

31. The mantra previously mentioned is a composite

105. TA. 10. 47. 1

106. Vidyeśvarasaṁhitā (17.44) enumerates these five forms as सद्योजात, वाम, अघोर, पुरुष and ईशान

of five letters. The same attains the form of a Yantra. I shall mention the details of its mystic diagram.

32. Yant·a is in the form of the deity; the deity is in the form of the universe; the preceptor too is in the form of the universe and the disciple is of the body of the preceptor.

33. Om is everything, everything is Brahman. (Om Itīdam Sarvam Iti Sarvam Brahma) This Vedic Text establishes the link between the word and its meaning.

34-35. The places of articulation, O goddess are: Ādhāra (support) Maṇipūra (jewel-refill) Hṛdaya (heart) Viśuddhi (purity) Ājñā (order) Śakti (power) Śānti. Beyond Śānti is the lord who is greater than the greatest. The authorised person is he whose non-attachment is firm and stable.

36-37. O goddess, I shall be the theme, thanks to the concept of the identity of the individual and the universal soul. The subject has been clearly mentioned. O goddess, now listen. The link of the Jīva and the Ātman with me and the Praṇava is as between the word and its sense.

38-42. A brahmin with the following characteristics shall approach the preceptor with the requisite qualifications. He shall be regularly engaged in holy rites, be calm, perform penance, shall have self-control, be a brahmin well-versed in the Vedas and endowed with cleanliness and good conduct, unattached to the pleasures of this world and of the next and of the worlds of the gods. He shall perform the holy rites of Śiva. The preceptor shall be one who has understood the tenets and the meanings of sacred texts; who has mastered Vedānta; who is an ascetic and the most excellent of intelligent men. After approaching him the intelligent brahmin shall prostrate before him and propitiate him by reverential deeds. That disciple is the most excellent who possesses good behaviour and the qualities of peaceful calmness. The disciple shall realise that preceptor is Śiva and Śiva is the preceptor. Then he shall reveal his thought.

43-52. After being permitted by the preceptor the brahmin devotee shall perform holy rites without taking anything except milk, for twelve days on the sea-shore, or on the banks of a river, or on a mountain or in a temple of

Śiva. On the fifth or the eleventh day of the bright half he shall take his bath early in the morning. The intelligent devotee pure in mind shall perform his daily duty. He shall invite the preceptor duly and perform Nāndīśrāddha. He shall get himself shaved of the hair on the head and the moustache and the beards. The hair in the armpit and the private parts must not be shaved. The nails shall be cut. He shall perform his ceremonial ablution with restrained mind. He shall eat only powdered fried grain. In the evening he shall take his bath and perform Sandhyā. In the presence of the preceptor he shall perform the Aupāsana rites in the evening. To Śiva in the form of the preceptor he shall give Dakṣiṇā according to the scriptures. He shall collect articles for Homa, place the holy fires, laukika and others, with the rules of his Gṛhya Sūtra. A brahmin who consecrates the sacred fire shall perform this Aupāsana in the sacrificial fire consecrated by the Prājāpatya sacrifice, reciting mantras from the Vedas and offering due Dakṣiṇās. Then the brahmin shall superimpose the fire in the Ātman and formally renounce the world. The food-off ring shall be cooked with the fire-wood and cooked rice and ghee. He shall perform the sacrifice repeating the Puruṣa Sūkta.[107] The ghee shall be offered at the end of every stanza. The Sauviṣṭakṛti shall be performed in accordance with the rules of his own Sūtra. After the sacrifice he shall perform Tāntric activities. The learned devotee shall sit on a cloth, deer-skin or Kuśa grass to the north of the fire. He shall repeat the Gāyatrī mantra silently till the Brāhma Muhūrta, and stabilise his mind firmly.

53. Then he shall take bath and cook the Caru. He shall perform the sacrifice beginning with Puruṣa and ending with the Virāja sūktas.

54. The procedure may follow the opinion of Vāmadeva or of Sanaka and others. But the important one is that of Vāmadeva because he was a liberated soul even while he was in the womb.

107. VS. 31.

55. After performing the remaining rites of the sacrifice he shall perform the Aupāsana rites of the morning. Then he shall superimpose Agni in the Ātman and perform the morning prayers.

56. When the sun has arisen he shall recite Sāvitrī. He shall eschew the three Eṣaṇās and repeat the Preṣa[108] mantras.

57. He shall abandon the tuft, the sacred thread and the girdle too. He shall start to the east or to the north.

58. He shall take with him a staff and a loin-cloth and such other things as are necessary for life. If he is totally detached he need not take these things too.

59. He shall approach the preceptor and prostrate before him thrice. Standing up he shall sit at the feet of the preceptor.

60-61. The teacher shall take the white ashes from the Virāja fire and smear it over the body of the disciple. Repeating the mantra "Agniriti" etc. he shall make the three marks Tripuṇḍra on his forehead. He shall think of me stationed in the lotus of the heart along with you.

62-63. Then the teacher shall place his hand on the head of the disciple. With a delighted mind, the preceptor shall utter the Praṇava mantra thrice in the right ear of the disciple mentioning the sage etc. Then he shall tell him the sixfold meaning.

64. The disciple shall bow prostrate before the preceptor on the ground twelve times. He shall remain subservient to him and practise the study of the Vedānta strenuously.

65. He shall ponder and meditate in the pure Ātman without aberrations, upon me the great Ātman, the Sākṣin of Brahman, the unchanging.

66. Here the person authorised is the ascetic engaged in the pious activities of self-restraint, the master of Vedāntic knowledge and free from rivalry.

67. The lotus of the heart is free from dust, devoid of sorrow, clear and great. It has eight petals with filaments and it shines above the pericarp.

108. Ibid. 5.7.

68. After thinking about the region from the Ādhāra-Śakti to the three Tattvas the Dahara Vyoman (the ether-heart) shall be imagined and conceived in the middle.

69. Repeating the single-syllabled Brahman Om, he shall with alert mind think of me along with you in the middle.

70. O beloved, he who performs the rite of this type attains my world. After securing the knowledge of my principles he will attain Sāyujya salvation as the fruit.

CHAPTER FOUR

(*The daily conduct of a Sannyāsin*)

Lord Śiva said :—

1. O goddess, after this I shall mention the daily routine during the Sannyāsa according to the convention. It is out of my affection for you that I am narrating the same.

2. The ascetic shall get up in the Brāhma Muhūrta and think about the preceptor Śiva seated in the thousand-petalled lotus on the head.

3. The preceptor resembling pure crystal, with two eyes and holding the mystic gestures of boon and protection in the hand is conceived as Śiva of beautiful form in the soul.

4. He shall bow to the preceptor with palms joined in reverence and worship him with scents, fragrant flowers etc. created by his imagination.

5. He shall pray thus—"O lord, let whatever I do from morning till sunset and from sunset till daybreak be your worship."

6. After intimating to the preceptor thus and securing the permission he shall retain the breath and sit down, with his mind and the sense-organs under full control.

7-8. He shall then meditate on the six-fold wheel[109] from the root to the Brahma Randhra. In the middle he shall think of me, the Nirguṇa Sadāśiva, free from ailment, the great Brahman, with the lustre of crores of lightning, identical with splendour, with the body of existence, knowledge and bliss.

9. He shall realize identity with me in the form "I am he". The intelligent ascetic then shall go out far according to convenience.

10. The intelligent devotee shall cover the head along with the nose with a piece of cloth. He shall spread some grass on the ground and evacuate his bowels there duly.

11. He shall stand up holding the penis and go to the water-pond. He shall take out water and use it for cleansing carefully.

12-13. He shall wash hands, feet and perform Ācamana twice remembering Om. He shall face the north and clean his teeth always with leaves or grass except on the eleventh and the New-moon day. He shall rinse the mouth by gargling twelve times.

14. After performing Ācamana twice he shall clean the hips with water and clay. At the time of dawn he shall take his bath using clay.

15. The bath and the Sandhyā prayers shall be performed with thoughts on the preceptor and me. The procedure of bath is not detailed here for fear of prolixity. That shall be seen elsewhere.

16. Joining the palms so as to from the Śaṅkhamudrā water shall be poured over the head repeating the Praṇava, twelve times, six times or three times.

17. He shall go to the bank and wash the loin-cloth. He shall perform the Ācamana twice. Repeating the Praṇava he shall sprinkle water over the towel and wipe off the body.

18. He shall wipe off his face first and then the head and other parts of the body standing by the side of the preceptor.

109. The six mystical circles of the body are मूलाधार, स्वाधिष्ठान, मणिपूर, अनाहत, विशुद्ध, आज्ञा

19. A pure loin-cloth shall be tied with its string with the knot on the left side. Then he shall smear his body with the ashes. O daughter of the mountain, now I tell you the procedure thereof.

20. After performing the Ācamana twice he shall take the ashes repeating the Sadyādi mantra[110]. Then repeating the mantras "Agniriti"[111] he shall touch the body.

21-22. Repeating the mantra "Āpo vai—[112]" he shall mix the ashes with water. He shall make two balls of the pasted ashes with the mantras "Om Āpo Jyotī"[113] and "Mā Nastoke"[114]—He shall divide one of the balls into five, O goddess, and apply each respectively to the head, face, chest, private parts and the feet.

23-25. He shall repeat the mantra beginning with "Īśāna[115]—" and ending with "Sadya." After applying the ashes he shall repeat Om touching all the parts of the body. He shall wash his hands, feet and take the other ball. Adoring as before he shall apply three parallel lines on the forehead repeating the mantra 'Tryāyuṣa'[116] and the 'Tryambaka'.[117] He shall apply the same on the chest with the Praṇava and on the shoulders with "Oṁ Namaḥ Śivāya."

26. Uttering Pañcīkaraṇa mantra, the scholarly ascetic shall think of his preceptor. In the manner as explained hereafter he shall perform six Prāṇāyāmas.

27-28. Touching the navel, the joints of the arms and the back in order he shall wash both the hands duly and perform Ācamana twice. He shall take some water in the right hand and cover it with the left hand. Praṇava is then repeated twelve times.

29-31. Sprinkling this water thrice on the head he shall drink water thrice meditating on Oṅkāra—Śiva with

110. VS. 29. 36
111. P. 154 note
112. TA. 10. 22. 1
113. Ibid. 10. 15. 1
114. VS. 16. 16
115. Vidyeśvara Saṁhitā recounts the five forms as सद्योजात, वाम, अघोर, पुरुष, ईशान in the reverse order.
116. VS. 3, 62
117. Ibid 3. 60

pure mind—Śiva who is stationed in the middle of the solar disc, the god consisting of all splendour, possessing eight arms, four faces, the wonderful form half-female, endowed with wonderful qualities and bedecked in ornaments. After meditating thus duly he shall offer three Arghyas.

32. After performing the Japa of Gāyatrī hundred and eight times, he shall offer Tarpaṇa twelve times. After performing the Ācamana he shall perform Prāṇāyāma thrice.

33. Then he shall go to the hall of worship thinking on Śiva. After reaching the door he shall wash his feet silently and perform Ācamana twice.

34. He shall enter it duly placing the right foot at first. Inside the Maṇḍapa there, he, the intelligent ascetic, shall draw the mystic diagram in due order.

CHAPTER FIVE

(The rules governing the mystic diagram of the ascetic)

Lord Śiva said :—

1-2. The ground shall be tested duly on the basis of smell, colour and taste. In a spot pleasing to the mind the space above shall be covered with a canopy, the ground below shall be scrubbed and cleaned so much as to appear like the surface of a mirror. A square of sides two Aratnis each shall be drawn.

3. Make small squares within the width of a palm-leaf each. Thus there shall be thirteen equal squares in each column.

4-6. The ascetic shall put the piece of palm leaf inside the square and sit facing the west. Towards the east a strong coloured thread shall be fixed. Threads shall be put in all the four directions. Thus there will be one hundred and sixtynine squares. The middle square is the pericarp. The squares adjoining it around in the outside, eight in number, are called eight petals.

7-8. All the petals shall be made white completely. The pericarp shall be made yellow in colour and a red circle shall be drawn within. O goddess, beginning with the petal of Indra to the right hand side the bordering lines shall be coloured alternatively black and red.

9-10. The Yantra illuminating the meaning of the Praṇava shall be written inside the pericarp. The pedestal shall be drawn beneath. Śrīkaṇṭha shall be drawn above it. Amareśa shall be drawn above it and Mahākāla in the middle. On the top of it the staff and beyond that Īśvara shall be drawn.

11. The Pīṭha shall be coloured blue. Śrīkaṇṭha in yellow, Amareśa in red, and Mahākāla in black.

12. The scholarly ascetic shall make the staff smoky coloured and Īśvara white in colour. After drawing the Yantra the red one (Amareśa) shall be encompassed by Sadya.

13. O goddess, only through the Nāda Īśāna shall be known. The rows of its residence shall be taken in order from the south-east one.

14-15. The four squares at the four corners, O beautiful lady, shall be painted white. The first four letters a, ā i and ī shall be written with red minerals and these four are conceived as doors. The two squares adjacent to each of these four shall be painted yellow.

16. In the yellow square in between the south-east squares a lotus of eight petals shall be drawn red in colour with yellow pericarp.

17-19. With purity of mind he shall draw the letter 'ha' in the middle along with the Bindu. In the south-west square of this lotus he shall draw another red lotus with yellow filaments and pericarp. The third letter of the class of Śa along with the sixth vowel and the fourteenth vowel decorated with Bindu and Nāda is, O gentle lady, the excellent Bīja which shall be written in the middle of the lotus.

20-22. In the north-east square of the lotus another lotus shall be drawn with the third letter of the class of "ka"

118. The mystical syllables as mentioned in the verses indicate the following incantations सू (सूर्याय नमः), गु (गुरवे नमः).

along with the fifth vowel. In its middle Bindu and Kaṇṭha shall be decoratively written. In the three columns outside it, beginning with the eastern one five squares shall be taken, O Śivā, daughter of the lord of mountains. The pericarp shall be taken in the middle painted yellow with a red circle.

23. The most excellent of the knowers of the rules shall make the leaves red in colour. Outside the leaves the cavities shall be filled with black colour.

24. The south-east square and others, four in number, shall be filled with white paint. With six Bindus a six-sided figure shall be drawn in black in the east.

25. To the south it shall be painted red. In the north a triangle is painted in white. In the west a crescent moon is painted in yellow.

26-27. The four Bījas shall be written in the squares in order. The Bindu shall be drawn in the east in white. In the south is painted in black the letter U; in the north, letter ma' is painted in red; in the west letter 'a' is painted yellow; thus the four letters are written.

28-29. In the second row from the top O beautiful lady, one shall begin. The first four squares are respectively painted yellow, white, red and black. Below that the four are painted white, blue, yellow and red respectively. O good-faced lady, below that in the triangle it shall be painted red white and yellow.

30. O goddess, from the south to the north the same procedure shall be adopted. In its external row it shall be painted from the east to the middle.

31-36. The colours are yellow, red, black, blue, white and yellow. O beloved, from the south-east onwards colours are red, blue, white, red, black and red. Thus the colours of the six squares are mentioned: from the south to the east; from the south-west to the south-east; from the west to the south; from the north-west to the south-west; from the north to the west; from the north-east, to the north-west. O goddess, thus the procedure of the diagram has been mentioned to you. Having drawn the diagram thus the ascetic with restrained mind shall worship the sun with devotion.

CHAPTER SIX

(*Rules of Nyāsa in the path of Renunciation*)

Lord Śiva said :—

1-4. The ascetic shall spread a beautiful tiger's hide to the south of the diagram and sprinkle pure water over it repeating the Astra mantra. After uttering the Praṇava at the outset he shall utter the Ādhāra and the Śaktikamala. He shall sit on the tiger's hide repeating the mantra with the dative case ending with Namaḥ.[119] He shall face the north. After performing the Prāṇāyāma duly preceded by the utterance of the Praṇava he shall smear the body with the ashes with the mantras "Agniriti"[120] After bowing to lord Śiva he shall arrange the diagram again.

5-7. Outside he shall adore in order the diagrams of triangle circle and square repeating Om. He shall fill the conch with fragrant pure water repeating the Praṇava. He shall place the conch on the diagrams and worship it with scents, flowers etc. repeating the Praṇava seven times. After repeating the mantra he shall show the Dhenumudrā and Śaṅkhamudrā. He shall sprinkle it with the Astra mantra.

8. He shall sprinkle himself and the scents, flowers and other materials of worship. After performing Prāṇāyāma thrice he shall utter the names of the sages etc.

9-10. Of this mantra of the glorious sun the sage is Devabhāga, the metre is Gāyatri, the deity is the sun. The six-organed Nyāsa shall be made with 'Hrām' etc. Then he sprinkles the Padma not within the purview of Agni.

11-14. The learned ascetic shall worship in it Prabhūtā, Vimalā, Sārā from the former to the latter in order. Then he shall worship Kālāgnirudra, Ādhāra, Śakti, Ananta, Pṛthivī Ratnadvīpa, imaginary trees and garden a house of jewels and the gemset seat at the feet; beginning with the east the gods of virtue, knowledge, detachment and supremacy shall be worshipped. He shall also worship the gods of evil etc. in the corner quarters such as south-east and others.

119. The text indicates the basic mantra of Śiva: ओं शिवाय नम:

120. See P. 153 note.

15-20. He shall worship the lower lid of Māyā and and the upper lid of Vidyā. Thereafter Sattva, Rajas and Tamas shall be worshipped in order. In the quarters beginning with the east and in the middle he shall worship the following:—Dīptā, Sūkṣmā, Jayā, Bhadrā, Vibhūti, Vimalā, Amoghā, Vaidyutā, Sarvatomukhasañjñā, Kandanāla, Suṣira, then Tantukaṇṭakas, then the root lid, filament, (light) and Sakalātman, the five-knotted pericarp and the petals, then the filaments, Brahmā, Viṣṇu, Rudra and Ātman. After worshipping the inner Ātman in the great Ātman of knowledge he shall worship the Yogapīṭha called the Saura. The knower of the root shall conceive the idol as stationed on the pedestal.

21-24. The ascetic sits checking the vital breath with the root from the root. With the power of its splendour he raises the Śakti through the path of the Piṅgalā nerve of the sun stationed in the circle. He causes it to come out with the handful of flowers. Of Śiva whose body is as red as the vermillion, who has his wife as his left half, who is wearing Rudrākṣa garland and holding a noose, a club called Khaṭvāṅga, a skull, a goad, a lotus a conch and a discus; who has four faces, twelve eyes and a spear within the lotus of his heart, he utters the Praṇava first and then Hrām, Hrīm and Saḥ.

25-27. Thereafter he invokes the sun along with the light and power saying 'I invoke obeisance'. He shows the mystic signs of Sthāpanā etc. After performing the Nyāsa of the limbs with the mantra Hrām, Hrīm, Hrum and conceiving the five services O great goddess, he shall worship thrice the six organs in the filaments of the lotus.

28-30. In the second covering the four deities shall be worshipped in the south-east, north-east south-west and the north-west. O Pārvatī, from east to north at the roots of the petals Āditya, Bhāskara, Bhānu and Ravi shall be worshipped in order. O beloved, in the third covering, Arka, Brahmā, Rudra and Viṣṇu shall be worshipped in the north-east and other quarters.

31. In the middle of the leaves from the east onwards he shall worship the Moon, Mars, Mercury, Jupitre, Venus, Saturn and Rāhu.

32. Or he shall worship the twelve Ādityas in the second covering and worship the twelve signs of zodiac in the third covering.

33-34. He shall worship the seven oceans[121] and seven Gaṅgās[122] on its outer side and then the sages, gods, gandharvas, serpents, celestial damsels, the village chiefs, the Yakṣas, Yātudhānas, the seven horses in the form of the Vedas and the Bālakhilyas.

35-37. After worshipping the sun of three coverings and then arranging the square diagram with pious attention he shall place a copper vessel that can hold a prastha of water on its stand. He shall fill it with pure water rendered fragrant with flowers. He shall worship it with scents, flowers and kneel on the ground. The arghya vessel shall be lifted upto the middle of the eyebrows.

38. He shall recite the hymn to the sun-god yielding all accomplishments. O goddess, it yields worldly pleasures and salvation always.

39-40. Obeisance to you of the colour of vermillion, of good disc wearing diamond for the ornament, having eyes resembling lotus, of good lotus and cause of Brahmā, Indra and Viṣṇu. O lord, be pleased to accept this holy arghya offered by me along with the red powder, cloured water, garland, vermilion, kuśa grass, flowers and a golden pot.

41. He shall recite this and offer the arghya to the sun-god and perform obeisance. He shall recite the following piously.

42. "Obeisance to Śiva accompanied by Pārvatī and the Gaṇas. Obeisance to you the primordial cause, of the form of Trinity, Rudra, Viṣṇu and Brahmā".

43-44. After saying this and bowing he shall seat himself. He shall mention the names of the sages etc. again

121. The purāṇas mention seven oceans viz. salt, sugar-cane, wine, ghee, curd, milk and water which surroun d जम्बु, प्लक्ष, शाल्मलि, कुश क्रौञ्च, शाक and पुष्कर continents respectively.

122. The river Gaṅgā rising from Bindusara (a Himālayan lake) has seven currents of which the three नलिनी, ह्लादिनी, पावनी go to the east, the three सीता, चक्षु and सिन्धु flow to the west and the seventh following the course channelled by Bhagīratha waters the northern region. Cp. Matsya P. cxx. 42.

and wash his hands with water. He shall apply the ashes again as mentioned before. He shall then perform Nyāsas expressive of his devotion to Śiva.

45. After worshipping lord Śiva with bent head and fivefold services he shall bow to the Praṇava in the dative case ending with Namaḥ.

46-47. He shall meditate upon the Praṇava consisting of five letters including the Bindu and fifth vowel 'U' without the fifth vowel and with the Bindu. After uttering this with Bindu he shall utter the composite unit.

48. With these Bījas duly uttered the scholarly ascetic shall bow to the preceptor and the lord of Gaṇas stationed on the arms and thighs.

49. He shall bow to Durgā and Kṣetrapāla also, with palms joined in reverence. He shall repeat "Om Astrāya Phat" six times and wipe off his hands.

50-51. He shall recite the mentra "Apasarpantu"[123] and repeat "Astrāya Phaṭ." Clapping the palms thrice and kicking thrice he shall remove the obstacles; he shall gaze at the heaven-dwellers, the skyfarers.

52. He shall restrain the vital breath and remember the Haṁsa mantra. Through the Brahma Nāḍī he shall then bring about the living consciousness in the heart.

53. He shall meditate on the supreme god of the form of cit in the middle of lunar sphere of cit within the great lotus of thousand petals, full-blown and stationed in the twelve (?)

54. For sixteen, sixty-four and thirty-two seconds he shall perform Pūraka, Kumbhaka and Recaka through Śoṣa Dāha and Plava.

55-58. After retaining the breath as mentioned in his particular Veda through wind, fire, water etc. he shall bring the nerve which is at the Mūla to the cerebral aper-

123. This is the Purāṇic mantra for warding off the demons. The full text is:—

अपसर्पन्तु भूतानि पिशाचाः सर्वतोदिशम ।
सर्वेषामविरोधेन पूजाकर्म समारभे ॥

'अपक्रामन्तु' is a variant for 'अपसर्पन्तु' ।

Cp. अपहता असुरा रक्षांसि वेदिषदः VS. 2. 27.

ture. When the body is bathed in the exquisite nectarine current issuing from the lunar sphere of Cit, within the lotus of thousand petals within the twelve, it is purified and thrilled with good emotions. He makes the Ātman descend to the lotus of the heart realising "I am he". He thrusts the Ātman into the Ātman through the nectarine current. Thus he shall piously stabilise the vital breath duly.

59-60. The Yogin with mental concentration shall ponder over the Mātṛkā. He shall fix the developed Mātṛkā through the Praṇava externally. He shall carry out nourishment etc. with restricted vital breath. Thinking upon Śiva in the mind he shall dedicate himself quietly.

61. O goddess, the sage of Praṇava is Brahmā, the metre is Gāyatrī and the deity is the great Ātman, Sadāśiva that is I myself.

62. The letter 'A' is the seed; the letter 'U' is Śaktī; the letter 'M' is Kīlaka. It is used for the sake of liberation.

63. Beginning with the two thumbs and ending with the palms, the hands are wiped off. O goddess, saying 'Om' he shall begin the Nyāsa of the hands.

64. He shall perform the Nyāsa starting with the thumb of the right hand and ending with the little finger of the left hand.

65. Everywhere 'A', 'U', 'M' with the Bindu, and the mantra ending with Namaḥ shall be uttered and the Nyāsa of the hand in the heart etc. be performed.

66. After uttering 'A' at the outset the identity of Brahman and Ātman shall be practised. The mantras ending with 'Ḍe' and 'Namaḥ' shall be utilised in the heart.

67. The Nyāsa of 'U' along with Viṣṇu is made on the head; that of 'M' along with Rudra in the tuft.

68. O Goddess, the sage practising the mantra shall make the Nyāsa of the Kavaca in the eyes and the forehead with an attentive mind.

69-74. The different organs, faces and digits shall be fixed in the five Brahmans. Īśāna's five digits shall be fixed in the head, face, heart, private parts and the feet. The four digits of the Puruṣa shall be fixed in the four faces.

Aghora's eight digits shall be worshipped in the heart, neck, shoulders, navel, belly, back and the chest. Vāmadeva's thirteen digits shall be fixed in the anus, penis, thighs, knees, calves, buttocks, waist and the sides. Sadya's eight digits shall be fixed in eight eyes. The most excellent of the knowers of kalpa shall fix these digits in the feet, hand, vital breath, head and arms.

75. Thus making the Nyāsa of the thirtyeight Kalās the intelligent knower of Pranava shall proceed with the Nyāsa of Praṇava.

76-77. After making the Nyāsa in the arms, elbows, wrists, sides, belly, calves, feet and the back, the devotee, an expert in the Nyāsa, shall perform Haṁsanyāsa, O lady enlightener of the great Ātman.

CHAPTER SEVEN

(*The worship of Śiva*)

Lord Śiva said:—

1-6. The ascetic devotee shall make the square diagram to his left and worship it with Om. He shall place the conch and the missile, with its stand and worship it with the Praṇava after filling it with the water scented with the sandal paste. He shall worship it with the scents and flowers and repeat Praṇava seven times. He shall show the mystic sign of the cow and the conch making a square diagram in front and a semicircle in the middle, a triangle, hexagon and a circle within each in order. After worshipping the diagram with scents, and flowers, he shall place within it the vessel of Arghya on its stand and worship it with scents, repeating the Praṇava. He shall pour holy water and fill it.

7-11. In the vessel, O good-faced lady, tips of Kuśa grass, raw rice grains, barley, other grains, gingelly seeds, ghee-fried object, flowers and ashes too shall be put. It shall be worshipped with scents, flowers and the "Sadyojāta mantras" with their six ancillaries, Praṇava and the Varma mantras. After veiling it with the Astramantra he shall show the mystic sign of the cow for the sake of protection. The water within it shall be used for sprinkiing himself and the materials of worship—scents, flowers etc., repeating the Astramantra. After saying "Obeisance to the seat of the preceptor" he shall assign the lotus to the north-east of the diagram as seat repeating the Praṇava. As enjoined the idol of the preceptor too shall be conceived there itself.

12-13. After saying "Oṁ guṁ gurubhyaḥ namaḥ" he shall invoke the preceptor and meditate on him as seated facing the south, with a delightful face, looking gentle and crystal pure, showing the mystic gestures of boons and protection with his hands in the form and features of Śiva but with two eyes.

14-15. After meditating thus he shall worship Gaṇapati with scents, flowers etc. in the proper order assigning him a seat on the lotus to the south-west of the mystical diagram with the mantra "Gaṇānāntvā"[125] etc. After invoking the lord he shall meditate on him with concentration.

16-18. He shall be conceived as red in complexion with a huge body bedecked in ornaments holding a noose, a goad, boons and teeth, with elephantine face destroying the hindrances and obstacles of his devotees. After meditating thus he shall worship him with scents, flowers and other services. After offering him the Naivedya of plantain fruits, coconuts, mango fruits and sweet balls he shall make obeisance to the god.

19. In the lotus to the north-west of the diagram the devotee shall conceive the form of Skanda and invoke him too.

20-21. Repeating Skandagāyatrī he shall meditate on Kumāra shining as the rising sun, seated on the peacock, with four arms and splendid limbs, bedecked in coronet holding mystic signs of boons and protection, a spear and a cock[126] as well.

125. VS 23. 19.

126. According to the legend, the cock was presented as a gift by Tvaṣṭṛ. This cock could assume any form ददौ क्रीडनकं त्वष्टा कुक्कुटं कामरूपिणम् (M.P. 159. 10.)

22-26. After meditating thus and worshipping with scents and other services, he shall worship Nandin, the chief of the harem in the right wing of the eastern doors, with the lustre of the golden hill bedecked in ornaments with the crescent moon constituting his coronet, of gentle aspect, with three eyes and four arms, holding a trident, a hind, an axe and a golden staff, with his face lustrous as the moon's disc or as the face of a monkey. To his north he shall worship his wife Suyaśā, the daughter of the Maruts of good rites, engaged in bedecking mother Śiva's feet duly with scents, flowers and other services.

27. He shall sprinkle the diagram with the water from the conch veiled by the Astramantra. Then the seat, stand etc. shall be conceived in the proper order.

28-30. On the ground beneath he shall conceive the holy Ādhāra Śakti of dark blue complexion. In front of her he shall conceive the serpent-chief with lifted five hoods and coiling shape, licking the sky as it were with hoods. He shall conceive above it the dignified seat with four lion's feet symbolical of virtue, knowledge, detachment and prosperity. They shall be worshipped beginning with the southeast corner in colours white, yellow, red and dark-blue.

31. Adharma etc. shall be conceived from the east to the north in due order. He shall conceive its body with the lustre of the jewel Lājāvarta.

32. The lower and upper lids, the bulbous root, the stem, the neck, the petals and the pericarp shall be conceived in order and worshipped.

33-35. He shall conceive the eight Siddhis in the petals, the Śaktis in the filaments, the eight Rudras, Vāma and others from the east, all round in order; the Vairāgya in the pericarp and the nine Śaktis in the Bījas, Vāma and others alone beginning with the east and ending with Manonmanī, the Dharma of Śiva in the bulbous root, the Śaivite knowledge in the stem and the zones of fire, sun and the moon above the pericarp.

36-37. The science of the Ātman, and the trio of principles named Śiva shall be conceived thereafter. Above these seats he shall conceive the seat of the deity shining with

127. I. 164. 41

the flowers of various colours and brilliance due to the Lore Paravyomāvakāśa.

38-40. From the Ādhāra Śakti to the seat of the sacred lore the devotee shall repeat the mantra. ओं शिवाय नमः

This is the procedure everywhere. As before, the five Brahmans shall be conceived in the idol in view of the difference due to limbs, faces and digits. The devotee, expert in the mystic signs shall invoke the lord standing with a handful of flowers.

41-45. Uttering the mantra beginning with "I resort to Sadyojāta" and ending with Om repeating the Nāda arising from the Ādhāra and concluding at the Brahmarandhra, along with the twelve knots he shall meditate on the lord in Oṅkāra, pure as crystal, the unsullied, the imperishable, the cause of creation, identical with the worlds, stationed within and without, pervading all, smaller than the smallest and greater than the greatest, visible to the devotees without strain, the unchanging incomprehensible to the gods, Brahmā, Indra, Viṣṇu, Rudra and others, the essence of the Vedas, declared as invisible, by the learned devoid of beginning, middle and end and the panacea for all worldly ills.

46-47. After meditating on him thus with concentration, the devotee shall perform obeisance after showing different mystic signs and performing the rites of invocation, installation, concentration and observance. He shall meditate on lord Śiva himself, of Sakala and Niṣkala forms.

48-63. He shall conceive the lord as pure as crystal, with cool lustre resembling the circular lightning, of delightful aspect bedecked in matted hair and coronet, clad in the tiger's hide with his lotus-like smiling face, with his palms, soles and lips having the lustre of the petals of the red lotus, endowed with all characteristics, bedecked in holding ornaments, divine weapons, perfumed with divine unguents and scents, with five faces, ten arms, the crescent moon for his crest jewel. His gentle face facing the east is lustrous as the rising sun. It has three lotus eyes. The infant moon adorns the crest. His right face has the charming lustre resembling the lustre of the blue cloud. It has crooked eyebrows, three circular and red eyes, is terrible by its curved fangs, inaccessible to the eyes and has sprout-like lips throbbing. The northern face has the lustre of the coral, is decorated with blue forelocks, has three eyes of graceful movements and crest decorated with the semicircular moon. The western face has the lustre of the full moon brilliant with the three eyes. It is gentle with the crescent moon and is charming with gentle smile. The fifth face is brilliant like crystal and shines with contours of the moon. It is very gentle and dazzling with the three beaming eyes. His right hands hold trident, axe, thunderbolt, sword and dazzling fire. In the left hands he has the bow, arrow, bell, noose and the goad. He has the Nivṛtti Kalā upto the knees, the Pratiṣṭhā Kalā upto the navel; the Vidyā Kalā upto the neck; the Śāntā Kalā upto the forehead and the Śāntyatīta Kalā beyond that. Thus he has a body of five Kalās. He pervades the five paths. He has Īśana for the crown. He is the primeval lord Puruṣa. He has Aghora for the heart, Vāmadeva for his private parts and Sadyojāta for his form. He has thirty-eight Kalās. He is Īśāna identical with the Māṭṛkās and the five Brahmans; he is identical with Oṅkāra, Haṁsanyāsa, the five-syllabled and the six-syllabled mantras, the six mountains and the Jātis.

64-65. After meditating thus, O goddess, he shall meditate on you as Manonmani to my left. Repeating the mantra "Gaurīrmimāya"* preceded by the Praṇava he shall invoke you as before and perform the rites ending with prostration. The sage of pious concentrated mind shall meditate on you, O goddess.

66-70. You have the lustre of the blooming lotus, eyes expansive and wide, face lustrous as the full moon, curly dark hair, complexion of the brilliant blue lotus, crest decorated with the semicircular moon, breasts rounded, plump protruding, smooth and stout, slender middle large buttocks and fine yellow garment. You are endowed with ornaments. In your forehead you have a shining Tilaka. Flowers of various colours decorate your braid of hair. Your feature befits your nature. Your face is bent

*RV. 1. 164. 41.

due to bashfulness. You hold splendid golden lotus in your right hand. You are seated on a cosy seat with your left hand placed like a staff.

71. After meditating on me and you like this, O goddess, the ascetic of restrained mind shall perform ablution with the water in the manner of Pranava —prokṣana.

72. He shall offer Pādya repeating mantra "Bhave bhave nātibhave.[128] He shall offer water for Ācamana by uttering "Vāmāya namaḥ"

73. He shall offer a fresh piece of cloth saying Jyeṣṭhāya Namaḥ" (obeisance to the eldest). He shall offer the sacred thread saying Śreṣṭhāya Namaḥ (obeisance to the most excellent).

74. He shall offer water for Ācamana once again saying "Rudrāya Namaḥ" (obeisance to Rudra). He shall offer well consecrated scent saying "Kālāya Namaḥ.

75. He shall offer raw grains saying "Kalavikaraṇāya Namaḥ". He shall offer flowers, saying Balavikaraṇāya Namaḥ"

76. He shall offer incense assiduously saying "Balāya Namaḥ". "He shall offer good lamp saying "Balapramathanāya Namaḥ."

77-78. Along with the Vedas including their six ancillaries, Mātṛkā, Pranava and Śiva joined with Śivā, he shall show mystic signs to me and to you, O good-complexioned lady. First he shall render service to me, then to you.

79-80. When he offers things and performs rites to you he shall use the feminine gender. O Pārvati, none but this is the difference. After performing meditation and worship duly in accordence with the rules the expert devotee shall begin the Āvaraṇa Pūjā.

128. TA 10. 43. 1.

CHAPTER EIGHT

(*Śiva's Mental worship*)

Lord Śiva said :—

1. O goddess, there are five Āvaraṇas here. The five Āvaraṇa-worships shall be performed thus.

2. Where they had been previoushy worshipped, the lords Gaṇeśa and Kārttikeyu shall be worshipped in order.

3-5. The five Brahmans shall be worshipped in order in the north-east, east, south, north and west. The devotee shall worship the six ancillaries then. He shall worship the eye and Astra in the southeast, northeast, southwest, north-west and in the middle. Thus the first Āvaraṇa is mentioned. Now listen to the second Āvaraṇa.

6-7. He shall worship Ananta in the petal in the east; the Sūkṣma in the South; Śivottama in the west; Ekanetra in the north; Ekarudra in the northeast; the Trinity in the southeast; Śrīkaṇṭha in the south-west and Śikhaṇḍīśa in the north-west.

8. In the second Āvaraṇa he shall worship the Emperors. (Now the third Āvarana). The devotee shall worship Vṛṣeśāna in the middle of the eastern door.

9-12. Nandin shall be worshipped to the south and Mahākāla to the north of it, Bhṛṅgīśa to the west of the southern door. Vināyaka shall be worshipped in the square to the east of that with scents; Vṛṣabha in the northwest and Guha in the southern square. To the east of the northern door the following eight shall be worshipped in accordance with the rules of circumambulation. They are Bhava, Śarva, Īśāna, Rudra, Paśupati, Ugra, Bhīma and Mahādeva. Such is the worship in the third Āvaraṇa.

13. After invoking Lord Śiva with the mantra "Yo Vedādau Svaraḥ"[129] he shall worship him in the lotus above the pericarp in the east.

14. He shall worship Lord Śiva in the eastern, Viśveśa in the southern, Parameśāna in the northern and Sarveśa in the western petal.

129. TA 10. 10. 3.

15. He shall worship Rudra in the south after invoking him with Ṛk "Ā vo rājānam"[130] in the petals and the pericarp with scents, flowers etc.

16. Śiva shall be worshipped in the east; Hara in the south; Mṛḍa in the north and Bhava in the petal in the western quarter. They shall be worshipped in this order.

17. After invoking Viṣṇu by uttering the mantra "Pra tad Viṣṇu"[131] etc. he shall worship him in the north on the pericarp and the petals with scents, flowers etc.

18. He shall worship Vāsudeva in the east; Aniruddha in the south; Saṁkarṣaṇa in the north and Pradyumna in the west.

19. The knower of Mantras shall invoke Brahmā with the mantra "Hiraṇyagarbhaḥ Samavartata"[132] etc. and worship him in the lotus to the west.

20. He shall worship Hiraṇyagarbha in the east; Virāja in the south; Puṣkara in the north and Kāla in the west.

21-24. (Now the fifth Āvaraṇa). In the topmost row the Lokapālas shall be worshipped in different spots beginning with the last and proceeding in the manner of circumambulation. The following ten are the Bījas for the Lokapālas :— Rānta (ending with 'Ra'), Pānta (ending with 'Pa'), Jñānta (ending with 'Jña') Lānta (ending with 'La') twice, Apūrvaka (beginning with 'A'), Ṣānta (ending with 'Ṣa'), Sānta (ending with 'Sa') Vedādya (Praṇava) and ŚriBīja. He shall worship the Lokapālas with these Bījas. He shall worship Brahmā and Viṣnu in accordance with the rules and proper means of service in the north, south-west, south and north-east. He shall worship Deveśa in the outer lines of the fifth Āvaraṇa.

25-26. He shall worship trident in the north-east, thunderbolt in the east; axe in the south-east; arrow in the south; sword in the south-west; noose in the west; goad in the north-west and bow in the north.

130. RV. 4. 3. 1.
131. VS. 5. 20.
132. Ibid. 13. 4.

27. For the satisfaction of Śiva, the knower of the rules shall worship Kṣetrapāla of Rudra facing the west, in accordance with the rules.

28. All these shall be thought of as standing with palms joined in reverence, their faces beaming with smile and glancing at the lord and the goddess with devotion always.

29. After performing the Āvaraṇa worship thus, the devotee shall worship the lord of the gods again for allaying his mental disturbance. He shall know Praṇava as Śiva.

30. After worshipping duly thus with scents and other services he shall offer Naivedya prepared in the proper manner.

31. He shall give water for Ācamana and the Arghya as before, and then offer Tāmbūla and water in accordance with the rules.

32. After performing Nīrājana the balance of the worship shall be completed. After meditating on the lord and the goddess he shall repeat the mantra hundred and eight times.

33-34. Then he shall stand up with a handful of flowers, O Goddess, meditate on lord Śiva with the mantra beginning with "Yo devānām"[133] and ending with "Yo vedādau svaraḥ proktaḥ". The handful of flowers shall be dedicated and he shall perform circumambulation thrice.

35. He shall prostrate with eight parts of the body touching the ground. Endowed with great devotion he shall perform circumambulation again, make obeisance once more.

36-38. While sitting there, he shall adore the lord with the eight names. Then he shall pray thus : "O lord Śiva, good or bad whatever I have done is your great service." After saying this, flowers shall be offered along with the water from the conch. After worshipping him who is worthy of worship he shall repeat the eight names with significant meaning. O goddess, I shall tell you the same because of your devotion to me.

133. VS. 11. 39

CHAPTER NINE

(The mode of interpreting the Praṇava)

Lord Śiva said :—

1-2. The following eight names indicate Śiva—Śiva, Maheśvara, Rudra, Viṣṇu, Pitāmaha, Saṁsāravaidya, Saravajña, Paramātman.

3. The five names of Sadāśiva are dependent on their condition. If the condition alters the name too alters.

4. The word is permanent. The object indicated by the word is non-permanent. The words are transferable since those indicated by the words are released.

5. Even when words are transferred there are conditions again. The first five names denote things other than Ātman.

6. The other three names derive their origin from difference in the material cause. Śiva exists by creating three types of conditions.

7. Due to the antecedent non-existence of the contact with the primordial Avidyā he is naturally pure-souled and is called Śiva.

8. Lord Śiva who is richly endowed with good attributes is called Śiva by the experts in the Śaiva cult.

9-11. Prakṛti is yonder than the twentythree principles Purusa, the twentyfifth principle is yonder than Prakṛti. The Puruṣa is called Svara as expressed in the Vedas. He becomes intelligible and recognizable only through the Vedas and the Upaniṣads. As the enjoyer he becomes merged in Prakṛti. He who is beyond this Puruṣa is named Maheśvara.

12-13. He is rightly termed Maheśvara because Prakṛti and Puruṣa are subservient to him. Or Māyā is the principle with the three attributes which is imperishable. Know that Māyā is the Prakṛti and Māyin (the wielder of Māyā) is Maheśvara who is eternal and the releaser from Māyā. Hence the name Maheśvara is applicable to him.

14. The word Rud means misery or cause of misery.

The lord who dispels it is called Rudra,[134] lord Śiva, the great or ultimate cause.

15. Śiva is called Viṣṇu because he pervades the principles of Śiva ending with the earth and the bodies, pots etc.

16. Śiva is called Pitāmaha because of his fatherhood of the Trinity which in turn is the cause of the universe.

17-18. A pathologist diagnoses correctly and cures illness through medicines. Similarly Śiva the cause of dissolution, sustenance and origin of the world as well as the router of the gross is called the physician of the world by those who know the nature of the principles.

19-21. Atoms enveloped by the dirt of the ocean of Māyā do not know the gross and subtle things that occur in the three periods of time even when they have the sense-organs for imbibing the five-fold knowledge. But Sadāśiva knows every existent object naturally, even though he has no sense-organs yielding the knowledge of all existent objects. Hence he is called omniscient.

22. Śiva is the great Atman because he is the Ātman of all, he is for ever endowed with the great qualities and there is no greater Ātman than him.

23-26. After eulogising Mahādeva, identical with Praṇava, the imperishable and offering gifts on the head of Īśāna, he worships the lord with the purity of mind, by means of the praṇavā. He shall then take a handful of flowers, join palms in reverence, inhale through the left nostril, identifying the inhaled air with Śiva and exhale through the right nostril bidding the ritualistic adieu to the goddess. He shall realise the identity of Śiva with himself. "I am Śiva alone." He shall make the ritualistic dismissal of the deities conceived in the heart.

27. After worshipping the lore and the preceptor he shall fix in the heart the mantras of the conch and the vessel of Arghya.

28-30. After consigning the remnants of the floral offerings to Caṇḍeśa in the north-east quarter he shall restrain

134. For a different derivation and meaning of the word Rudra see Vāyavīya Saṁhitā 1. 12. 30

the vital breath and utter the names of the sages. This Maṇḍala is technically known as Kailāsaprastara. This shall be worshipped every day, or every fortnight, or every month or once in six months or once in a year or during the Cāturmāsya festival. A theist shall necessarily worship my Liṅga every day.

31-32. O goddess, in this context a special order shall be observed. On the day of initiation he shall worship the Liṅga along with the preceptor and bow thrice in front of the preceptor : "Till my death I shall worship Śiva".

33. O beloved, he shall worship it, as mentiond above. He shall pour water from Argha above on the top of Liṅga.

34. After worshipping it with Praṇava he shall offer incense and the lamp. After propitiating Caṇḍa in the north-east he shall offer Nirmālya.

35-36. The Liṅga and the altar shall be washed with the filtered water. Repeating the Praṇava he shall put a flower on the top of the Liṅga. He shall mentally conceive everythig from the Ādhāra Śakti to the seat of the holy lore and install the supreme god.

37-39. He shall perform the ablution of the lord with Pañcagavya etc. or with holy water rendered fragrant with scented articles repeating the mantras from the Ṛg or Sāmaveda such as 'Pāvamāna' 'Rudra' 'Nīla' or 'Tvarita' along with the five Brahmans. The Praṇava or the name of Śiva can be used as mantra. The ablution shall be made with the Arghya water repeating the Praṇava.

40. After wiping the Liṅga with a piece of cloth he shall put a flower on the top. After installing the Liṅga on the pedestal he shall perform the worship of the sun.

41-42. He shall worship the Ādhāraśakti and Ananta beneath the pedestal. After worshipping the throne duly with the lower and upper lid he shall worship Skanda on the foot of the Pīṭha. After conceiving me in the Liṅga he shall worship me along with you.

43-44. The ascetic shall think on me with devotion in accordance with the rules. O beloved, thus I have narrated to you a great secret that shall be guarded assiduously. It shall not be imparted to any one and everyone. It shall be given to my devotee, to an ascetic free from passion and lust.

45-46. It shall be given to a person devoted to his preceptor, who is calm and who engages in Yoga for attaining me. The foolish fellow who transgresses my directives and gives this away is my enemy. Surely he will go to hell. O goddess, imparting it to my devotee he will become my favourite. After enjoying all pleasures here he shall attain my presence.

Vyāsa said:—

47-48. On hearing this speech of Śiva, the goddess eulogised the lord with various hymns containing the purport of the Vedic mantras. She bowed at the feet of her lord. O excellent sages, she rejoiced with a delighted heart.

49. O brahmins, this is a great secret. It illuminates the meaning of the Praṇava. Leading to the knowledge of Śiva it destroys all your miseries.

Sūta said:—

50-52. After saying this, the excellent sage of great penance, the son of Parāśara, worshipped and honoured with intent devotion by the sages and propounder of the Vedas, thought of the mount Kailāsa and left that hermitage. Delighted in their hearts, at the end of the sacrifice they too worshipped the moon-crested god and the goddess Umā with great devotion. They engaged themselves in Yogic practices of restraint etc. and continued to meditate on Śiva.

53. This was mentioned to Guha by the goddess who mentioned it to Nandin. Lord Nandin mentioned it to the sage Sanatkumāra.

54. O leading sages, from him this was obtained by my preceptor Vyāsa of immeasurable splendour. This holy lore was obtained from him by me also.

55. On knowing your love for the lord and realising that you are his favourite devotee, this secret of secrets has been narrated to you by me.

56. This secret lore dear to Śiva shall be given by you only to ascetics of quiet minds, devotees of Śiva's feet.

57. After saying this the blessed Sūta, most excellent of Paurāṇikas, wandered over the earth, visiting the holy centres.

58. After securing this great secret from Sūta, the sages remained in Kāśī and attained Śiva's abode by attaining salvation.

CHAPTER TEN

(*Sūta's instruction*)

Vyāsa said :—

1. When Sūta had left, the wondering sages thought and spoke to one another—"What the great sage said about Vāmadeva's opinion has been forgotten. This is indeed distressing to us.

2. When shall we see the excellent sage again? His sight dispels the vast miseries of worldly existence. May the great sage appear again as a result of the merit accruing from the worship of lord Śiva.

3. The sages who were worried with these thoughts worshipped Sūta in the lotus of their heart and stayed there being eager to see him.

4. At the end of a year, the sage, engaged in devotional activities of Śiva, the wise propounder of the meaning to the Purāṇas, came to Kāśī again.

5. On seeing Sūta coming, the sages delighted in their minds, worshipped him duly rising up and offering seat and Arghya.

6. He too congratulated the sages with a smiling face. With pleasure he took the bath in the holy waters of the Gaṅgā.

7. He propitiated the sages, the gods and the Pitṛs with gingelly seeds and rice grains. He came to the bank and put on his dress after sprinkling it with water.

8-9. He performed the Ācamana twice and took the Bhasma repeating the Sadyādi mantras. Wearing the garland of Rudrākṣa beads he applied the Bhasma to his body and made the Tripuṇḍra marks on the limbs. He then performed his routine rites.

10. With great devotion he eulogised, bowed to and worshipped lord Śiva and Umā along with his sons and chief Gaṇas.

11-12. He worshipped Kālabhairava in accordance with the rules after circumambulating him thrice. He prostrated five times and circumambutaled again. Thinking upon his lotus-feet he eulogised him again with the great hymn.

13-14. He performed the Japa of the sacred Pañcākṣarī lore one thousand and eight times. Standing in front of lord Śiva's image he begged for forgiveness. After worshipping him he took his seat in the the middle of Muktimaṇḍapa offered by the sages who had mastered the Vedas.

15. When all had taken their seats after due obeisance with the recital of the mantras he spoke in accents that increased the piety of the sages.

Sūta said:—

16. O intelligent sages, you all who have fulfilled your vows are blessed. I have come for your sake. Please listen in details.

17. After telling you the meaning of the Praṇava I went on a pilgrimage. Now hear the details.

18. O leading brahmans, after starting from here I went to the southern ocean. I took bath therein and worshipped the goddess Śivā, Kanyākumārī. On my return I came to the river Suvarṇamukharī[135].

19-25. I reached the wonderful city on the Kālahasti Śaila. I took my bath in the waters of Suvarṇamukharī[136] and performed Tarpaṇa to the gods and the sages. Remembering Śiva with the mystic signs I worshipped Kālahastīśa with the lustre of the lunar stone, the lord with the face directed to the west, the wonderful lord of five faces, the lord who

135. This sacred river of South India issues from the Agastya mountain, flows in the North Arcot district near Kālahasti mountain and falls into the southern sea.

136. It is an unidentified town on the sacred hill of Kālahasti on the river Suvarṇamukharī in the North Arcot district.

dispels all sins at his very sight, the lord Triguṇeśvara who bestows Siddhis, worldly pleasures and salvation. Then with great devotion I worshipped Śivā stationed to his right, the goddess who is the bud of the flower of knowledge and the mother of the universe. I performed the Japa of the holy Pañcākṣarī Vidyā one thousand eight times. I circumambulated, eulogised and bowed again. Thus I went round the hill every day with great devotion. I observed all restraints and performed rites every day with rejoicing mind.

26. O great sages, I spent four months there by the favour of the goddess—the bud of the flower of knowledge.

27-28. Once I spread the cloth, deerskin and the Kuśa grass on the seat. Seated on it silently with restrained mind I entered into the mystic trance. "I am Śiva the solidified knowledge and bliss, the perfect one for ever." This realisation dawned in my heart and I was free from agitation.

29-32. Then my preceptor, the ocean of mercy, resembling the dark cloud, with matted tawny hair resembling the lightning, the tall sage bearing the water-pot and staff and wearing the antelope's skin, with the body turned white with the ashes having all auspicious marks with the Tripuṇḍra shining on the forehead, decorated with Rudrākṣa garlands and the two lotus-like wide eyes gleaming, appeared in the lotus of my heart. Thereafter I swooned soon, O theists, this was the wonderful incident indeed.

33. Then I opened my eyes and cried. The tears I shed quashed out like a mountain stream.

34. Then a celestial unimbodied voice was heard from the sky. It was wonderful. O brahmins, listen to that devotedly.

35-36. "O blessed son of Sūta, go to Vārāṇasī; the sages whom you had instructed before, are desirous of the pleasure of your arrival. They are on fast theretoo." After saying this the voice stopped.

37-39. I got up immediately and circumambulated the lord and the goddess with devotion. I bowed and prostrated for twelve times. Considering it the order of my preceptor and of Śiva and Śivā I set out from the temple. O excellent sages, I have come here in forty days. Please bless me. Please tell me what I shall say now.

40. On hearing the words of Sūta, the sages were delighted in their minds. They bowed to the sage Vyāsa again and again and said.

CHAPTER ELEVEN

(*Description of the Brahman Vāmadeva*)

The sages said:—

1-2. O Sūta, O blessed Sūta, you are our excellent preceptor. We ask you if there be your blessing for us, your faithful disciples, as it has been shown by you who are always affectionate to us.

3. The opinion of Vāmadeva was hinted at by you at the time of Virajā homa formerly. O sage, it was not heard by us in detail.

4. Now we are eager to hear it reverentially and devotedly, O ocean of mercy. It behoves you to narrate it with pleasure.

5-6. On hearing this, Sūta was thrilled with delight. After making obeisance to lord Śiva, the preceptor of preceptors, to the goddess-mother of the trio and to his preceptor Vyāsa with devotion he spoke in a majestic tone delighting the sages.

Sūta said:—

7. O sages, hail to you. May you remain happy always; devotees of Śiva steady-minded and propagators of devotion to Śiva.

8. That wonderful thing has been heard from the lotus-like mouth of the preceptor. This was not mentioned by me before, being afraid of revealing a secret.

9. Indeed you are highly fortunate devotees of Śiva

and stable in your rites. Convinced of this, I shall mention it to you. May this be heard joyously.

10-15. Formerly in the Rathantara kalpa the sage Vāmadeva, roaming over the earth, entered Kumāraśikhara,[137] the southern summit of Meru where the peacock-vehicled lord Kārttikeya, son of Śiva, stays joyously. The sage was a liberated soul even while he was in the womb. He was the most-honoured among the knowers of Śiva's cult. He knew the reality, and the principles of the Vedas, Āgamas, Purāṇas and other sacred scriptures. He knew the births and activities of all living beings, gods, Asuras, mortals and others. The ashes made his body white. He was bedecked in the knots of matted hair. He had no permanent abode, no desire, no egotism and none of the mutually opposing feelings and emotions. He was unclad. He was very wise like Śiva himself. He was surrounded by the leading sages who were like him and who had become his disciples. He sanctified the earth by the pious touch of his feet. His heart dwelt in the great splendour.

16. Lord Kārttikeya, the hero possessed of the power of knowledge, the suppressor of the Asuras, stays there along with Gajavalli and bowed to by all the gods.

17-21. Near the lord there is a lake Skandasaras[138] as vast as an ocean with plenty of deep, sweet, cool, clear water of wonderful attributes. The sage Vāmadeva took his bath there along with his disciples. He saw Skanda seated on the summit attended by the sages, shining like the rising sun, with the peacock as his vehicle. He had four arms and splendid body. He was bedecked in coronet and other ornaments. He was reverentially attended by two excellent Śaktis. He held Śakti and a cock. He showed the mystic gestures of boons and protection with his hands. On seeing Skanda the sage worshipped him with devotion and began to eulogise him.

137. It is not identified.

138. This lake formed of the waters of the Kumāra hill lying to the south of Meru remains unidentified.

Vāmadeva said:—

22. Om, obeisance to the meaning of the Praṇava, to the enterpreter of the Praṇava, to the Bīja of the letters of the Praṇava.

23. Obeisance to the lord in the form of the purport of the Upaniṣad, to their enterpreter and the knower of their purport.

24. Obeisance to Guha, to the deity concealed in the cavities of the hearts of all living beings. Obeisance to the secret one of secret form. Obeisance to the knower of the secret sacred lore.

25. Obeisance to you the minutest of the minute, the greatest of the great, the knower of the greater and the lesser, the lord in the form of the great Ātman.

26. Obeisance to Skanda; to the lord of splendour as red as that of the sun in the form of Skanda; to the lord who wears the coronets adorned with the garlands of the flowers of the divine Mandāra tree.

27. Obeisance to the disciple of Śiva; to the son of Śiva, to the bestower of bliss and happiness, to the beloved of Śiva; to the storehouse of pleasure of Śiva and Śivā.

28. Obeisance to the son of the Gaṅgā, to the intelligent Kārttikeya, to the noble son of Umā, lying in the grove of Śara plants.

29. Obeisance to the six-faced god of six imperishable bodies to the one who interprets in six ways, to the lord whose form is beyond the sixfold path.

30. O soul of the twelve (?) obeisance be to you with twelve wide eyes, with twelve uplifted arms and twelve types of weapons.

31. Obeisance to the four-armed lord, to the calm lord who bears Śakti and a cock, to the bestower of boons; the learned or to one with a bird in his hand. Obeisance to the splitter of the Asuras.

32. Obeisance to the lord whose chest is marked by the saffron that had been smeared over the breasts of Gajavallī. Obeisance to the one whose heart is delighted by the pleasures of the elephant-faced lord Gaṇapati.

33. O lord, whose song of praise is sung by Brahmā

other gods, sages and the Kinnaras, obeisance be to you who are the abode of fame reflected upon by the pious. O lord, whose lotus-like beautiful feet deserve the worship of the garlands that decorate the splendid crowns of the gods, obeisance be to you.

34. He who reads or listens to this divine prayer to Skanda, uttered by Vāmadeva, attains the supreme goal.

35. This prayer sharpens intelligence, enhances devotion to Śiva, increases longevity, imparts health and affluence and yields all desires always.

36-37. O brahmins, after eulogising lord commander-in-chief of the gods thus, circumambulating him thrice and prostrating on the ground Vāmadeva bowed to him once again and went round him. Then he stood bowing down with humility.

38-39. On hearing the eulogy of Vāmadeva, unfolding the facts, the lord, son of Maheśvara, was delighted and said "I am delighted by your worship, devotion and eulogy. Welfare be to you. What shall I do for you ?

40. O sage, you are the chief of Yogins, perfect and free from avarice. There is nothing for people like you which has to be solicited.

41. Still saintly men like you move about in the world for upholding virtue and blessing the worlds.

42. O Brahmin, if it is fit to be heard you shall speak it out. I shall expound it to the people for their welfare.

43. On hearing the words of Skanda, the sage Vāmadeva, bowed with humility and spoke in a tone as majestic as the sound of clouds.

Vāmadeva said:—

44. O lord, you are the great Īśa, the bestower of prosperity to all and sundry. You are omniscient; creator of all and the lord bearing all Śaktis.

45. We are insignificant creatures to speak before you who are a great lord. Still it is your blessing that you speak to me.

46. O intelligent one, I have but a particle of wisdom. Urged thus I ask you. My transgression must be excused.

47. Praṇava is the word that expresses lord Śiva. Lord Paśupati is the goal, the releaser of the bondage of the Paśus, the individual souls.

48. Invoked with the mantra he releases the Jīva instantaneously. Hence siddhi is achieved with the mantra Om for Śiva.

49. The eternal Śruti says, "Verily all this is Om; Om is Brahman. Everything is Brahman."[139]

50. O commander of the gods, obeisance to you, the lord of the gods and of ascetics. Obeisance to you the perfect one.

51. In this situation, there is nothing distinct from Śiva in this world. Śiva is the lord who assumes all forms. Maheśvara is all-pervasive.

52. The universal and the personal application of Praṇava was heard by me. O lord, but I have never had a preceptor like you to tell me that.

53. Hence take pity on me and reveal its meaning in accordance with the rules of instruction and the conduct of the good.

54. My lord alone is the preceptor who cuts off the bondage. O preceptor, now favour me with the exposition of its meaning.

55. Thus requested by the sage, Skanda bowed to Sadāśiva, the very praṇava itself who is characterised by thirtyeight excellent digits, who is accompanied by Umā at his side and who is followed by the excellent sages. He then began to expound the path of welfare well guarded in the Vedas.

139. T. U. 1. 8. 1.

CHAPTER TWELVE

(*The procedure of Sannyāsa*)

Subrahmaṇya said:—

1. Well done, well done, O fortunate Vāmadeva, O great sage, you are a great devotee of Śiva and the most excellent of those who possess Śiva's knowledge.

2. Nowhere in the world is there anything not known to you. Still I shall tell you since you wish to bless the worlds.

3. All the individuals in the world are deceived by the Māyā of Iśa. They are deceived by various sacred scriptures.

4. They do not know the great lord, the meaning of the Praṇava, the Nirguṇa and Saguṇa Brahman, the great progenitor of trinity.

5. I shall lift up my right hand and swear unto you truth again and again.

6-12. Śiva is declared as the purport of the Praṇava in the Śruti and Smṛti texts, Purāṇas and the Āgamas; from whom words recede unable to reach him along with the mind; the knower of whose bliss does not have fear from anywhere;[140] from whom this entire universe, beginning with Brahmā, Viṣṇu and Indra is born at the outset with the groups of sense-organs and elements; that which has no cause anywhere at any time; which neither the lightning nor the sun nor the moon does illuminate; by whose splendour this entire universe is resplendent all round; he who is endowed with prosperity himself in the name of Sarveśvara; who is worthy of being meditated upon by those who are desirous of salvation; he who is the cause of welfare; who is in the middle of the firmament; who is omnipresent, whose soul is light, who is in the form of splendour, knowledge and consciousness; whose splendid Śakti is comprehensible only through emotion and who is both Nirguṇa and Saguṇa, unsullied and auspicious.

13. Three types of his form—gross, subtle and causal

140. Ibid. 2. 9. 1.

shall be meditated upon by those seeking salvation, O sage, and by the Yogins in the proper order.

14. The unsullied being, the primordial and the eternal lord of all who is stated to be the supreme soul has knowledge and the ritual as his innate nature.

15-16. The image of the lord of the gods is Sadāśiva himself, the lord with five mantras for his body and the five digits for his physical form. The lord is as bright as crystal, has cool lustre and is delightful. He has five faces, ten arms and fifteen eyes.

17-18. He the ancient lord has Īśāna for his coronet; Puruṣa for his face; Aghora for his heart; Vāmadeva for his private parts and Sadya for his foot. He is both Sakala and Niṣkala. The six Śaktis, omniscience etc. constitute his six limbs.

19. He is infused with the power of the word throbbing in the lotus of his heart; he is bedecked on his left by Manonmanī, his own Śakti.

20. With reference to the six entities, Mantra, etc., I shall explain the Pranava-souled lord in his composite and personal nature.

21. The order of instruction shall be mentioned at first. Please hear, O sage, indeed the four castes are well known in the world.

22. The Vedas enjoin rituals for the first three castes. The Śūdras are excluded since their only activity is service.

23-25. Nothing but the holy rites of the Śrutis and Smṛtis shall be performed by the first three castes in their respective stages of life. Following the conduct of life enjoined for different stages and castes, excellent sages have attained Śāyujya form of liberation.

26. The Śruti says that the sages are satisfied by Brahmacarya; the gods by sacrifice; and the Pitṛs by progeny.

27-28. Freed from this threefold debt and entering the Vānaprastha stage the devotee shall bear both pleasure and pain, chillness and heat; shall subjugate the senses, control the diet. The ascetic shall practise restraint and other means of Yoga so that the intellect becomes stable and unswerving.

29-30. Thus he becomes pious and free from activities. After eschewing all activites he shall be devoted to the pursuit of knowledge. That alone bestows the fruit of living liberation and identity with Śiva. It is most excellent and renders free from aberrations those who have restrained their minds.

31. I shall explain different modes of the same with a desire for blessing the worlds. O intelligent one, it is out of affection for you that I do so. Please listen with attention.

32. The ascetic shall approach a preceptor, the most excellent among intelligent ones; the preceptor who knows the principles of sacred scriptures and has mastered the Vedāntic knowledge.

33. After approaching him in accordance with the rules, the ascetic devotee shall please him assiduously by obeisances, prostration etc.

34. The preceptor is Śiva and Śiva is the preceptor. After deciding this in mind he shall express his intention.

35-36. Permitted by the preceptor he shall subsist on milk diet and perform rites for twelve days. On the fourth or the tenth day in the bright lunar fortnight he shall take his early morning bath. With pious mind, he shall perform his routine. He shall invite the preceptor and begin the Nāndī śrāddha.

37-39. The Viśvedevas are Satyavasus. In the Śrāddha of the gods, Brahmā, Viṣṇu and Śiva, in that of the sages, those born of celestial damsels from human beings, in that of the Pitṛs, Vasu, Rudra and Āditya, in that of human beings, the four sages, Sanaka and others, in that of the Bhūtas the five great elements are included.

40. The group of sense-organs consists of the eye, etc; that of the Bhūtas is of four types. In the Pitṛ Śrāddha the father, grandfather and greatgrandfather are included.

41-42. In the Mātṛśrāddha, the mother, grandmother and the greatgrandmother are mentioned. In the Srāddha of the Ātman the four, viz. himself father, grandfather and greatgrandfather and their wives are mentioned. In the Śrāddha of mother's father the three ancestors of the maternal grandfather are mentioned.

43. In every Śrāddha a pair of brahmins shall be invited and their feet washed. He shall then perform the Ācamana assiduously.

44-46. He shall pray thus:—"May the dust-particles from the feet of the brahmins sanctify me. They are the cause of prosperity. They destroy all adversities and constitute the bridge on the vast ocean of worldly existence. Like suns they remove the pitch darkness of distress. Like divine cows they meet the desired objects. They are the embodied holy waters in every pilgrim centre." After praying thus he shall bow and prostrate with eight limbs touching the ground. He shall then face the east and remember the lotus-feet of Śiva.

47-49. Wearing the Pavitra in the finger and the sacred thread on the shoulders, being pure and steady he shall perform the Prāṇāyāma thrice. Mentioning the Tithi etc. he shall continue—"As an ancillary rite to my formal renunciation I have to perform eight Śrāddhas beginning with the Śrāddha of Viśvedevas and ending with the Śrāddha of Mātāmaha. I shall perform these with the rules governing the festive rites, with your permission." After proclaiming the intention he shall cast off the Darbha grass to the north.

50. He shall touch water and stand up to begin the formal invitation to the brahmins. With the Pavitra in the hand he shall touch the hands of the brahmins and proclaim:

51-53. "For the sake of Viśvedevas I invite you both and conclude. You shall favour me." This is the procedure throughout. After this he shall draw ten Maṇḍalas beginning from the north. He shall worship these with Akṣatas and ask the Brahmins to stand there.

54-55. He shall utter the names of Viśvedevas in the vocative case. "Here is water for washing the feet". Saying this, he shall offer water from the Darbha grass, flowers and

Akṣata as Pādya. He shall wash his own feet too facing the north. He shall perform Ācamana and ask them to sit in pairs on their seats.

56-57. "Here is the seat to the brahmin in the form of Visvedevas." Saying this he shall offer a few Darbha grass blades. He himself shall stand holding the Darbha grass and say, "In this Nāndīmukhaśrāddha for the sake of Viśvedevas I invite both of you to be present."

58. Then he shall say "Both of you shall accept my invitation." The two brahmins shall say "We accept."

59. He shall request the brahmins—"May you bless me. Let the rite be complete. Let me attain my desires."

60-63. He shall then place cooked rice and other food-stuffs in well washed plantain leaf cups. They shall be covered with Darbha grass. He shall sprinkle water over them. The leafcups shall be lifted up by the hands. He shall offer the food-stuffs into fire saying "Svāhā." The names of the deities shall be used in the dative case. The Mantras "the earth is your vessel,"[141] etc. shall be repeated. After worship the devotee shall say "Na Mama" (not for me). Everywhere this is the procedure.

64 "I salute lord Śiva accompanied by Ambā, the recollection of whose feet and the repetition of whose names makes deficient rites perfect and complete.

65-67. After repeating the prayer he shall say. I have completed Nandīmukhaśrāddha. Confirm that I have done it. He shall propitiate the leading brahmins, let some water drop from his hand, bow to them, stand up and say to them. let the food be even as nectar. Then with palms joined in reverence he shall pray with pleasure.

68. He shall recite Śrīrudra, Camaka, and Puruṣa sūktas duly. After meditating on Sadaśiva he shall repeat the Japas of the five Brahmans.

69. At the end of the meal he shall recite Rudra Sūkta. He shall ask forgiveness of the brahmins. After food he shall offer water.

70. Washing his feet and performing the Ācamana he

141. Āpg. 8. 21. 8.

shall approach the Piṇḍas. Facing the east he shall sit silently and perform Prāṇāyāma thrice.

71-72. "I shall perform the rite of offering the Piṇḍas as an ancillary to the Nāndīmukhaśrāddha." After deciding thus he shall draw nine lines from south to north. He shall place twelve Darbhas with their tips to the east over the lines. These are the five places for the gods Dakṣa and others.

73-75. In these places the akṣata grains and water shall be offered silently. In the other places he shall sprinkle water with the mantra "Atra Pitaraḥ",[142] and offer the Akṣata grains and water for worship. The names of different gods shall be mentioned with the dative case ending. Three Piṇḍas shall be offered to each in the five places.

76. The Piṇḍas shall be given separately along with Akṣatas for the full efficacy of the Pitṛs as explained in the Gṛhyasūtra.

77-79. He shall meditate on lord Sadāśiva in the lotus of the heart reciting the verse. By remembering his lotus-like feet he shall give fees to the Brahmins according to his ability. He shall ask forgiveness and bid them farewell. He shall give Piṇḍas to the cows or cast off into running water. After performing "Puṇyāhavācana" he shall take meals with his kinsmen.

80-81.. After getting up early in the morning next day the devotee shall perform his routine. He shall observe fast, shave hair except in the armpits and the private parts. He shall cut the moustache, the nails and shave his head.

82. He shall take bath and wear a washed and dried cloth. He shall be pure in thought and body. Silently he shall perform Ācamana twice and apply ashes duly and perform the Puṇyāhavācana.

83. Except the materials for the homa and the articles of gift for the preceptor—because they are naturally pure, every other article shall be sprinkled with holy water.

84. He shall make gift to brahmins especially to devotees and to Śiva in the form of preceptor.

142. VS. 2. 31.

85-87. He shall give cloths and the fee also. He shall prostrate before him. He shall take the loin-cloth, its string, staff and the articles for homa—sacrificial twigs etc. He shall go to sea-shore or a mountain or a river-bank or a Śiva temple or a forest or a cowpen. He shall sit on a good place and perform Ācamana. He shall make his mind pure like a flower bunch.

88-90. He shall repeat Vedic mantras along with Oṁ and recite "Namo Brahmaṇe"[143] etc. thrice. Then he shall repeat the mantra "Agnimīle purohitam",[144] perform the great rite and repeat. "Agnirvai"[145] "Iṣe tvorje tvā", then repeat the Mantras "Agna āyāhi vītaye",[146] Śanno devīrabhiṣṭaye"[147] along with Ma, Ya, Ra, Sa, Ta, Ja, Bha, Na, La, and Ga.

91-92. This shall continue for five years. This is the tradition. Then he shall repeat the text of grammar, Mīmāṁsā and Vedānta. He shall repeat the names of the gods as well.

93-96. He shall perform the Japa of Brahmā, Indra, Sun, moon, Prajāpati Jñānātman and Paramatman with Praṇava in the beginning, namaḥ in the end using the dative case. He shall take some flour of fried grain, eat it with Pranava, perform Ācamana twice, wash his hands, repeat the mantras mentioned hereafter. He shall repeat the names of Ātman, Antarātman, Jñānātman beginning with Praṇava and ending with Namaḥ. After repeating the mantra of Ātman he shall repeat the mantra of Prajāpati.

97-98. He shall then perform the Japa ending with Svāha. Repeating Praṇava he shall take in milk, curd and ghee separately thrice and perform Ācamana twice. With the mind steady he shall sit firmly facing the east and perform prāṇāyāma thrice in accordance with the rules.

143. AB. 8. 9. 5.
144. RV. 1.1.1.
145. VS. 1.1. 22; 7. 30; 14. 22.
146. Ibid 11. 46.
147. Ibid 26. 12.

CHAPTER THIRTEEN

(*The Procedure of Renunciation*)

Subrahmaṇya said :—

1. Then at midday he shall take bath. With the mind fully controlled he shall gather materials for worship such as fragrant flowers, Akṣatas etc.

2. With the mentra, "Gaṅānām tvā" he shall as enjoined invoke lord Gaṇapati worshipped by the gods. He shall worship him in the south-west.

3-5. After invoking the elephant-faced lord Gaṇapati son of Śivā, of red colour, huge body, bedecked in ornaments and holding noose, goad, Rudrākṣa and boon in his lotus-hand he shall worship him at dusk. He shall offer milk pudding (sweet pie), coconut jaggery and other things as Naivedya and also the leaf. After propitiating and bowing to him he shall pray for warding off evil.

6. Thereafter the rites of sacrifice concluding with the sharing of clarified butter shall be performed in the Aupāsana fire according to the rules of one's Gṛhyasūtra.

7. After offering the Pūrṇāhūti with the three Ṛks "Bhūḥ Svāhā[148] and concluding the rites he shall repeat Gāyatrī assiduously till late in the afternoon.

8. He shall perform the evening prayers after bath and the sacrificial rites and inform his preceptor accordingly.

9-10. After offering the Caru therein e shall perform Homa with different faggots of sticks, cooked rice and ghee repeating Rudrasūkta. He shall conceive Lord Śiva in the fire along with Ambā and the five Brahmans—Sadyojāta etc. He shall remember Gaurī and perform homa with the mantra "Gaurīrmimāya[149] etc.

11-12. He shall perform sacrifice, repeat the mantra "Agnaye sviṣṭakṛte svāhā"[150] and then show mystic gestures. Being of steady mind he shall sit on the seat of cloth, deerskin or Darbha grass to the north of the fire and perform the Gāyatrī japa silently till the brāhma muhūrta.

148. VS. 3. 5. 37.
149. RV. 1. 164. 41; TB 2. 4. 6. 11
150. TB. 3.12. 2. 2-8.

13-19. He shall then take bath. If he is feeble he shall smear Bhasma only. He shall cook Caru in the fire and pour ghee over it. Thus sanctifying it he shall consign it to the fire. He shall perform the Japa of the Vyāhṛtis, Rudra Sūkta and the five Brahmans. He shall fix his mind in the lotus-feet of Śiva. He shall perform the Japa of Prajāpati, Indra, Viśvedevas and Brahmā also, with dative case-endings. Praṇava and other mantras shall be repeated ending with Svāhā. He shall perform Puṇyāhavācana, say Agnye svāhā, show mystic gesture in front of the fire. Then he shall repeat Prāṇāya svāhā and offer five Āhutis to Sviṣṭakṛt fire. He shall repeat Rudrasūkta, the five Brahmans, the Caturvyūha mantras, Homa and mystic gestures in accordance with his Vedic branch.

20-21. The same procedure he shall adopt for the other gods, along with their ancillary rites. After these rites beginning with the fire, the Virajā homa of the Ātman shall be performed for the purification of the self in the form of twentysix principles.

22-23. He shall say "Let these Tattvas be purified." For the purity of the principle—Ātman, the mantras 'Āruṇaketukas' shall be repeated. He shall silently perform the Homa with the Caru and ghee and remember the lotus-feet of Śiva. O sage, the principles begin with Pṛthivī and end with Puruṣa.

24-27. Pṛthivī, Sound, Speech, Ear—these are five each. The four head, sides, back, belly and the calves shall be added afterwards in the group—skin etc. The Dhātu group consists of seven. Prāṇas are five in number. Anna etc. are the five sheaths. Mind, Citta, intellect, ego, Khyāti come under Saṅkalpa. Guṇas come after; Prakṛti and Puruṣa follow these. Puruṣa is the only enjoyer and the five principles are the objects of his enjoyment.

28. O great sage, destiny, time, attachment, Vidyā, Kāla—this set of five is born of Māyā.

29. The Vedas declare:" Māyā is identical with Prakṛti." The principles as mentioned in the Śruti are born of that.

30. The Vedas declare "Destiny is the nature of Kāla." This set of five is also called "The wheel of five."

31-33. Though sentient, the Puruṣa is confused in thought, not knowing the five principles. Though superior to nature he falls below Prakṛti as the eye of the crow. This set of five—the pure Vidyā Maheśvara, Sadāśiva, Śakti and Śiva is called Vidyātattva or Śivatattva. This is implied in the Vedic text "Prajñānam Brahma."

34. O Sage, the purity of the principles from Pṛthivī to Śiva is effected through the dissolution of its cause.

35. With the eleven mantras he shall mention the god. The word Śivajyotis shall be used in the dative case.

36-38. After Svāhā" he shall say "Na mama" (not to me). By this, renunciation of motive is indicated. In the mantras "Vividyā" "Kaṣṭapotā" after the word Vyāpakāva the word Paramātmane shall be used. The words "Śivajyotis" "Viśvabhūta" and "Ghasanotsuka" shall be mentioned in dative case. After mentioning the god by name the word Devāya shall be uttered.

39. After "Viśvarūpāya" in the mantra "Uttiṣṭhasva" the word "Puruṣāya" shall be uttered and the words "Om Svāhā" shall be added.

40. At the end of the word "Lokatraya" the words "Vyāpine Paramātmane Śivāyedam Na Mama" shall be added.

41-42. He shall conclude the rite according to his own branch of the Veda. He shall eat Caru mixed with ghee and then give fee of gold etc. to the priest. After the ritualistic dismissal of Brahmā he shall perform the morning worship.

43-45. He shall recite the mantra "Saṁ mām siñcantu Maruta."[151] He shall warm his hand over the fire repeating the mantra "Yā te Agne[152] and superimpose the fire in his own Ātman, abode of the universal soul. He shall perform the morning prayers and pay respects to the sun. He shall enter water upto the navel, perform the Japa of the mantras with pleasure, devotion and steadiness.

46. The devotee who had been maintaining sacrificial

151. AV. 7. 33. 1.
152. VS. 5. 8

fires regularly shall perform the Prājāpatya rite in the sacrificial fire and give his entire possession as gift.

47-51. The brahmin shall superimpose fire in his Ātman and leave the house. In the Sāvitrī mantra he shall utter the first foot and say 'I enter Sāvitrī Bhūḥ Om.' Then he shall utter the second foot and say I enter Sāvitrī Bhuvaḥ Om. He shall utter the third foot and say I enter Sāvitrī Suvaḥ Om. Then he shall repeat all the three feet and say Sāvitrīm Praveśayāmi, at the end of which he shall say Bhūḥ Bhuvaḥ Suvaḥ Om with great pleasure and steady mind.

52-56. He shall then think—"This is Goddess herself having half the body of Śiva. She has five faces, ten arms and fifteen eyes. She is bedecked with a crown set with nine gems over which the crescent moon rises. She is auspicious, pure as crystal and bears ten weapons. Her body is adorned with necklaces, shoulderlets, bangles and anklets. Her ornaments are studded with gems. She wears brilliant garments. She is served by Viṣṇu, Brahmā the leader of the gods, sages, Gandharvas and human beings. She is Śivā pervading all Ātmans. She is charming wife of lord Sadāśiva. She is the mother of the universe and the trio. She is unborn. She is Saguṇa and Nirguṇa as well."

57. After thinking thus the intelligent devotee shall perform the Japa of Gāyatrī the primordial goddess comprising three metrical feet. She is unborn and the bestower of brahminhood

58. The sinner who repeats Gāyatrī in any other manner is tortured in the terrible hell for the period of kalpa.

59. She is born of and merged into Vyāhṛtis. Vyāhṛtis are born of the Praṇava and are merged in Praṇava.

60. Pranava is the initial of all mantras of the Vedas. It expresses Śiva. It is the emperor of all mantras. It is the great Bija, the greatest mantra.

61. Śiva is Praṇava, Praṇava is Śiva since there is no difference between Śiva and Praṇava that expresses Śiva.

62. It is this very mantra that Śiva speaks to in-

dividual souls who leave off their bodies at Kāśī to attain liberation hereafter.

63. Hence good ascetics worship Śiva the single-syllabled lord who being the cause of the universe is stationed in the lotus of the heart.

64. Men desirous of salvation and unattached to worldly pleasures worship Śiva after realising the futility of worldly pleasures.

65. After dissolving Gāyatrī in the Praṇava identical with Śiva he shall recite the hymn "ahaṁ vṛkṣasya reriva."[153]

66. He shall repeat the hymn beginning with "Yaḥ Chandasām Ṛṣabhaḥ"[154] and ending with "gopāya." Then he shall say I have got up.

67. O sage, he shall recite the mantras in the low, medium and high tone beginning with the Praṇava in the order of creation, sustenance and dissolution.

68-69. In this order he shall say Om Bhūḥ I have renounced. Om Bhuvaḥ I have renounced. Om Suvaḥ I have renounced. Then he shall say the composite Vyāhṛtis Om Bhūḥ, Bhuvaḥ, Suvaḥ.[155]

70. O sage, he shall say "I have renounced after meditating on Sadāśiva in the heart in the low, medium and high pitch gradually.

71. After muttering the Preṣa mantras with attentive mind he shall say "Let all living beings have fearlessness from me, Svāhā."

72. He shall take water in the cupped palms and pour it to the east. He shall uproot the tuft and take out the sacred thread.

73-74. Taking the two in the cupped palms along with water he shall say Om Bhūḥ "Go thou to the ocean" after uttering Suāhā, the name of the wife of the fire. Along with the water in the palms he shall put the two in the water uttering Preṣa mantras. After performing Ācamana thrice he shall come to the bank and cast off all the clothes.

153. TA. 7. 101, TU. 1. 10. 1
154. Ibid. 7. 4. 1; 10. 6. 1.
155. BDH 2. 10. 17. 27

75-76. He shall then foot a short distance more than seven paces facing north or the east. Then the preceptor shall ask him to stop saying, "for your stay and activity in the world, O holy one, accept this loin-cloth and staff." He shall hand them over to him with his own hands.

77-78. After giving the loin-cloth with its string, and the ochre-coloured robe he shall ask him to wear them. After performing Ācamana twice he shall tell the disciple thus "You are the thunderbolt of Indra."[156]. After praying and saying "A good companion", he shall take up thestaff.

79. He shall approach the preceptor remembering the lotus-like feet of Śiva and fall at his feet thrice with fully restrained mind.

80. Standing up again he shall approach the feet of the preceptor with palms joined in reverence, glancing at his preceptor with love.

81-82. Before the rites are begun he should collect cowdung and make them into balls of the size of a myrobalan fruit and dry them in sunshine. The balls shall be placed in the sacrificial fire at the advent of homa. At the conclusion of the homa the ashes shall be collected and preserved.

83-85. The preceptor shall take the white ashes of the Viraja fire. Repeating the mantras "Agniriti Bhasma"[157] he shall apply the sacred ashes over the body of the disciple from head to foot. Repeating the five mantras "Īśāna"[158] Tryāyuṣa"[159] "Tryambakaṁ Yajāmahe[160] he shall apply the Tripuṇḍra marks too beginning with head.

86. Then the disciple shall meditate devotedly on Śiva, the consort of Umā in the lotus of his heart.

87. Putting his hand on the head of the disciple the preceptor shall utter the Praṇava thrice into the right ear of the disciple along with the names of the sage etc.

88. The excellent preceptor shall be sympathetic and explain Praṇava with the knowledge of the six-fold topics.

156. VS 9. 5.
157. Śiras U 5..
158. TA. 10. 47. 1
159. VS. 3. 62
160. Ibid 3. 60.

89. The disciple shall make obeisance to the preceptor by prostrating twelve times. He shall remain subservient to him always. He shall not do anything else.

90. At his bidding the disciple shall pursue Śaivite knowledge in conformity with the Upaniṣadic doctrine and based on the difference of Saguṇa and Nirguṇa.

91. The preceptor shall make the disciple perform all the rites in the morning up to the Japa including the practice of hearing etc.

92. The disciple shall perform the worship in the maṇḍala Kailāsaprastara as enjoined by Śiva.

93. If he cannot worship the deity worshipped by his preceptor he shall take up Śivaliṅga of crystal along with the pedestal.

94. "I shall rather cast life and cut off my head than take meals without worshipping Śiva."

95. Thus shall the disciple devoted to Śiva take vow in the presence of the preceptor which he shall repeat thrice with a steady mind.

96. Thus the disciple shall worship Lord Śiva every day with devoted and diligent mind, following the path of five Āvaraṇas.

CHAPTER FOURTEEN

(*The Praṇava in the form of Śiva*)

Vāmadeva said:—

1-2. O Kārttikeya, the nectarine ocean of perfect knowledge, son of Śiva the lord of gods and the dispeller of distress of the devotees what is perfect knowledge of the sixfold topics that bestows all desires? What are the six topics? What is the perfect knowledge?

3. What is explained therein? What is the fruit of that knowledge? Please mention all that I have asked.

4. Without knowing this I have been deluded by Śiva's Māyā. I am ignorant of the Pāśupata Śāstra.

5-6. I have sought refuge in your lotus-feet. Glancing at me for a long time with your eyes drenched with the nectar of sympathy you shall bless me so that I shall I become free from delusion, drink in the nectarine potion of the knowledge of the feet of Śiva.

7. On hearing these words of the sage the lord bearing the trident of knowledge said words causing fears to other systems of theology.

Subrahmaṇya said:—

8-9. O revered sage, you have enquired about the perfect knowledge of Śiva in his composite and individual state. O performer of good rites, I shall explain that in detail. Perfect knowledge comprises the meaning of Praṇava by realising the unity of six topics.

10-11. The first topic is the mantra; the second Yantra; the third deity; the fourth the cosmos; the fifth the preceptor; the sixth the Ātman of the disciple.

12. O excellent sage, I shall explain to you the form of the mantra which makes a man possessed of perfect knowledge.

13. The first and the fifth vowels, the fifth letter of the fifth class of consonants, Bindu and Nāda these five letters are mentioned by the Vedas.

14-15. The initial mantra of the Vedas i.e. Oṁ is of the composite form. Nāda too is the composite of all. The set of four with Bindu as the fifth is established as Vyaṣṭi in the Praṇava that expresses Śiva. O intelligent one, now listen to the form of Yantra that is Śivaliṅga.

16-17. Beneath all, the pedestal shall be drawn; then the first vowel—A; then the letter U, the final letter of the class of Pa i e. Ma followed by Bindu and Nāda. When the Yantra becomes perfect, all desires are achieved.

18. The Yantra is encompassed by the Pranava itself. The Nāda shall be known through the Nāda arising therefrom.

19. O sage, I shall now explain the secret topic of the deity. I shall mention it, out of my affection to you, in the manner explained by Śiva.

20. Beginning with "I resort to the lord born all of a

sudden" and concluding with "Sadā Śivam" the Vedic text clearly expresses the five Brahmans.

21. The five deities shall be known comprising the subtle form of Brahman. These are enlarged in the form of the idol of Śiva too.

22. The Mantra that expresses Śiva expresses his idol too, since there is not much of difference between the idol and the original.

23. I have already referred to the form of Śiva with Īśāna at the head. Now listen about his five faces.

24. Beginning with the fifth one the Sadyojāta and proceeding till Īśāna upwards are the five faces.

25-26. The four Brahmans constitute a Caturvyūha for lord Īśāna, the famous Brahman. These five together constitute the composite. O sage, from Puruṣa to Sadyojāta the four constitute the individual.

27. This set of five is the 'wheel of blessing'. It is the same as Brahman. It is subtle ; free from aberration and ailment.

28. The Anugraha or blessing is twofold : appearance and disappearance. The lord who bestows the greater and the lesser salvation to the souls is another.

29. This is the twofold function of Siva for ever. The five functions of creation etc. come under Anugraha.

30. O sage, there too the deities Sadya etc. are of the form of the great Brahman. The five always bestow happiness.

31. The Anugraha cakra is the greatest bliss presided over by Sadāśiva. It consists of the digit beyond calmness.

32. This region is attainable by the pious ascetics who worship Sadāśiva, with the minds fixed on the Pranava.

33-34. After attaining this region and enjoying vast pleasures along with the lord in the form of Brahman the sages attain equality with Śiva at the advent of the great dissolution. They never fall again in the ocean of the universe.

35. The eternal Veda says "Te brahmaloke"[161] etc. The glory of Śiva is the composite form itself.

36. The Vedic text Atharvaśirṣa says "Equipped with

161. TA. 10. 10. 3.

glory and prosperity". The ability to bestow glory shall be mentioned of him alone.

37. There is no higher region than that of Śiva. This universe is only an extension of the five Brahmans.

38. Nivṛtti and the Kalās are the offshoots of five Brahmans. They are in the form of subtle elements well known as causes.

39. O sage of good rites, the set of five Brahmans is the cause of gross cosmos.

40. Puruṣa, ear, speech, sound and ether, this set of five is pervaded, O excellent sage, by the Brahman in the form of Īśāna.

41. Prakṛti, skin, hand, sense of touch and wind, this set of five, O great sage, is pervaded by Brahman as Puruṣa.

42. The ego, eye, foot, colour and fire, this set of five is pervaded by Aghora Brahman.

43. The intellect, tongue, arms, taste and water, this set of five is pervaded by the Brahman Vāmadeva.

44. The mind, nose, organ of generation, smell and earth, this set of five is pervaded by the Brahman Sadya. The whole universe is identical with the five Brahmans.

45-46. Praṇava expressive of Śiva is taught through yantra. It is the composite of five letters. The four viz, Bindu etc. constitute the form of yantra in the Śaiva cult. Praṇava is the highest Mantra—the very Śiva himself.

CHAPTER FIFTEEN

(The idol of Śiva for worship)

Subrahmaṇya said :—

1. Henceforth I shall explain, O good-faced Vāma, the mode of creation for the set of four, Maheśa etc. from Sadāśiva.

2. Sadāśiva the lord of ether is the composite. The set of four, Maheśa etc. is the individualistic form.

3. Maheśa is a thousandth part of Sadāśiva. It has the form of Puruṣa for its face. It is the lord of wind too.

4. He is associated with Māyā Śakti on his left. He is Saguṇa having much activity. The set of four Īśvara etc. is his own Vyaṣṭi.

5. This set of four comprising Īśvara, Viśveśvara, Parameśvara and Sarveśvara is the excellent Tirobhāvacakra.

6. Tirobhāva is twofold. One concerns Rudra, the other the individual souls in view of their physical bodies.

7. The latter remains till equality in activity is achieved. When this is achieved, there remains only the lord of the form of blessing.

8. There all the Īśvaras who are glorified as the deities, are identical with the great Brahman itself, free from alternatives and ailments.

9. The Tirobhāva Cakra consists of the Śāntikalā. This excellent region is presided over by Maheśvara.

10. This region is attainable by those who serve Maheśa etc. It yields Sālokya liberation to the devotees of Maheśvara.

11. The image Rudra is born of a thousandth part of Maheśvara. He has Aghora for his face. He is the lord of the principle of fire.

12. He is associated with Gaurīśakti on his left. He is the cause of dissolution of the universe; of him alone is the Vyaṣṭi born—the set of four, Śiva etc.

13. This set of four consists of Śiva, Hara, Mṛda and Bhava. This wheel of dissolution, O sage, is wonderful and divine.

14-16. Dissolution has been classified into three. The first Nitya is the daily slumber of living beings. The second is the conditioned dissolution of Brahmā. The third is the final dissolution. The three have been indicated by the Vedic texts. O excellent sage, the dissolution has been classified into three by the illustrious Rudra for the maturing of the activities of individual souls and for their rest. The souls released from their recurring births are ultimately placed in the great Ātman itself.

17. Thus I have mentioned the three activities of

Rudra in respect of dissolution. The five activities of the lord in respect of creation shall also be explained to you.

18. O sage, the deities Bhava etc. are identical with the great Brahman, being the cause of bliss.

19. This wheel of dissolution has Vidyārūpa Kalā. This healthy region is presided over by Rudra himself.

20 This region is attainable by those who desire the propitiation of Rudras. O sage, it yields the Sāyujya of Rudras gradually through Sālokya.

21. Viṣṇu was born from a thousandth part of Rudra. In the form of Vāmadeva wheel he is the presiding deity of the principle of water.

22. He is associated with Lakṣmī Śakti on the left. He is the protector of all. He has four arms. He has eyes as splendid as the lotus. He is dark-complexioned and bears the characteristics of Śaṅkha etc.

23. Of him alone is the set of four Vāsudevas in the Vyaṣṭi form. It bestows liberation on the devotees of Viṣṇu engaged in worship through meditation.

24. This set of four consists of Vāsudeva, Aniruddha, Saṁkarṣaṇa and Pradyumna. This excellent wheel of sustenance is well known.

25. Sustenance means the protection of the existing universe along with its creator until the completion of the pleasures of the souls, the reapers of the fruit.

26. Protection is the activity of Viṣṇu. In the sustenance also the lord has five activities, viz; creation etc.

27. The deities of whom Pradyumna is the chief are absolute and without distress. They cause bliss to liberated souls.

28. O Brahmin, this wheel of sustenance which is permanent is presided over by Viṣṇu. It is the highest abode.

29. This region is attainable by those who serve the lotus-feet of Viṣṇu. This wheel yields Sālokya etc. to the devotees of Viṣṇu.

30. Brahmā was born of a thousandth part of Viṣṇu. He has the face of Sadyojāta and is the presiding deity of the principle of earth.

31. He is accompanied by the goddess of speech on his left. He is the creator and lord of the universe. He has

four faces. He is red in complexion and his form is possessed of Rajas attribute.

32. Hiraṇyagarbha, Virāṭ, Puruṣa and Kāla, the four constitute his personal form.

33. O Brahmin, this wheel of creation is the cause of Brahmā's sons and other sages. It bestows desires and happiness to the devotee.

34-35. Those who have the knowledge of creation know this to be the function of Brahman. Creation is the process of re-unification of the soul with the body previously annihilated—the body which along with the means, ancillaries and results comes out of Prakṛti for gradual enjoyment. It is pleasing as long as it holds good.

36. O sage, in the creation of the universe there are five functions of the lord. The present time etc. are the deities there.

37. This wheel of creation is in the form of turning round. This charming region is presided over by Brahman.

38. This region is attainable by those who have dedicated their minds to Brahmā. This indeed bestows Sālokya and other liberations on the devotees of Brahmā.

39. Even in regard to the set of four wheels the Praṇava indicates Maheśa etc.

40. O sage, this wheel of universe is glorified by the Śrutis. The Vedas eulogise it as the wheel with five spokes.

41. Although the wheel of the universe with its five constituents: creation etc. has five spokes, it develops and increases by Śiva's energy.

42. It is called a "wheel" because it moves round and round with incessant dissolution and recreation like the whirling fire-brand.

43-44. Because of the immensity of creation it is called Pṛthu, the resultant of the Śakti of lord Śiva of immense splendour and of golden features. The wheel is dependent on golden splendour and is surrounded by water encompassed by fire.

45. Fire is surrounded by wind; wind by ether; ether by the primordial element and that by intellect.

46. Intellect is encompassed by the unmanifest. O sage, the universe is thus explained by the learned preceptors.

47. Such are the seven sheaths which protect the universe. The expanse of water is ten times more massive than the wheel.

48. The world above is ten times more than the one below. O leading sage, the universe shall be known thus by those who desire to know that.

49. It is by accepting this sense that the Śruti says "In the middle of water". Of course the earth rotates as the wheel.

50. That Śiva alone accompanied by Śakti performs incessant sports through blessing, disappearance, dissolution. sustenance and creation.

51. O sage, of what avail is much talk? I shall tell you the essence. Śiva endowed with Śakti is all this. It is definite conclusion.

CHAPTER SIXTEEN

(*Śiva's principle*)

Sūta said:—

1. On hearing this truthful purport enunciated, by the preceptor the leading sage asked him about his doubt concerning the great Ātman.

Vāmadeva said:—

2-3. O lord endowed with the power of knowledge and of the form of great bliss, I have heard the sweet meaning of Praṇava from your glorious lotus-like mouth and nourished intellect. My doubts have gone. O lord, Mahāsena, I ask you something else. Please listen.

4. Surely this universe from Sadāśiva to a worm is reflected in male and female forms everywhere.

5. Is the eternal cause of the universe in the form of a woman, or of a man or a eunuch?

6. Or is it a mixture of both or something else? There has been no decision so far. Deluded by sacred scriptures scholars argue on this point in various ways.

7. The Vedas expatiating on the creation of the universe itself, Viṣṇu, Brahmā and other gods and the Siddhas do not know it.

8-10. Please explain so that the conflicting views may be resolved into one truthful interpretation. We say—"I know," "I do". This is accepted by all. There is no dispute about this. But I have some doubts. "Is there a form of the Ātman or is the Ātman identical with the body, sense-organs, mind, intellect and ego? The two are the points of dispute among many.

11-12. O lord, uproot this poisonous tree of doubt arising from ignorance. I shall be enlightened by you so that my mind may become the fertile ground for the growth of monistic knowledge of the Śaivite cult. O lord of gods, by your benign favour I shall become wise.

Sūta said:—

13. On hearing the enquiry of the sage full of Vedāntic topics, the lord smiled a little and unfolded the secret.

Subrahmaṇya said:—

14. O sage, this very secret was narrated by Śiva while goddess Ambā and I listened.

15. Then I was fully satiated with the drink of her breast-milk. I listened to it and I came to a decisive thought.

16. O sage, I shall sympathetically explain the same to you. O son, it is the greatest secret. Please listen to it now.

17. The arguments in the philosophical text books are extensive beginning with those on Karmans and the principle of existence. But O sage, those arguments shall be listened to with discrimination by a wise person. Then it may yield wisdom.

18. You have taught many disciples. But among them

who is like you? Those base persons are rotting in delusion even now, wrangling in the philosophical texts propounded by Kapila and others.

19. They indulged in insulting Śiva and hence were cursed by the seven sages. Their views should not be heard because they explain false notions.

20-22. There is no scope for inference that consists of the five syllogisms. On seeing smoke they say that there is fire too. But here, O sage, the world is the object of perception. Its cause and support, the great Ātman Śiva must be known directly. The universe in the form of male and female is directly perceived.

23-24. The physical body consists of six sheaths. The first three are born of the parts of the mother and the other three of the parts of the father. So says the Śruti.

25. The Śruti speaks of the Brahman as having the form of existence, knowledge and bliss. The word 'existence' is used in order to exclude the 'non-existent'.

26-27. The exclusion of the insentient is effected by the word sentient. Of course the word Cit is used in all the three genders but it signifies here a male being. The word Cit in the feminine gender is a synonym of the word knowledge. If it is taken to mean 'Light', it is clear that it illuminates.

28. The pair Light and Cit is the cause of the universe. Similarly the Sat and the Cit are the causes of the universe.

29. In the self-same individual the feeling of Śiva and Śakti exists. If there is dirt in the oil or the wick there may be dirt in the light too.

30. Thus dirt and inauspiciousness is seen in the funeral fire also. Śivatva is due to illusion there.

31. There is weakness in the power of Cit in the individual soul. It is to exclude it that the conception of Śakti is ever present.

32. O sage, people say in the world: he is strong, he is powerful and in the Vedas too there is a similar expression.

33. Thus the Śivatva and Śaktitva is present in the

great Ātman. The bliss from the union of Śiva and Śakti is ever rising.

34. Hence, O sage, sinless ascetics aiming at bliss fix their minds in Śiva and attain untainted auspiciousness.

35. The word Brahman in the Upaniṣads signifies Ātman collectively. It can be traced to the root Bṛh to increase or grow.

36. Growing in size and massiveness is ever present in Śiva constituting the five Brahmans. The word Brahman denotes the universe.

37. O Vāmadeva, due to my affection for you I shall explain the origin of the Praṇava when the word Haṁsaḥ is reverted. Listen attentively.

38. If the consonants Sa and Ha are removed it becomes Oṁ. It is the expression of the great Ātman.

39. It shall be known as the great Mantra by the expert sages. This great Mantra is subtle. I shall tell you its analysis.

40. The great Mantra is formed with स and the sixteenth vowel (:) = सः and अ + ह with the fifteenth vowel (ṁ) = अहम् = (सोऽहम्)

41. It is the inverted form of Haṁsa. The meaning of the letter 'Sa' is Śiva. The conclusion is, the Śakti form is expressed by the great Mantra.

42-43. At the instruction of the preceptor, the great mantra is Śiva in the form of Śakti. Hence the great mantra is the individual soul too. The individual soul is in the form of Śakti and is a part of Śiva. Due to the identity with Śiva it attains equality with Śiva. In the passage (of the Vedas) "Prajñānam Brahma" the meaning of "Prajñānam" is seen.

44. Undoubtedly the word "Prajñānam" is a synonym of consciousness. O sage, there is the aphorism.

45. Caitanya is the freedom in respect of the knowledge and activity of every thing in the universe. He whose nature is this is glorified as Ātman.

46-47. Thus a gloss on the aphorisms of Śiva has been mentioned by me. In another aphorism of Śiva viz; "Jñānaṁ Bandhaḥ" the lord speaks of the nature of individual souls. There the word Jñāna refers to vague knowledge and activity.

48-49. These two (knowledge and activity) are the first throbbing of the great Śakti. It is this Parā Śakti that the Śvetāśvataras eulogised joyously saying "Power of knowledge and activity is natural" They know the three eyes of Śiva constitute knowledge, will and activity.

50. When these reaching the centre of the mind become the object of perception on the part of sense-organs the individual soul enters these, then knows and acts.

51. Hence these are the features of the Ātman alone. I shall now explain then meaning of the creation indicating the identity with the Praṇava.

52. The eternal Śruti says "Om is this all." Beginning with "verily from it", the creation of the universe is glorified.

53. I shall mention the purport of the Vedic passage. Listen to that, O Vāmadeva, due to affecion for you I say this. It is developed by the sense of discrimination.

54-55. It is certain that the union of Śiva and Śakti is the great-Ātman From Parāśakti is born the citśakti. Born of it is the power of bliss. The power of will is born of that. From this is born the power of knowledge and from this is born the power of activity, the fifth one. O sage, the Kalās—Nivṛtti etc. are born of these Śaktis.

56-57. Nāda and Bindu are born of cit and Ānanda Śaktis. O sage, the letter 'ma' is born of Icchāśakti. The fifth vowel 'U' is born of Jñāna Śakti and the letter 'A' is born of Kriyāśakti. The origin of the Praṇava has been mentioned thus. Now listen to the origin of the five Brahmans.

58. From Śiva is born Īśāna; from Īśāna the Puruṣa, from Puruṣa Aghora, from him Vāmadeva and from him Sadyojāta.

59-60. From these mātrās (of the praṇava) are born the thirty eight Kalās, Śāntyatītakalā is born of Īśana; Śāntikalā of Puruṣa; Vidyākalā of Aghora; Pratiṣṭhā and Nivṛtti of Vāmadeva and Sadyojāta. There are five pairs such as Īśāna and cit-śakti etc.

61. This set of five is the cause of activities such as Anugraha etc. as mentioned by the sages who know the principles.

62-63. O sage, the five elements beginning with the ether are born of this set of five letters of the Praṇava which constitute pairs based on the relationship of the word and its meaning.

64. Ākāśa has the only attribute of sound. The wind has the two: sound and touch. The fire has three : sound, touch and colour.

65. The water has four : sound, touch, colour and taste. The earth has five : sound, touch, colour. taste and smell.

66. This is the Vyāpakatva (pervasiveness) of the Bhūtas. The Vyāpakatva is in the inverse order beginning with smell.

67. The five Bhūtas constitute the universe. Virāṭ is the composite form of all. The universe is thus created.

68. It begins with the element of the earth and ends with the element of Śiva. After merging with each other they merge in the individual soul ultimately.

69. Accompanied by the energy it comes out again for the purpose of creation. It appears in the form of the gross cosmos and functions till the period of dissolution.

70. The primeval oozing of Śiva who attempts to create the universe at his will is called Śivatattva.

71. In view of its conformity with the activities this alone becomes the principle of his power of will. Between the two Śaktis of knowledge and activity if the knowledge predominates, the principle is Sadāśiva.

72. O sage, know that as Maheśvara Tattva when the activity is predominant. If there is equality between the two Śaktis know that as the form of pure knowledge.

73-74. After withdrawing his form of great glory with the intellect comprehending the difference between the illusion and reality among various emotions in the form of his own part when Śiva becomes the recipient of all objects through illusion, he is called Puruṣa, the creator. The Vedic text says "Tatsṛṣṭvā" (after creating it).

75. He is transformed as the individual soul deluded by Māyā and devoid of the knowledge of Śiva. His intellect is deluded by different activities.

76. It is the individual soul that is deluded and not the lord. Because the former considers himself different from Śiva.

77. As the magician so also the Yogin has no illusion. Śiva is of perfect knowledge and this is revealed by the preceptor.

78-79. The five Śaktis of Śiva are: activity, knowledge, completeness, eternality and pervasiveness. Even in their shrinking forms they shine always.

80-81. There is a set of five Tattvas of the individual soul, viz, Kalā, Vidyā, Rāga, Kāla and Niyati. Kalā is the cause of doing anything. Vidyā is the means of certain Tattvas. Rāga is the attachment to the sense-objects.

82. Kāla is the illuminator of positive and negative appearances. Being a separating factor it is called Bhūtādi.

83. Niyati means the factor that discriminates and ordains. "This shall be done and this shall not be done by me." It is a Śakti of the lord. Setting it at nought the individual soul falls.

84. This set of five is called "the five sheaths" in view of its nature of enveloping the form. It is the innermost and most essential means.

CHAPTER SEVENTEEN

(The non-dualistic nature of Śiva)

Vāmadeva said:—

1-2. You have mentioned before[162] that the Puruṣa is placed beneath the Niyati and is above Prakṛti. How is it that you say now that it shrinks in form through Māyā and

162. Kailāsa S. 13 31.

is beneath it. O lord, it behoves you to clear this doubt of mine.

Subrahmaṇya said:—

3. This is the Śaivite philosophy of non-dualism. Nowhere does it brook duality. Duality perishes and the non-dualism remains imperishable.

4. The omniscient, omnipotent, Śiva, the Nirguṇa lord of all, the progenitor of the three deities, the Brahman, is formed of existence-knowledge-bliss.

5. That lord Śiva himself, out of his own will, through his own Māyā appears shrinking in size and becomes Puruṣa.

6. He is conceived as the enjoyer through the set of five—Kalās etc. Thus the Puruṣa stationed in Prakṛti enjoys the Guṇas born of Prakṛti.

7. The presence in two places of the Puruṣa is not incompatible. He is the composite of Jñana etc. of both shrinking and intrinsic forms.

8-9. The principle of the mind Prakṛti consists of Buddhi, Manas and Ahaṁkāra achievable through the Guṇas Sattva etc. The Guṇas are born of the Prakṛti, the Sāttvaic from Sattva and so on. From the Guṇas the intellect takes its origin. It is the cause of decisiveness in the objects.

10. From Buddhi the principle of intellect is born and from it ego. From the ego the sense-organs of knowledge. The mind has two aspects—thought and doubt.

11-12. The sense-organs are ears, skin, eyes, tongue and nose and the qualities particularly sensed through those organs are sound, touch, colour, taste and smell. The Tanmātras are born from the Vaikārika Ahaṁkāra.

13. They are called subtle principles by the sages. Now understand the organs of activity and their functions.

14. O sage, they are the organs of speech, hand, feet, anus, penis and the vaginal passage. Their functions are speaking, handling, moving, evacuation and the sexual pleasure.

15. The subtle elements originated in order from the

ego, are the cause of the elements. Their subtle forms are sound etc.

16. From them are born in order the ether, wind, fire, water and the earth. O sage, they are known as the five elements.

17. Their functions are giving space, blowing, cooking, force and supporting.

Vāmadeva said:—

18. O Skanda, you have mentioned before that the elements were created from Kalās etc. How is it that it is being mentioned in another manner? I have great doubt here.

19. "The letter 'A' is the Ātmatattva; the letter 'U' is 'Vidyā; the letter 'Ma' is Śivatattva. O Vāmadeva let this be thought over thus.

20. "The Bindu and Nāda have essence of all the principles. O sage, listen now to what the deities therein are.

21. They are Brahmā, Viṣṇu, Rudra, Maheśvara and Sadāśiva. They are the images of Śiva himself well known in the Vedas

22. This is what you have said before. Now you say in another manner that they are born of the subtle elements. I have a great doubt in this matter.

23. Therefore, O Skanda, it behoves you to favour me by clearing the doubt. On hearing the words of the sage, Kumāra replied thus.

Subrahmaṇya said:—

24-26. O intelligent sage, listen with respect and attention. O sage, in accordance with the Vedic text "Tasmād Vai Etasmād" etc. it is certain that the five Bhūtas are born of the Kalās. They are in the form of the gross cosmos. This explains the body of the lord of Bhūtas (Śiva). In the order of the coming up of the Tattvas from Śiva Tattva to the principle of the earth, O sage, they shall be mentioned as originating from the subtle elements in order.

27. There shall be identity between the subtle elements and the Kalās as causes of the Bhūtas. O excellent among those who know the Brahman, know that there is no mutual antagonism here.

28. In the cosmos both subtle and gross are born the planets: moon, sun stars, etc.

29-32. The deities Brahmā, Viṣṇu, Maheśa and others, the various living beings, Indra and other guardians of the quarters, gods, Pitṛs Asuras, Rākṣasas, human and other mobile beings, beasts, birds, worms, serpents, trees, hedges, creepers and herbs, the eight mountains,[163] the seven rivers[164] Gaṅgā and others, the oceans of great prosperity whatever object is there in the world all are established here.

33. This universe of the form of female and male, of the form of Śiva and Śakti shall deserve attention of learned men like you, experts in the Śaiva knowledge.

34. O sage, the Śruti says "Think that everything is Brahman, everything is Rudra." Thus Sadāśiva is the Ātman of the universe.

35. Due to the concept of thirtyeight Kalās the concept of duality is ever present but he who has purified the Ātman by the concept "I am Sadāśiva" becomes the preceptor Śiva.

36. Such a disciple becomes the preceptor Śiva himself. He attains the form of the Yantra, mantra and the cosmic deity itself.

37. O Brahmin, the disciple whose bondage is severed due to the favour of the preceptor and who is engaged in Śiva's worship becomes a lofty soul indeed.

38. They say that whatever exists whether a composite unit or an analysed piece is the meaning of the Praṇava in view of the predominence of the Guṇas.

39. Out of affection I have explained the non-dualis-

163. The eight principal mountains are महेन्द्र, मलय, सह्य, शुक्तिमत्, ऋक्ष, विन्ध्य and पारियात्र।

164. The Purāṇas describe the seven streams of Gaṅgā thus : Sītā, Cakṣu, Sindhu, Bhāgīrathī, Nalinī, Hlādinī or Hrādinī, Pāvanī. These originate from the Bindusaras identified with the Mānasa lake.

tic principle to you. It is pleasing to Śiva, it is devoid of aberrations; it is the essence of the Vedas.

40-41. If anyone whether a god or a human being, Siddha or Gandharva, out of arrogance considers this statement otherwise, I shall cut off his head evenly with my good trident which is like a black fire to the enemies.

42. O sage, you yourself are the most excellent of those who know the non-dualistic nature of Śiva. You are the guide for good behaviour on the occasion of the instruction of Saivite knowledge.

43. An impious ghost got his sins removed by the contact with the ashes on your body. By your grace he attained the supreme goal.

44. You are a Śiva yogin, an asset to the three worlds. At your benign glance even the individual soul becomes the supreme soul.

45. It is for instructing the world that a noble soul as yourself look up to me with respect. Indeed the saints wander here and there for helping the wide world.

46-47. This great secret is founded in you. You too, abide by the Praṇavas alone with respect, faith and devotion and unite them with Parameśvara helping people grasp Śaivite conduct including Bhasma and Rudrākṣa.

48. You are Śiva indeed. You follow Śaivite conduct and have understood the concept of non-dualism Wandering about for the welfare of the world you will attain an everlasting happiness.

Sūta said :—

49. After hearing this wonderful cult of Vedānta, explained by Kārttikeya the sage became very humble. He bowed many times and prostrated before him. He behaved like a bee hovering round his lotus-like feet.

CHAPTER EIGHTEEN

(*The procedure of initiating a disciple*)

Śaunaka said :—

1. On hearing that extremely wonderful secret, the essence of the Vedānta, what did Vāmadeva ask of the son of Maheśvara ?

2. Blessed indeed is the Yogin Vāmadeva, who is ever engaged in Śaivite activities and about whom this divine and highly sacred story has come about.

3. On hearing these words, pregnant with love, of the sages, the delighted Sūta, the scholar whose mind is attached to Śiva, spoke to them.

4. You are all blessed. You are the devotees of lord Śiva You help all the worlds, O sages, you hear further their conversation.

5. On hearing the words of Kārttikeya, that quell dualism and produce non-dualistic knowledge the sage became delighted.

6. After bowing to Kārttikeya, son of Śiva and eulogising him in various ways the great sage asked him again regarding the principles, with great humility.

Vāmadeva said:—

7. O lord Kārttikeya, O ocean of nectar, O knower of all principles, how can the ascetics of purified souls attain the position of a preceptor?

8. They cannot have the authority to instruct without a tradition following which the individual souls attain worldly pleasures and salvation.

9. Similarly how is the ceremonial ablution an ancillary to the rite of shaving? O lord, herein I intimate to you this doubt of mine. It behoves you to clear it.

Subrahmaṇya said:—

10. On hearing the words of Vāmadeva Kārttikeya began to explain after thinking upon Śiva and Śivā.

11. I shall explain Yogapaṭṭa whereby one attains the state of a preceptor. It is a great secret that yields salvation and O Vāmadeva, it is due to my affection to you that I mention it to you.

12-15. During any of these months Vaiśākha, Śrāvaṇa, Āśvina, Kārttika, Mārgaśirṣa or Māgha, on an auspicious day in the bright half, either on the fifth or on the full moon day the disciple shall finish his daily morning duties. Taking permission from the preceptor he shall take his bath. With restrained mind he shall sit on his hams. With a cloth he shall wipe off the limbs. He shall wear two cloths after tying the waist-band with twice-spun thread. He shall then wash his feet and perform Ācamana twice. After dusting his body with Bhasma he shall wear Tripuṇḍra marks with Sadyādi mantra.[165]

16-17. O sage, the preceptor shall grasp the disciple with his hands and make him sit facing east on a well decorated platform on a pure excellent seat—a cloth, a deerskin or Darbha grass. The disciple shall be wrapped in the cloth.

18. Then he shall take a conch with its stand and purify it with Astra mantra. He shall then place it in front of him on a favourable position.

19. After worshipping the conch with its pedestal with flowers he shall pour pure water into it sanctified by Astra and Varma mantras.

20. After filling it, it shall be worshipped again in the manner mentioned in Ṣaḍaṅga Pūjā. Then he shall repeat the Praṇava seven times.

21. He shall worship it with scents and flowers and show lights and incense. He shall then cover up the conch with Astra and Varma mantras.

22-23. He shall then show the mystic gestures of the cow and conch. In a pure spot to the south of the conch and in front of him he shall make a beautiful and auspicious Maṇḍala according to the rules of worship and worship it with sweet scents and flowers.

24-25. He shall place a pot on its pedestal. It shall be pure and scrubbed well. Threads should be neatly tied round it. It shall be fumigated with incense and filled with pure fragrant water. Five barks, five sprouts and five types of clay shall be mixed with sweet smelling substances and smeared over it, O great sage.

165. See P. 1688 note 110.

26. That pot shall be decorated and embellished with cloths, mango leaves, Dūrvā grass, coconut flowers and other articles.

27. O great sage, he shall put five gems into the pot or if they are not available he shall put gold into it.

28. The five gems are: amethyst, ruby, gold ingot, coral and onyx.

29. After uttering the mystic syllables "Nṛmlaskam" and "Glūm" in the end he shall perform worship in a favourable manner in accordance with the rules.

30. He shall invoke the lord along the path of five coverings in the manner prescribed for sacrifices, beginning with Ādhāra Śakti and then worship.

31. He shall offer milk pudding and cooked rice as Naivedya and the betel leaves as before. After the adoration with the repetitions of eight names, the other mantras shall be chanted.

32-33. Praṇava shall be repeated hundred and eight times. The five Brahmans beginning with Sadyojāta and ending with Īśāna shall be meditated upon. It shall be covered with Astra and Varma mantras. Incense and lights shall be waved with devotion. He shall then show the mystic gestures of cow and the vaginal passage clearly.

34. The preceptor shall then cover the vessel on the top with the Darbha grass. He shall then make a square to the northeast of the Maṇḍala.

35. Then a beautiful seat shall be put over the square in accordance with the rules. He shall then make the boy disciple sit on it in a comfortable posture.

36. The preceptor shall raise the vessel. Repeating "Svasti" he shall pour water on the head of the disciple making a circle with the inverted pot.

37. After uttering the Praṇava once first and then seven times with the names of five Brahmans he shall encircle him at the end of the ablution with the water from the conch.

38. After the rite of waving the charming light he shall wipe him with a towel The disciple shall be made

to wear a new waistband, a loin-cloth and two wearing cloths.

39-40. The feet shall be washed and Ācamana performed twice. Holding the ashes in his hands the preceptor shall smear it over the body of the disciple who is led into the Maṇḍapa and comfortably seated.

41. The precep or shall be seated with the disciple facing the east and desirous of spiritual knowledge. The preceptor shall tell him—"Be pure in soul."

42-43. He shall sit steady in a trance for a short while thinking "I am the preceptor—Śiva. He shall open his eyes with the mind favourably disposed towards him and without xcitement glance at the pupil who is sitting with palms joined in reverence.

44. With his hand smeared with the ashes he shall touch the head of the pupil and instruct in his right ear clearly "Haṁsaḥ Soham."

45. "The first Ham means Śakti-Soul. Saḥ means Śiva. I am he alone." Thus he shall reveal the meaning.

46-47. After instructing him in the meaning of 'Yaḥ Aṇu' he shall express clearly the meaning and purport of the statements in the middle. He shall tell him clearly, "O Brahmin, I shall tell you the statements. Listen and retain them in your mind."

CHAPTER NINETEEN

(*The rules of Yogapaṭṭa*)

Subrahmaṇya said :—

Now the great statements: perfect knowledge is Brahman; I am Brahman; thou art that. This Ātman is Brahman. All this is pervaded by the lord. I am the vital breath. Ātman is perfect knowledge; what is here is there; what is there is here. It is other than what is known; verily it is other than what is unknown too. This is your soul, the immanent and the deathless one. He who is in this

Puruṣa and he who is in the sun both are the same. I am the great Brahman, the greatest, greater than the greatest. I am myself (the Brahman) characterised by bliss, since I am the master of the Vedas and the Śāstras. Brahman is stationed in all living beings. Undoubtedly I am that alone. I am the vital breath of the elements : of the earth, of the waters, of the fire, of the wind, of the ether and of the three Guṇas. I am all. I am the Ātman of all. I transmigrate. I am without a second because I have everything in my Ātman—past, present and future. Indeed all this is Brahman. I am all. I am the liberated. He who is this is I; I am he; I am Haṁsa; I am he. This shall be meditated upon always and everywhere.

1. The meaning of the statement—"Perfect knowledge is Brahman" has already been made known. Parameśvara the Śakti-soul is the meaning of the word Aham.

2. 'A' is the foremost among all letters. It is the greatest splendour 'Śiva'. The letter Ha is of the form of firmament. It is glorified as the Śakti-soul.

3. Bliss is ever-rising due to the union of Śiva and Śakti. The word Brahman indicates the state of being Ātman of all, of Śiva and Śakti.

4. That has been taught before. The devotee shall meditate "I am he" "That you are;" in this the meaning of "That" has already been explained.

5-6. Otherwise there is a likelihood of opposite conception in "I am he" whereas the word "I" is in the masculine, the word "That" is in the neuter. Hence due to the incompatibility they cannot be interpreted together. The cause of the universe, of male and female forms, cannot be otherwise. The concept of the meaning of the instruction is: "Thou art that."

7. In the statement "This Ātman is Brahman" both the words are in the masculine. All this worthy of protection is pervaded by the lord.

8-9. "The Ātman is the perfect knowledge: what is here is there; he who is here is there." The concept is very well interpreted by the scholars.

10-12. In the statement "It is other than what is

known and what is unknown", there is a likelihood of adverse interpretation and conception in regard to the fruit of salvation. I shall explain, O sage, how this misinterpretation shall be prevented. "What is known" means "what is known not properly." What is unknown" means "What is not known before." Otherwise the expression may not be conducive to any meaning.

13-14. "This is your soul, the immanent, and the immortal one." It is Śiva himself, who is in the Puruṣa, or in the sun. Here the two conditions indicate that there is no separateness in the lord.

15-17. Verily the Vedas mention lord Śiva as golden. "Golden-armed" refers to his limbs being golden. Otherwise the lordship cannot be his. In the Chāndogya also in the passage "He who is in Śiva" is mentioned with golden moustache, golden tresses. Everywhere from the nail till the hair he is golden.

18. I shall tell you the purport of the statement "I am the great Brahman". Please listen.

19. The meaning of 'Aham' is Śakti-soul. Siva is indicated thereby. "I am he alone". The statement can be construed thus.

20-21. He is mentioned as the great Brahman, most sublime and the soul of all: "Para, Apara, Parātpara." The words Rudra, Brahmā and Viṣṇu are mentioned in the Vedas. The lord is greater than these. This is indicated by the word 'Para'.

22. By pondering over and practising the words of the Vedas, Śāstras and the preceptor, Śiva, the blissful lord appears in the heart of the pupil.

23. Śiva is stationed in all living beings. Undoubtedly I am he. I am the vital breath of all the Tattvas. I am Śiva.

24-26. After mentioning the Tattvas the Śāstras mention the Tattvas and Guṇas severally. The statement "I am the vital breath of all", O sage, includes the principles in entirety. By saying "I am all" he means "I am the vital breath of the Vidyātattva and the Tattvas of Śiva and Ātman."

Hence "I am the Ātman of all." Since the individual soul is immanent as well, I am his Jīva always.

27. What is past, what is yet to be, what is present—all these are identical with me. Hence I am all. All is Rudra.

28. O sage, the Śruti says that it has originated from Śiva's mouth. "I am the soul of all", because the great qualities are ever present in me.

29. "I am without a second" because there is no other Ātman distinct from the self. The statement "indeed all this is Brahman" has been explained before.

30. I am complete because of my positive aspect. I am ever liberated. All the souls resorting to my nature are liberated due to my grace.

31. "I am he who is Śiva, the soul of all and identical with all. I am Haṁsa. I am Śiva." This is the meaning of all statements, O Vāmadeva, as mentioned by Śiva.

32. The preceptor shall communicate to the pupil the meaning as declared by Śiva and explained in the Vedic passages. It establishes the identity of men with Śiva Himself.

33. He shall then take the conch with the pedestal and purify it with Bhasma and the Astra mantra. He shall put it before the disciple on the square and worship it.

34. He shall worship it with scents repeating Om. It shall be filled with scented water invoked by Astra mantra and filtered with a cloth. It shall be worshipped with the Praṇava Om.

35-36. It shall be worshipped repeating Om seven times. He who makes the slightest slip has to face the greatest terror. So says the Śruti. He shall then address the disciple himself, "Be steady-minded and fearless". Meditating on the lord he shall continue the worship.

37. He shall worship the seat of the disciple with the rite of "Ṣaḍutthāpana." After conceiving Śiva's seat he shall instal an idol of Śiva.

38-39. He shall fix on the head and the body of the disciple, the five Brahmans, beginning with the head and ending with the feet. He shall also fix the Kalās of the Praṇava too in the forms of the thirtyeight mantras as distinguished by the trunk, face and Kalās. After invoking Śiva he shall show the mystic gestures of the Kalās.

40. He shall then perform the Nyāsa of the limbs. The sixteen forms[166] of ancillary services beginning with the offering of the seat shall also be performed.

41. Milk pudding shall be offered as Naivedya repeating Om Svāhā. The rites of offering water for gargling and Ācamana, Arghya, incense, lights etc. shall also be performed.

42-45. After worshipping with the eight names he shall perform the Japa along with brahmins well-versed in the Vedas. Passages from the Śrutis: "The knower of Brahman attains.." "Bhṛgu the son of Varuṇa" "He who of gods"[167] and ending with "He who is the greatest is Maheśvara" shall be recited. Taking a garland of Kalhāra flowers he shall stand up and recite the "Siddhi Skandha" section in the Pañcāśika Text of Śrīvirūpākṣa. Thereafter thinking thus "This is my fame. I am complete" and feeling favourably disposed towards him the preceptor shall put the garland round the neck of the disciple.

46. The caste mark on the forehead and the application of the unguent over the body shall be carried out in accordance with his cultural custom.

47-49. The preceptor shall assign a name to him prefixed with the title Śripāda. He shall offer him an umbrella and sandals. He shall delegate to him the power of oratory, authorise him to accept seat in front since the disciple has now become Śiva himself. He shall tell him to be conscious that he is Śiva. The preceptor shall make obeisance in accordance with the tradition in the cult.

50. The disciple shall then stand up and prostrate

166. The sixteen ways of doing homage to a deity are:

आसनं स्वागतं पाद्यमर्घ्यमाचमनीयकम् ।
मधुपर्कांचमस्नानं वसनाभरणानि च ।
गन्धपुष्पे धूपदीपौ नैवेद्यं वन्दनं तथा ।

167. MŚ 1. 3. 4. 3; MG. 2. 2. 19

before his preceptor, the preceptor's preceptor and the other disciples of his preceptor.

51. When the disciple has finished the customary obeisance he shall stand humbly and silently like a well behaved disciple. The preceptor shall tell him like this.

52. "From now onwards be engaged in blessing the worlds. Accept a disciple only after testing him for a year. Accept him duly.

53. Eschew the faults of lust etc. and be devoted to meditation on Śiva. Associate with those who have inherited good tradition and not with others.

54. Till the end of your life never take food without worshipping Śiva. Abiding by your devotion to the preceptor be happy, be happy."

55. In this manner the excellent preceptor, sympathetic and scholarly, shall be favourably inclined towards the disciple.

56. O Vāmadeva, O great sage, out of affection for you the mode of the consecration of the disciple has been mentioned to you though it is a great secret.

57. After saying this Kārttikeya narrated the procedure of hair-cutting and ablution in detail intending to favour the ascetics (anxious to hear him).

CHAPTER TWENTY

(*Rules for hair-cutting and ablution*)

Subrahmaṇya said:-

1. O sage Vāmadeva I shall now explain the rules of hair-cutting and ablution. These if performed immediately are conducive to great purity of the ascetic.

2. O sage, after the consecration as a disciple he shall observe the other rites and get ready for the tonsorial ceremony.

3. He shall bow to the preceptor and secure permission

from him. After washing the head and performing the Ācamana he shall have the tonsure while putting on cloth.

4. After that he shall wash the cloth, the razor etc. with water and clay. The barber also shall be given clay and asked to wash his hands.

5-6. Repeating "Śivam" "Śivam" he shall sprinkle every object with water. He shall then close his eyes with the ring-finger and the thumb. Repeating the Astra mantra he shall open his eyes and look at the razor and other implements of tonsorial rite. Repeating the mantra twelve times he shall sprinkle them with the Astra mantra.

7. He shall take the razor and cut off a patch of hair on the right side. Then a few hair on the front, then the entire hair shall be shaved off.

8. The hair shaven off shall be put on a leaf and not allowed to fall on the ground. The beards, the moustache also shall be shaven. Nails of the hands and feet shall be pared.

9-10. He shall take clay from the root of Bilva, Asvattha or Tulasi. He shall plunge into water twelve times and come to the bank. He shall place the clay on a pure spot of ground and divide it into three parts. Each part shall be divided into three. It shall be sprinkled with water with the Astra mantra.

11. Taking a lump of clay he shall wipe off his hands with it twelve times. Each of the hands shall be separately washed with water.

12. Another lump of clay shall be used similarly for the feet, another lump for the face, another for the arms and so on. After smearing and washing he shall enter water again.

13. Another lump of clay shall be divided into twelve and applied over the beard. He shall then plunge into the water again.

14. He shall come to the bank, gargle sixteen times, perforn Ācamana twice and Prāṇāyāma sixteen times repeating the Praṇava.

15. He shall divide another lump of clay into three. With one part he shall purify the hips and feet and perform Ācamana twice.

16. Repeating the Praṇava he shall perform Prāṇāyāma silently sixteen times. He shall take another part of the clay lump and apply it on his thighs thrice repeating "Om".

17. He shall sprinkle water over it repeating Om seven times. He shall apply the clay on the palms once in the beginning and thrice afterwards. Then he shall glance at the holy disc of the sun.

18-19. With another lump of clay he shall purify the armpits by means of the hands on the opposite sides. With steady and pure mind the disciple shall take another lump of pure clay and smear his body fromhead to foot with devotion to the preceptor and eyes fixed in the sun.

20. Fixing the staff on the ground he shall stand up and remember his preceptor who has taught him the mantra with devotion strengthened by wisdom.

21. He shall devoutly remember Sāmba, Maheśāna, Śaṅkara, the moon-crested Śiva, the lord of prosperity and glory.

22. He shall prostrate before the preceptor Śiva thrice with eight limbs and once with five limbs touching the ground and stand up making obeisance.

23. He shall enter the river again and plunge once. Coming up he shall apply the clay on the shoulders in the manner mentioned before.

24. The remaining clay he shall take up and dissolve it in the water and then apply it all over his body.

25. He shall repeat 'Om' thrice and remember the lotus-like feet of Śiva which enable him to cross the ocean of worldly existence.[168]

26. Repeating Om he shall pour water over his body besmeared with the Bhasma of the Virajā Homa. He shall wipe the body, take his bath and apply Bhasma.

27. O sage, then he shall carefully apply Tripuṇḍra in accordance with the rules.

28. After paying obeisance to Maheśvara, the preceptors, holy centres and others he shall perform the midday rites.

168. The last pāda of this verse is defective.

29. O sage, with great devotion he shall worship Śiva accompanied by Śivā and the bestower of perfect knowledge, the protector of the three worlds.

30. With steady mind, abiding by his virtuous duties and pure in body, he shall go to good brahmin householders for alms.

31. He shall divide the alms into five parts and do with them as proper. He shall avoid defiled food.

32. A mendicant shall perform four activities : Purificatory rites, ablution, begging for alms and resorting to isolated places for meditation. He has no fifth rite.

33. He shall use only four types of begging bowls, that made of dried gourd, or of bamboo, or of wood or of clay. He shall not take any other type of bowl.

34. Six things are forbidden to the ascetics: chewing the betel, using the metallic vessel, emission of semen, white cloth, sleeping during the day and taking meal at night.

35. If they observe the rules they are wise. If they do not they are Rākṣasas. The ascetic shall never indulge in activities contrary to the rules.

36. He shall perform the post-shaving ablution assiduously for purity, remembering mentally the supreme Brahman Sadāśiva.

37. O sage, thus out of affection for you, the rites of post-shaving ablution I have explained to you. What else do you wish to hear?

CHAPTER TWENTYONE

(*The duties and rites up to the tenth day after the death of ascetics*)

Vāmadeva said:—

1-2. There are no crematory rites for the liberated ascetics. I have heard that they are buried. O Kārttikeya, my preceptor, please mention that rite lovingly. There is none in the three worlds who can explain the same.

3-4. O lord, son of Śiva, considering me as your disciple please tell me lovingly the mode of departure for those who are liberated from the corporal cage after realising perfect identity with the Brahman and who have attained their goal after liberation through the path of Upāsanā.

5. On hearing the request of the sage, the son of Śakti, destroyer of demons spoke about the great secret which had been heard from Śiva by Bhṛgu.

6. It is this secret, O sage, that was explained to Bhṛgu, the devotee of Śiva by the omniscient Pināka-bearing lord himself.

7. O Brahmin, I shall explain it to you. It shall not be given to any or every one indiscriminately. It shall be given to a calm disciple equipped with devotion to Śiva.

8. If there is any ascetic who has quit his body while in trance with his devotion for Śiva he becomes Śiva himself.

9. If there is such a person devoid of concentration who does not attain Samādhi, I shall mention the means of remedy for him. Listen attentively.

10. On hearing from his preceptor the lore of Vedānta and Āgamas along with the explanation he shall practise Yoga by means of Yama, Niyama etc.

11. O sage, practising it regularly the ascetic shall be attached to Praṇava and be well-engaged in the meditation on Śiva.

12. If he is devoid of courage due to physical weakness, he shall remember Śiva with specific desires and cast off his worn-out body.

13. O sage, there are five deities in the forms of messengers who by the favour of Sadāśiva are put in the charge of Nandin.

14-16. One of them has the shape of a self-killer (fire). Another has a mass of splendour as body. A third is the presiding deity of the day. The fourth is the presiding deity of the bright half of the month and the fifth one is in the form of the sun's transit from capricorn to cancer. These five are engaged in blessing. Another set of five deities is also well known: Dhūmrā, Tamasvinī, Rātri, Kṛṣṇapakṣābhimāninī, Dakṣiṇāyana. O great sage Vāmadeva, now listen to their activities.

17. The five deities, O sage, take the souls interested in performing holy rites to the heaven by their merit.

18. After enjoying the pleasures in heaven as mentioned, at the diminution of the merit they return to the human realm and take births as before.

19-20. The deities employed in activities divide the sphere beginning with the earth into five in the order of fire etc. They then take the ascetic to Sadāśiva's region. Having led him to the honoured feet of the lord, the deities of blessing stand behind the lord.

21-22. On seeing him come, if he is unattached, Sadā-Śiva lord of the gods teaches him the purport of the great mantra; crowns him as the chief of the Gaṇas and gives him a body similar to his. Śiva lord of all, leader of all, blesses him thus.

23-31. The ascetic is decorated with the deer-skin, axe, trident and the gesture of offering boons. He has three eyes. His matted locks shine by the splendour of Gaṅgā and the crescent moon. He is seated on a splendid aerial chariot. He is delegated the power of bestowing all desires. If he is attached the lord blesses him with an aerial chariot having the speed of the mind, capable of going everywhere, shining like a crore of suns, cool like a crore of moons, full of vessels with celestial nector and divine water, decorated with divine garments, garlands, unguents and ornaments charming with the sounds of dance, music, Mṛdaṅga and other instruments and surrounded by Rudra virgins. When he has enjoyed all pleasures, when his eagerness for enjoyment subsides lord Śiva blesses him imparting to him the purport of the great mantra. He blesses him with immovable trance in the form "I am Śiva, I am perfect." He blesses him with unrestricted Siddhis capable of creating the sun etc. The Siddhis are in the form of throbbings arising from realisation that he is the slave of Siva. The preceptor of the world bestows on him the greatest salvation devoid of return even when the life of the lotus-born deity comes to an end.

32. The attainment of this region is the accumulation of all prosperity and glory. It is the highway to salvation, the conclusion of Vedāntas.

33. When the ascetic of good tradition is slowly dying the other ascetics shall stand around him with their attitude in conformity with their wishes.

34-35. They shall recite the statements beginning with Praṇava and explain their purport with the pious mind. They shall remind him of Śiva the great Nirguṇa splendour and make obeisance to him till he expires.

36. The procedure of obsequies shall be followed. If their bodies are not cremated they are likely to miss the good goal.

37. Since they have renounced all their activities and have resorted to Śiva, if the king defiles their bodies his kingdom will be ruined.

38. The people of that village too will suffer distress. The following procedure shall be taken up to avoid that default.

39. Humbly the king shall begin with "obeisance to Iriṇya"[169] and recite the mantra ending with "obeisance to Āmivatkas".[170]

40. Repeating Om in the end he shall complete the worship of the lord. O great sage, this procedure will quell the defect.

41. His sons and relatives shall perform the obsequies according to the rules.

42-43. He shall be bathed with water and worshipped with flowers etc. repeating the mantras of Śrirudra, Camaka and Rudrasūkta in order. The conch shall be placed before him and he shall be sprinkled with the water therein. A flower shall be placed on the head and his body shall be wiped repeating the Praṇava.

44. The loin-cloth shall be taken off and fresh one shall be tied. His body shall be dusted with the ashes in accordance with the rules.

45. Tripuṇḍra marks shall be applied in accordance

169. VS. 16. 43.
170. TS 4. 5. 9. 2.

with the rules, and a sandalpaste mark shall also be made. The body shall be decorated with flowers and garlands.

46. Repeating the requisite mantras Rudrākṣa garlands shall be worn over the chest, neck, head, arms, wrists and ears in order.

47. After fumigating with incense the body shall be lifted and placed on a rope-swing. It shall be placed on a charming chariot of the form of five Bahmans.

48. The chariot shall be decorated with fragrant flowers and garlands with the five Brahma mantras beginning with Sadyojāta preceded by Om.

49. The body shall be taken round in procession around the village to the accompaniment of dances, music and chanting of Vedic mantras.

50-56. The ascetics shall dig a ditch as deep as the staff in a holy spot near a holy tree on the eastern or northern side. They shall sprinkle it with water repeating the Praṇava and the Vyāhṛtis. They shall spread the leaves of the Śamī tree and flowers with their tips pointing to the north. Above them Darbha grass shall be spread. His seat whether cloth, deerskin or mat of Darbha grass shall be placed over them. The body shall be sprinkled with Pañcagavya with Praṇava and Brahma mantras. It shall be bathed with the water from the conch repeating Rudrasūkta and the Praṇava. A flower shall be placed on the head. Repeating the Svastivācana mantras and Om the body shall be lifted and placed inside the ditch in the Yogic pose facing the east. It shall be decorated with fragrant flowers and fumigated with incense and fragrant gum resin repeating the mantra "O Viṣṇu, protect the Havya".

57-58. The staff shall be placed in his right hand and the vessel full of water in the left, repeating the mantra "Prajāpate natvadetā".[171] With the mantra "Brahmaja jñānam Prathamam"[172] etc. his head and with the Rudra Sūkta the middle of the eyebrow shall be touched.

171. VS 10. 20.
172. Ibid. 13. 3.

59. The skull shall be split with a coconut repeating the four mantras beginning with "Mā no Mahāntam[173] etc. Then the ditch shall be filled.

60-61. Touching the place, with the mind dwelling on nothing else, the performer of the obsequies shall repeat the five Brahma mantras and the mantra beginning with "Yo devānām"[174] and ending with "Yaḥ paraḥ sa Maheśvaraḥ" he shall worship Mahādeva, Sāmba, the panacea for the ills of the world, the omniscient, the non-dependent and the blesser of all.

62. Then a mud platform, two Aratnis square and one Aratni high, shall be erected and smeared with cow-dung.

63. A mystic diagram shall be inscribed in the middle and worshipped with fragrant flowers, Bilva leaves and Tulasī along with scented raw grains.

64. The waving of the lights fumigating with incense, milk and the food offering shall be offered with Praṇava. The grave shall be circumambulated. They shall them prostrate five times.

65. After repeating the Praṇava twelve times they shall again make obeisance. To every quarter and interstice food offering shall be offered with Praṇava.

66. Thus I have narrated the rites up to the tenth day. O great sage, now listen to the rites of the eleventh day for ascetics.

173. Ibid 16. 15.
174. See P. 1705 note.

CHAPTER TWENTYTWO

(The rites on the eleventh day for the ascetics)

Subrahmaṇya said:—

1. O sage, out of affection for you I shall explain the rite for ascetics on the eleventh day after death.

2-3. The performer of obsequies shall sweep the platform and smear it with cowdung. He shall sprinkle water with Puṇyāhavācana mantras five times from the west to the east. He shall sit down facing the north and draw the mystic diagrams himself, the middle square of 18 cms in length.

4. The Bindu, triangle, hexagon and circle shall be drawn in order. The conch shall be placed in front in accordance with the rules of worship.

5. He shall perform the Prāṇāyāma and after due Saṁkalpa rite, he shall worship the five deities mentioned as messengers before.

6-8. He shall cast off Darbha grass to the north and not touch it again. Beginning with the west the Maṇḍalas shall be worshipped according to the rules for the rite of "Sadutthāpana." Flowers shall be stacked within them like a pedestal with "Om Hrīm. I invoke the messenger goddess in the form of fire, obeisance." This latter portion is common to the five. The gestures of installation shall be shown severally to each.

9. The Aṅganyāsas for the deities shall be performed with Hrām, Hrīm etc. The messenger goddesses shall have the noose, goad, gestures of fearlessness and wish in their hands. They are as lustrous as the lunar stone.

10. They have changed (or enhanced) the hue of the quarters by the lustre of their gemset rings. They wear red garments and shine with lotus-like hands and feet.

11. They look charming with their faces resembling the full moon and brilliant with three eyes. They are decorated with the crescent moon shining above their ruby-set coronets.

12. Their swinging ear-rings tickle their cheeks. They have plump and elevated breasts. They are charming with their necklaces, shoulderlets, bangles and girdles.

13. Their waists are slender and buttocks large. They wear divine red garments. The ruby-set anklets jingle and tinkle in their lotus-like feet. The rings in their toes are very charming.

14. What blessing can be secured from a departed soul? Only from a powerful soul can everything be achieved as from Maheśa.

15. The five deities capable of all activities and eager to bless others are accepted by the lord as the bestowers of bliss.

16. After meditating on the auspicious deities eager to bless he shall offer Pādya at their feet with drops of water from the conch.

17. The water for Ācamana shall be offered in their hands and Arghya on their heads. He shall conceive of their ritualistic ablution with the drops of water from the conch.

18. Beautiful garments red in colour shall be offered along with upper cloths. Coronets and ornaments shall also be offered.

19. Fragrant sandal wood, auspicious Akṣatas and charming fragrant flowers shall also be offered.

20-21. Fragrant incense and lamp with wicks soaked in ghee shall be offered saying "I dedicate everything." Om should be uttered in the beginning and Namaḥ at the end. Then milk pudding with honey shall be offered along with ghee, sugar, sweet pie and plantain fruits stuffed with jaggery.

22. Different articles shall be heaped on separate plantain leaves and rendered fragrant. They shall be sprinkled with water uttering "Bhuḥ Bhuvaḥ Svaḥ."

23. Naivedya shall be offered with; "Om Hrīm Svāhā". With "Namaḥ" water shall be offered with great devotion.

24. O excellent sage, thereafter the rite of Udvāsana shall be performed with devotion. The place shall be mopped clean beginning with the east. Then water for gargling and Ācamana shall be offered with Arghya.

25. After offering Tāmbūla, incense and lights, the circumambulation and obeisance shall be performed. The

deities shall be prayed with the joined palms placed on the head reverentially.

26. "May the glorious mothers be delighted. At the lotus-like feet of Parameśa let them recommend the protection of the deceased ascetic who is desirous of attaining the region of Śiva.

27. After ritualistically dismissing them along the way they had come, the remanents of the Naivedya shall be distributed among the virgins.

28. It shall be given to the cows or cast off into water: There is no other way of disposal. Pārvaṇa and not Ekoddiṣṭa Śrāddha shall be performed for an ascetic.

29. I shall now tell you the rules for the Pārvaṇa for your welfare. O sage, listen.

30-32. The performer of the Pārvaṇa shall take his bath, perform Prāṇāyāma with pious mind wearing the sacred thread as usual. Wearing the Darbha ring he shall say "On this auspicious Tithi I shall perform the Pārvaṇa Śrāddha." In the place of Āsana Darbha grass shall be placed. After Saṁkalpa Darbhas shall be cast off to the north. Water shall be touched. He shall invite four Śaiva brahmins who are steady in their rites. The brahmins shall take oil bath after which they shall be made to sit.

33-34. "Ye all shall represent the Viśvedevas." After saying this he shall say "obeisance to Ātman, Antarātman and Paramātman." Then he shall touch their feet with devotion.

35. The feet of the brahmins shall be washed and they shall be made to sit facing the east. After decorating them with scents, sandal paste etc., they shall be fed in front of Śiva

36-39. The ground shall be smeared with cowdung. Darbha grass shall be spread with their tips to the east. He shall perform Prāṇāyāma and the rite of saṁkalpa "I shall offer the Piṇḍa." He shall then worship the Maṇḍala Ātman, Antarātman and the Paramātman turning the face back. "I am giving these Piṇḍas," saying this he shall offer the Piṇḍas with devotion. Water from the Darbha grass shall be offered. Getting up he shall perform circumambulation and the Namaskāra.

40. After giving gifts to the Brahmins according to the rules he shall offer Nārāyaṇa Bali at the same spot on the same day.

41. Everywhere Viṣṇu shall be worshipped for protection. He shall perform the worship of Viṣṇu and offer milk pudding as Naivedya.

42-43. He shall invite twelve brahmins who are masters of the Vedas. He shall worship them in the names of Keśava etc. with scents, flowers and Akṣatas. He shall propitiate them and offer them shoes, umbrella, cloth, according to the rules. He shall speak to them sweet, auspicious words.

44. He shall spread Darbha grass on the ground with their tips to the east. After saying "Bhūḥ Svāhā, Bhuvaḥ Svāhā, Suvaḥ Svāhā, Om." He shall offer milk pudding as oblation.

45. O great sage, the rite of the eleventh day has been mentioned by me. O brahmin, I shall now explain the twelfthday rites.

CHAPTER TWENTYTHREE

(*The twelfth day rites for Yatis*)

Subrahmanya said:—

1-2. He shall get up early in the morning on the twelfth day, take his bath and perform his daily rites. He shall invite some Śaiva ascetics or brahmin devotees of Śiva. After they had taken their baths they shall be fed at midday in accordance with the rules, offering them sweet and auspicious foodstuffs of various sorts.

3-4. In the presence of Parameśa they shall be worshipped in accordance with the Pañcāvaraṇa rites after performing Prāṇāyāma. As in the case of Mahāsaṁkalpa he shall perform the Saṁkalpa rite thus, "I shall perform the worship of the perceptor." He shall then touch the Darbhas.

5. After washing his feet and performing Ācamana he shall make them sit facing east. Ashes shall be smeared all over the body.

6. O sage, the eight—Sadāśiva etc. shall be meditated upon and the brahmins shall be treated with respect.

7. He shall then meditate on Parameṣṭhi Guru as Sāmba with his own name. Paramaguru and Parāt Paraguru shall also be meditated upon.

8-11. He shall say "Here is the seat" and offer seat. With Om as prefix his name shall be mentioned in the accusative case with the addition "I invoke, obeisance". He shall then offer Pādya, Ācamana, Arghya, cloth, scents and Akṣatas. They shall be decorated with flowers. Their names shall be mentioned in the Dative case with Om prefixed and worshipped with fragrant flowers. After fumigating with the incense and offering lights he shall say, "The entire rites of propitiation are over. May they be perfect and complete" and perform obeisance and get up.

12-14. Plantain leaves shall be spread and cleaned with water. Pure cooked rice, milk pudding, sweet pies, cooked dal, vegetable dishes, and other food stuffs shall be placed over them along with plantain fruits, coconuts and jaggery. Darbha grass is put under each leaf. These shall be sprinkled and the Pariṣecana, the sprinkling of foodstuffs shall be performed. He shall then say "Protect the Havya of Viṣṇu" and make them touch the articles.

15. He shall stand up and ofter giving water for drinking he shall request them thus, "May Sadāśiva and others be delighted with me and bestow boons on me".

16. He shall then recite the mantra "Ye devā"[175] etc. and scatter Akṣatas. He shall prostrate, stand up and say "Everywhere may there be nectar".

17-23. Saying this he shall propitiate them. Then repeating the mantra "Gaṇānāṁtvā"[176] he shall recite Rudra, Camaka, Rudrasūkta and Pañcasūkta. After the brahmins had taken their meals they shall be given as many Akṣatas as there

175. VS 1. 4.
176. Ibid 23. 19.

are mantras. Water shall be offered for drinking and washing hands, mouth and feet. When they had performed Ācamana they shall be comfortably seated. Pure water shall be given again. Camphor betel leaves shall be offered and Dakṣiṇās given. Gifts of sandals, seats, leaves, fans, planks and bamboo staff shall be made. They shall be circumambulated and prostrated and their blessings received. Making obeisance again they shall be requested for unflinching devotion to the preceptor. Saying "May Sadāśiva and others go delightedly and comfortably" he shall bid farewell to them. Till the door he shall follow them. When they forbid him follow further, he shall return and take food along with the other brahmins, kinsmen and the poor. He shall then feel contented and happy.

24. This is never affected. It is the truth. He who performs the rite of propitiation of the preceptor every year enjoys great pleasure here and attains Śivaloka hereafter.

25. After saying this to Vāmadeva his disciple blessed by himself, the wise lord Subrahmaṇya delighted in mind said:—

26. Since formerly this was mentioned to the sages of the Naimisa forest by the sage Vyāsa he is our first preceptor. You are the second one famous in the world.

27. Hearing this from the lotus-like mouth of yours the great sage Sanatkumāra, full of devotion to Śiva, shall mention this to Vyāsa. That excellent devotee of Śiva will mention this to Śuka.

28. For every leading sage there will be four disciples. They will be masters of Vedic study and establish virtuous sacred rites.

29. The four disciples of Vyāsa are Vaiśampāyana, Paila, Jaimini and Sumantu.

30. O sage Vāmadeva, your disciples are Agastya, Pulastya, Pulaha and Kratu.

31-32. Sanaka, Sananda, Sanātanamuni, and Sanatsujāta, these great yogins, favourites of Śiva, the knowers of the Vedas are the disciples of Sanatkumāra. Thus these preceptors, great preceptors etc. are worthy of being worshipped by the yogin Śuka.

33. This perfect knowledge of Praṇava is well established in the four classes of disciples. Being the cause of great glory it is the cause of salvation at Kāśī.

34. This Maṇḍala as the seat of the great Śiva is wonderful. It is worshipped by the great sages conversant with the essence of Vedānta. It is enveloped by the ether as mentioned in the Vedas. May it be conducive to your satisfaction and the welfare of the world. May it yield glory and prosperity.

35. This is the secret par excellence as mentioned by Śiva. It is the conclusion of the Vedānta tenet. O sage, since it has been heard by you from me people call it as your tenet.

36. Hence an ascetic who treads along this path attains Śiva like the rivers that fall into the sea. By the repeated practice of the meditation "I am Śiva", the ascetic becomes Śiva. He can grant salvation even to the class of beings Brahmā etc.

37-38. After teaching this to the sage the lord of gods remembered the lotus-like feet of his parents worshipped by the gods. Kumāra reached Kailāsa of many peaks, Kumāra the preceptor who bestows perfect knowledge.

39. Accompanied by his disciples and making obeisance to the peacock-vehicled lord, Vāmadeva too immediately left for the wonderful mountain Kailāsa.

40. After reaching the summit of Kailāsa the sage approached Śiva. He saw the feet of the lord and the goddess—the feet that bestow salvation and destroy illusion.

41. With great devotion he dedicated himself to him. He prostrated again and again and then got up.

42. Then the sage, with various Vedic and Śāstric hymns eulogised Śiva together with Ambā and their sons.

43. He put the lotus-like feet of the lord and the goddess on his head. With their blessings he stayed there comfortably.

44-45. All of you too shall learn the meaning of the Praṇava Maheśvara, the secret of the Vedas, of the Tāraka Brahman, the bestower of salvation. Remaining here itself comfortably you will attain the excellent salvation, the unequalled Sāyujya with the feet of Śrīviśveśvara.

46. I shall go to Badarikāśrama[177] for serving the lotus like feet of my preceptor. Let us aspire for the opportunity of having excellent talk again.

177. See P. 1327 note.

VĀYAVĪYASAṂHITĀ

Section I

CHAPTER ONE[178]

(Origin of the sacred lore)

Vyāsa said :—

1. Obeisance to Śiva accompanied by Umā, Gaṇas and his sons, the lord of Prakṛti and Puruṣa and the cause of creation, sustenance and annihilation.

2-3. I seek refuge in Śiva, whose power is unequalled, whose glory spreads everywhere, whose lordship and potency are said to be natural, who is unborn, who is the creator of the universe, eternal, auspicious and the unchanging great Ātman.

4-5. Noble sages engaged in truthful rites, highly fortunate and dignified performed a great sacrifice in the Naimiṣa[179] forest, a virtuous spot and a holy centre of many sacrifices at the confluence[180] of the Gaṅgā and Kālindī, a pathway that leads to Brahmaloka.[181]

6-9. On hearing that the sages of good rites were performing the sacrifice, Sūta the most excellent of Paurāṇikas came to that place, Sūta who was a noble disciple of the intelligent Veda Vyāsa the son of Satyavatī, who was very intelligent and famous in the world, who knew the faults and merits of syllogistic statements. He could satisfy even the queries of Bṛhaspati. He was an expert in narrating the stories of charming anecdotes. He knew the proper time for everything and the policy to be adopted. He was a poet.

10. On seeing Sūta come, the sages were delighted

178. Most of the verses of this chapter are identical in form and content with those of the first chapter in the Vidyeśvara Saṁhitā.

179. See P. 35 note 27.

180. See P. 76 note

181. A particular region is intended to be meant here.

in their minds. They received him and worshipped him suitably.

11. Accepting their welcome and worship he took the proper seat offered by them.

12. By their contact with him the sages of pious souls became eager and impatient to hear the Purāṇic lore.

13. Worshipping him with words of praise the sages sat in front of him and spoke.

14. O omniscient Romaharṣaṇa, the principal devotees of Śiva of great fortune and keen intellect, it is due to the weightiness of our good luck that you have come here now.

15-17. You have directly acquired the Purāṇic lore from Vyāsa. Hence you are a repository of wonderful tales, even as the ocean of precious gems. There is nothing in the three worlds past, present or future, which is not known to you. Fortunately you have come here to visit us. It does not behove you to go in vain without conferring blessing on us.

18. Please narrate to us the holy Purāṇa the storehouse of good stories and the essence of the Vedānta.

19. Thus requested by the sages, the habitual reciters of the Vedic texts, Sūta spoke auspicious words full of sweet and rational meaning.

Sūta said:—

20. I have been honoured, blessed and urged by you all. Why shall I not then expound clearly the Purāṇa, held in esteem by the sages.

21-22. After saluting Śiva, Pārvatī, Skanda, Geṇeśa, Nandin and Vyāsa the son of Satyavatī, I shall narrate the extremely meritorious Purāṇa which is on a par with the Vedas, which being an ocean of Śaivite knowledge directly yields worldly pleasures and salvation.

23. It is embellished with the topics of the Āgamas full of rational meaning. In the context of the Śveta Kalpa[182] it was narrated by Vāyu formerly.

24. Understand well even as I narrate the various sacred lores, the due order of the Purāṇas and their origin.

25. The sacred lore consists of fourteen texts viz., the

182. On Kalpa see P. 1070 note.

six Aṅgas, the four Vedas, Mīmāṁsā, Nyāya, Purāṇas and the Dharma Śāstras.

26. There are eighteen secular Vidyās—Āyurveda Dhanurveda, Gāndharvaveda etc. ending with Arthaśāstra.

27. Śruti mentions that the original exponent and poet of the eighteen Vidyās, each having its own individual path, is the trident-bearing lord himself.

28. Indeed he is the lord of the universe. At the outset, with the desire of creating the universe, he created Brahmā, as his son.

29. To his eldest son Brahmā, the cause of the universe, Śiva gave these lores in the beginning in order to facilitate the creation of the universe.

30. He created Viṣṇu for the protection, of even Brahmā himself and endowed him with the power of protection.

31. Purāṇa, the first among the Śāstras, was learnt by Brahmā who had acquired the lore and began the creation of the subjects.

32. The Vedas came out of his mouths. The Śāstras too had their origin from him.

33-34. When the people could not follow the big sacred texts, at the instance of Viśveśvara, lord Viṣṇu the sustainer and the soul of the universe incarnated on the earth at the end of Dvāpara Yuga, in order to abridge them. He walked about the earth in the name of Vyāsa.

35. O Brahmins, in every Dvāpara Yuga the Vedas are classified by him. The Purāṇas and other texts are written by him.

36. In this Dvāpara age he was born of Satyavatī in the name of Kṛṣṇadvaipāyana as fire from Araṇi.

37. He abridged and classified the Vedas into four groups. He is known as Vedavyāsa.

38. Purāṇas extending to a hundred crore Ślokas were condensed by him into four hundred thousand Ślokas. Even now in the Devaloka they have the original number.

39. Even if a brahmin knows the four Vedas with their Aṅgas and the Upaniṣads he is not an expert if he does not know the Purāṇas.

40. The knowledge of the Vedas shall be enlarged by

Itihāsa and the Purāṇas. The Vedas are afraid of a man of deficient knowledge thinking "This man will deceive me".

41. Purāṇas have five characteristics[183]—creation, subsidiary creation, genealogy, manvantaras and the chronological account of kings, these are described in every Purāṇa.

42. The sages reckon ten Purāṇas and eight big Purāṇas.

43. Brāhma, Pādma, Vaiṣṇava, Śaiva, Bhāgavata, Bhaviṣya. Nāradīya and Mārkaṇḍeya are the eight big Purāṇas.

44-45. Āgneya, Brahmavaivarta, Liṅga, Vārāha, Skānda, Vāmana, Kūrma, Matsya, Garuda and Brahmāṇḍa are the ten small Purāṇas. These are the eighteen Purāṇas in order. Śivapurāṇa, the fourth in the list belongs to Śiva and is conducive to the achievement of all objects.

46. It contains a hundred thousand verses. It is divided into twelve Saṁhitās. It is created by Śiva. All sacred rites are mentioned therein.

47. Men are classified under three castes in accordance with their duties. Hence he who wishes for liberation shall resort to Śiva alone.

48. Even the gods can attain liberation by resorting to him alone and not otherwise.

49. What I mentioned as the Śivapurāṇa on a par with the Vedas, know its creations as I briefly explain.

50-56. There are twelve Saṁhitās: Vidyeśvara, Rudra, Vaināyaka, Auma, Mātr, Rudraikādaśaka, Kailāsa, Śatarudra, Koṭirudra, Sahasrakoṭirudra, Vāyavīya and Dharmapurāṇa. Vidyeśvara contains ten thousand verses. There are eight thousand verses in each of the four—Raudra, Vaināyaka, Auma and Mātṛpurāṇa. Rudraikādaśa contains thirteen thousand verses; Kailāsa six thousand; Śatarudra three thousand; Koṭirudra nine thousand; Sahasrakoṭirudra eleven thousand; Vāyavīya four thousand and Dharma contains twelve thousand verses.

57. Thus Śivapurāṇa contains a thousand verses.

183. On the characteristics, nomenclature and number of the Purāṇas see Introduction to Vol. I.

This Purāṇa, the essence of the Vedas, yields worldly pleasures and salvation.

58. Śiva Purāṇa the fourth one was abridged into seven Saṁhitās with twenty four thousand verses.

59-60. The first Saṁhitā is Vidyeśvara; the second Rudrasaṁhitā; the third Śatarudra. Koṭirudra is the fourth. Umāsaṁhitā is the fifth; the sixth is Kailāsa. The seventh is Vāyavīya. These are only seven compendiums.

61-64. Vidyeśvara contains two thousand verses, Rudra ten thousand five hundred; Śatarudra two thousand one hundred and eighty; Koṭirudra two thousand two hundred and forty; Umā one thousand eight hundred and forty; Kailāsa one thousand two hundred and forty and the Vāyavīya four thousand verses. Thus is the holy text of Śivapurāṇa.

65. I shall now begin the Vāyavīya containing four thousand verses and consisting of two parts.

66. This excellent Śāstra shall not be mentioned to one who is not conversant with the Vedas nor to one who has no faith nor to one who does not know the Purāṇas.

67. It shall be given to a tested virtuous disciple uncontaminated by malice. He shall be a devotee of Śiva and a follower of the Śaiva cult.

68. Obeisance to the holy sage Vyāsa of brilliant splendour whose grace has endowed me with the Purāṇic lore.

CHAPTER TWO

(The problem of the sages)

Sūta said:—

1-3. When a long time had elapsed, many kalpas had come and gone, the present kalpa had started, the activity of creation had begun, and the customs among the enlightened subjects had become established, a dispute arose among the sages of six clans. One said "This is the greatest being."

Another said, "It is not." Because the greatest being could not be reviewed or defined no conclusion was arrived at.

4. In order to see the eternal creator they went where the lord was staying eulogised by gods and Asuras.

5-6. It was on the auspicious and charming peak of Meru,[184] where there were plenty of gods and Asuras where Siddhas and Cāraṇas thronged, where Yakṣas and Gandharvas frequented, where flocks of birds chirped and crew, which was embellished by jewels and corals and which shone due to streams and rivulets, caves and crevices, bushes and hedges.

7-8. There was a forest Brahmavana[185] which abounded in different species of deer. It was ten Yojanas wide and hundred Yojanas long. There were beautiful lakes full of sweet and clean water. It had plenty of trees in full bloom where swarms of bees hummed and hovered.

9. This was a great city as beautiful and brilliant as the midday sun. It could not be attacked by the haughty Daityas, Dānavas and Rākṣasas.

10. It had lofty ramparts and portals made of molten gold. It was embellished by hundreds of main streets, turrets and wooden ceilings.

11. It appeared to lick the sky with crores of huge mansions set with precious gems of variegated colours. It was decorated with many such mansions.

12-13. Lord Brahmā resides there along with his councillors. Going there the sages saw the lord, the noble Ātman served by the groups of gods and sages. He was shining like pure gold. He was bedecked in all ornaments.

14. He was gentle with delightful face. His eyes were as large as the petals of a lotus. He was endowed with a divine lustre. He had smeared divine unguents and scents.

15. He was clad in brilliant white garments. He was bedecked in divine garlands. His lotus-like feet were saluted by the gods, Asuras and leading yogins.

16. Accompanied by Sarasvatī whose body had all auspicious marks who held the chowries in her hands, he shone as the sun with his dazzling light.

184. See P. 310 note; P. 623 note.
185. It is not identified.

17. On seeing him the sages were delighted and their eyes and faces shone. With palms joined in reverence and held over their heads they eulogised the leading god.

The sages said:—

18. Obeisance to you in the form of Trinity, the cause of creation, sustenance and annihilation, the ancient Puruṣa, Brahmā the great Ātman.

19. Obeisance to the deity who has Prakṛti for his body, who is the cause of quickening Pradhāna, who though transformed into twentythree principles is yet free from aberration.

20. Obeisance to the deity who has universe for his body, who is stationed within the belly of the universe, who has accomplished his task and whose body is perfectly accomplished.

21. Obeisance to the deity identical with the world, the creator, the sustainer and the annihilator of the world.

22. O Brahmā, it is by you alone that the entire universe is created, sustained and annihilated. Still, due to illusion, O lord, we do not know you.

Sūta said:—

23. Thus eulogised by the fortunate sages, Brahmā spoke to the sages in a majestic tone delighting them.

Brahmā said:—

24. O blessed sages of great splendour and strength, why have you come here all together?

25. The sages foremost of those who know Brahman spoke with palms joined in reverence, with words couched in humility to lord Brahmā who spoke thus.

The sages said:—

26. O lord, we have been encompassed in deep darkness. We are distressed. Unable to understand the greatest being we are arguing among ourselves.

27. Indeed you are the creator of the universe. You are the cause of all causes. O lord, there is nothing here not known to you.

28. Who is that being more ancient than all living beings? Who is the greatest Puruṣa? Who is the purest, perfect, and eternal Being?

29. Who by indulging in wonderful activities has created the universe? O intelligent lord, please mention it and quell our doubts.

30-31. Thus questioned, Brahmā, with smiling eyes, stood up and meditated for long in the presence of the gods, Dānavas and sages. Uttering the words "Rudra" he joined his palms in reverence, with a blissful sensation moistening his body and spoke.

CHAPTER THREE

(*The Naimiṣa episode*)

Brahmā said:—

1-4. Śiva stationed in the middle of the ether shall be meditated upon by those desirous of salvation; Śiva from whom the words recede not approaching him along with the mind;[186] knowing and realising whose bliss-form one has no fear from anywhere; from whom every thing inclusive of Brahmā, Viṣṇu, Rudra, Indra, the elements, the sense-organs, is born at first, who is the creator, meditator and ultimate cause of all causes; who is not born from anything else at any time; who is endowed with glory and prosperity and who is known as Sarveśvara.

5. It was he who created me at the outset as his son and gave me perfect knowledge. It was due to his grace that the lordship of the people was attained by me.

6. He is the lord who stands in heaven like the lofty stump of a tree; and by whom, by the Puruṣa, the great Ātman, all this is filled up.

7. He is active among the inactive creatures; he who being single himself creates many is Maheśvara.

186. TU 2. 9,

8. He rules over all the worlds through the Jīvas. He is the only lord Rudra. There is none second to him.

9. Though he has entered and is ever present in the hearts of the people he is invisible to others; he occupies and views at the universe always.

10. He is the sole lord of infinite Śakti who presides over all causes and is released from Time—Death.

11. He has neither day nor night; neither equals nor superiors. The great knowledge and activity is innate in him.

12. That which is perishable and unmanifest, that which is imperishable and immortal—both these have the imperishable as their Ātman. The sole lord is Śiva himself.

13. By concentrating on him, the person of *Sāttvaic* feelings becomes the lord himself. At the end the universal illusion recedes from him.

14. The eternal Śruti says "In whom neither the lightning flashes nor the sun blazes nor the moon sheds light and by whose brilliance this universe comes in the limelight."

15. That lord Śiva shall be realised. There is no other region greater than his worthy of attainment.

16. He is the cause. He has no beginning, no end. He is naturally pure, independent and perfect. The mobile and immobile beings are subservient to his will.

17. His body is not the creation of Prakṛti. He is glorious, devoid of examples and definitions. He is both the liberated and liberator. He is not influenced by Time. He is the activiser of time.

18. He has taken up residence above all. He is the repository of all. He is the knower of all. He is the lord of the universe comprising the sixfold path.

19. He is the Being above all beings, one above the other. There is no being above him. He is the bee imbibing the honey of endless bliss.

20. He is an expert in solidifying the unsevered cosmic eggs. He is the ocean of benevolence, prowess, majesty and sweetness.

21. There is no object equal to him or excelling him. He stands as the unparalleled Emperor of all living beings.

22. The universe is created by him indulging in wonderful activities. At the time of dissolution this gets dissolved in him.

23. The living beings are under his control. He is the employer of all. He is seen by great devotion and not otherwise.

24. Sacred rites, charitable gifts, penances and observances, these are advocated by people for the purification of emotions. There is no doubt in this.

25. Viṣṇu, I, Rudra, gods and Asuras are desirous of seeing him even today by performing great penances.

26. He is invisible to fallen wicked men, the despicable and the stupid. He is worshipped within and without by devotees and can be spoken to.

27-28. Forms in the universe are threefold—the gross, subtle and that which is beyond. The gross is seen by us, the gods and others. The subtle is seen by the Yogins. That which is beyond the two, is eternal, knowledge, bliss and the unchanging can be seen by those who dwell in it, are devoted to it and are engaged in the rites concerning it.

29. Of what avail is much talk? Devotion to Śiva is the secret of secrets. He who is endowed with it becomes liberated. There is no doubt in this.

30. Devotion is the result of grace and grace is the result of devotion just as the sprout comes out of the seed and produces the seed.

31. The achievements of the individual are due to the grace of God. Lord alone is achieved in the end through all the means.

32. Virtue and holy rites constitute the means for the attainment of grace. That is indicated by the Vedas. By practising Dharma the sins and merits are levelled to equality.

33. Contact with grace yields excellence of Dharma. After attaining this excellence the sins of the individual decline.

34. When his sins decline through succession of births the devotion to Sarveśvara and Ambā is generated along with knowledge.

35. The grace of the lord varies in accordance with the purity of emotions. Due to grace, eschewment of rites results. Here the eschewment is of the fruits of rites and not the rites themselves.

36. As a result of the abandonment of the desire for the fruits of holy rites, the auspicious Śaivite virtues are attained. This is twofold : that dependent on the preceptor and that which is not.

37. That which is dependent on the preceptor is more important and hundred times more efficacious since in the Śaivite creed there is an association of Śaivite knowledge.

38. In view of the knowledge the man sees the defects in the worldly existence. Thereafter arises non-attachment to the sensual objects and thence Bhāva is attained.

39. When Bhāva is attained the man becomes more inclined towards meditation than towards rituals. A man endowed with knowledge and meditation becomes engaged in Yoga.

40. Through Yoga arises the great devotion and then grace of God. By means of the grace the creature is liberated and becomes equal to Śiva.

41. The different modes of blessings may not be in the order mentioned. The blessing is based on the ability of the man.

42. Some soul is liberated even while in the womb; another even while being born ; a third whether he be a boy or a youth or an old man.

43. A soul born as a lower species, a soul undergoing torture in hell, a soul achieving a heavenly region may be liberated when the tenure is over.

44. Some soul may return after the enjoyment of heavenly region and then liberated. Still another soul may be liberated on its way.

45. Hence there is no stipulated mode or order in the attainment of liberation. The supreme bliss is in accordance with the knowledge and emotion and attained by the grace of the lord.

46-48. Hence, in order to win his grace you shall avoid verbal and mental defects; meditate on Śiva alone along with your wives, sons and others ; abide by him ; be attached to him. You shall associate with him, resort to him, do holy rites with your minds fixed in him, continue a long sacrifice for a thousand divine years. At the end of the sacrifice due to the efficacy of the mantras Vāyu will come there.

49-50. He will tell you what is good for you along with the means. Then you shall go to the holy and auspicious city of Vārāṇasī where the glorious trident-bearing lord sports about with the goddess for blessing his devotees.

51. O excellent brahmins, after seeing the great wonder therein you come to me again. Then I shall tell you the means of salvation.

52. Thereby in a single birth, salvation comes within your reach, salvation which sets you free from the bondage of births and transmigrations.

53. Now I am releasing this mentally created wheel. The place where its rim gets shattered is auspicious for your penance.

54. After saying this Brahmā created a mental wheel as bright as the sun. After bowing to lord Śiva he released it.

55. Those delighted brahmins bowed to the lord and pursued the wheel to the place where its rim got shattered.

56. The wheel thus hurled fell on a smooth charming rock in a certain forest where the water was sweet and clear.

57. That forest became famous as Naimiṣa. It is worshipped by the sages. It abounds in Yakṣas, Gandharvas, and Vidyādharas.

58-59. Indulging in sexual dalliance with Urvaśī, Purūravas was moving about in the eighteen islands in the ocean. Urged by fate he came to this place and foolishly spoiled the golden sacrificial altar here. The infuriated sages hurled Kuśa grass at him which had the power of thunderbolt and felled him to the ground.

60. Formerly the Viśvasṛja Brahmeśa householders desirous of creating the universe began a divine sacrifice here.

61. There had been many scholarly sages here experts

in words, meanings and logical arguments. They performed rites by their power of intellect and yogic practice.

62. Here persons well-versed in the Vedas refute those who are excluded from Vedic path by their power of arguments. They speak eloquently.

63. This Naimiṣa forest was the fitting place for the penance of the sages. It was beautiful with nectarine clear water flowing from the bottom rocks of the crystalline mountain. It abounded in fruit-bearing trees and was free from beasts of prey.

CHAPTER FOUR

(*The advent of Vāyu*)

Sūta said :—

1. The fortunate sages of devout rites worshipped lord Śiva and began their sacrifice there.

2. The sacrifice of the sages functioned evoking wonder in everyone like that of the Viśvasṛjas formerly who were desirous of creating the universe.

3. After sometime when the Satra had concluded with the distribution of manifold gifts Vāyu himself came there at the instance of Brahmā.

4-7. Vāyu the disciple of Brahmā, the self-controlled lord who perceives everything directly; in whose bidding stay the fortynine Maruts[187] always; who sustains the bodies of all living beings urging them perpetually by his own functionaries Prāṇa and others; who is endowed with the eightfold glories; who supports the worlds with his holy hands; who is born of Ākāśa; who possesses the two qualities of touch and sound and whom the philosophers call the material cause of fiery principle.

8. On seeing him at the hermitage the sages who were busy in a long Satra remembered the words of Brahmā and felt unequalled pleasure.

187. According to the Vedic concept they are sons of Rudra but a legend represents their origin in an unborn son of Diti whom Indra dashed in the womb into fortynine pieces and gave the name Maruts.

9. Standing up they welcomed and bowed to him. They offered him a golden seat.

10. He seated himself there and was worshipped by the sages. Congratulating them he enquired after their health.

Vāyu said:—

11. O brahmins, hope you are all quite well, now that this great sacrifice has concluded. Hope that the Asuras, the enemies of the gods, the destroyers of sacrifices do not harass you.

12-13. Hope that imprecations and expiatory rites do not take place. Hope that the rites are duly performed by you after worshipping the gods, with Stotra and Śastra hymns and the ancestors with the rites due to them. What do you propose to do afterwards, now that the great Satra has been concluded?

14. When addressed thus by Vāyu, the meditator on Śiva, the sages were delighted in their minds. They considered themselves sanctified. They replied thus humbly.

15. Today we have attained bliss; our penances are rendered fruitful since you have come for the increase of our welfare.

16. Listen to an old anecdote. Formerly we meditated on Prajāpati when we were overwhelmed by darkness. We wanted to acquire perfect knowledge.

17. The lord Brahmā worthy of being sought refuge in, blessed us as we sought refuge in him and said, "O brahmins, Lord Rudra is superior to all. He is the ultimate cause.

18. Only the devotee sees the lord whose real nature cannot be reflected upon or argued over. Devotion is acquired through grace and through grace is bliss attained.

19. Hence, in order to propitiate him perform the Satra. Worship him who is the ultimate cause, perform Satra in Naimiṣa extending over a long period.

20. At the end of the Satra, by means of his grace Vāyu will come there. You will acquire perfect knowledge from his mouth and attain welfare.

21. Commanding thus Brahmā sent us all to this place. O fortunate one, we were eagerly awaiting your arrival.

22. We sat and performed the Satra for a thousand divine years. We had nothing to wish for except your advent.

23. On hearing thus this story of the sages who had performed the satra for a long time Vāyu was delighted in his mind and stayed there surrounded by the sages.

24. On being implored by the sages, the lord succinctly narrated the glory of Śiva beginning with creation in order to enhance their piety.

CHAPTER FIVE

(*The Principles of Śiva cult*)

Sūta said:-

1. There at the outset the fortunate residents of the Naimisa bowed duly to lord Vāyu and asked him.

The sages said:—

2. How did you, sir, acquire the knowledge of Śiva? Wherefore is your devotion to Śiva, the Brahman whose birth is unmanifest.

Vāyu said:—

3. The twenty-first kalpa shall be known as Śvetalohita. In that kalpa the four-faced lord, desirous of creative activity performed a penance.

4-5. Delighted by his austere penance his father lord Śiva, foremost among the handsome assumed the divine form of a bechelor. He became a sage Śveta and uttering divine words appeared in front of him.

6. On seeing his father, Brahmā bowed to him and secured perfect knowledge along with Gāyatrī.

7. Having acquired knowledge, the four-faced lord created all living beings—the mobile and immobile.

8. That immortal knowledge was acquired by me

through the power of penance from that face through which it was acquired by Brahmā.

The sages said:—

9. What is that knowledge attained by you—the knowledge that is auspicious, more truthful than the most truthful, abiding by which a man attains happiness.

Vāyu said:—

10. Great and steady devotion shall be applied by a man who wishes for happiness, for the perfect knowledge of the individual soul, illusion and the lord who releases from the bondage.

11-12. Misery arises from ignorance. It is removed by knowledge that is a correct and precise comprehension of objects. Object is twofold: sentient and non-sentient. There is a controller of the two. The three are called Paśu, Pāśa and Pati.

13. On many occasions knowers of reality call the three by Akṣara, Kṣara and Kṣarākṣarapara.

14. The Paśu is called Akṣara. The Pāśa is called Kṣara. Pati is called Kṣarākṣarapara.

The sages said :—

15. O Māruta, please mention. What is Kṣara? What is Akṣara? What is that which is greater and beyond these two?

Vāyu said:—

16. Prakṛti is Kṣara. Puruṣa is Akṣara. The one who urges these two is the greatest Parameśvara.

The sages said:—

17. What is this Prakṛti? Who is Puruṣa? What is the relationship between the two? Who is this instigator Īśvara?

Vāyu said:—

18. Māyā is the Prakṛti. Puruṣa is enveloped by Māyā. The relationship is through the root and Karman. Lord Śiva is the instigator.

The sages said:—

19. What is this Māyā that is mentioned? Of what form is he who is enveloped by Māyā? Of what nature is the root? Whence is it ? What is Śivahood ? Whence is Śiva ?

Vāyu said :—

20. Māyā is the Śakti of Maheśvara. The form of Cit is enveloped by Māyā. The dirt is that which covers the Cit. Śivatva is his own innate purity.

The sages said :—

21. How does the Māyā cover up the pervading one? What for ? Why is this covering up of the Purusa ? By what is it made to recede ?

Vāyu said :—

22. Even a pervasive can be covered just as Kalā etc. that are pervasive. The cause is Karman alone. The purpose is enjoyment. It recedes when dirt is quelled.

The sages said :—

23-24. What are these Kalā etc. ? What is Karman ? What its beginning and what its end ? What the fruit ? What the support ? Whose enjoyment ? What is enjoyed What is the means of enjoyment, the cause of the diminution of dirt ? Of what nature is the Puruṣa devoid of dirt ?

Vāyu said :—

25-28. Kalā, Vidyā, Rāga, Kāla and Niyati, these are certain entities The enjoyer is Puruṣa, Karman is merit and sin. The fruits are happiness and misery. The beginningless dirt till the enjoyment rests in the ignorant soul. Enjoyment is for quelling Karman. The unmanifest is what is enjoyed. The means of enjoyment is the body with external and the internal senses as doors. Dirt is quelled by grace acquired by piety. When the dirt is quelled the Puruṣa becomes equal to Śiva.

The sages said :—

29. What are the several functions of the five principles Kalā etc. ? Why is Ātman called the enjoyer and Puruṣa ?

30. Of what nature is that unmanifest ? In what

form is it enjoyed ? What is its instrument in the act of enjoyment ? What is it called body ?

Vāyu said :—

31. Vidyā (learning) that reveals the place and activity, time and passion these are the inducing agents. Time is the conditioning factor there ; destiny is the controlling factor.

32. The unmanifest is the cause. It consists of three Guṇas. It is the source of origin and the place of merger. It is called Pradhāna and Prakṛti by philosophers.

33. Characteristically unmanifest it becomes manifest through Kalās. It is of the form and content of happiness, misery and delusion while being enjoyed. It has the three Guṇas.

34. The Guṇas Sattva, Rajas and Tamas, originate from Prakṛti. Like oil in the gingelly seed they are present in the latest form in Prakṛti.

35-36. Happiness and its cause constitute briefly the Sātttvaic trait. The Rājasaic trait is its opposite. Stunned state and delusion are Tāmasic traits. The Sāttvaic movement is upward progress; the Tāmasic one is downfall ; the middle course is cited as Rājasaic.

37-38. Briefly the unmanifest with its ramifications is as follows :—five subtle and primary elements, five gross elements, five sense-organs of activity and the set of four, viz. Pradhāna, intellect, ego and mind.

39. When it is in the state of a cause, it is unmanifest ; when it is in the state of an effect such as the body, pot etc, it is manifest.

40. Just as the pot is not materially different from clay, so the manifest, body etc. is not materially different from the unmanifest.

41. Hence the unmanifest alone is the cause of the composite viz. organs, body but their support, the object of enjoyment is unmanifest.

The sages said :—

42. How can Ātman which is separate from the sense-organs and the body exist ?

Vāyu said :—

43. The separateness of all-pervading lord from the intellect, sense-organs and the body is definite. There is something called Ātman. A reason thereof is difficult to understand.

44. The intellect, the sense-organs and the bodies are not the Ātman due to indefinite knowledge and non-eternality.

45. Hence the one who has the cognition of experienced objects and comprehends the entire knowables, is sung about in the Vedas and Upaniṣads as the immanent soul.

46. It is eternal. It incorporates and pervades everything. It stands everywhere. Still it is not perceived by any one clearly anywhere.

47. This Ātman cannot be perceived by the eye nor by any other sense-organ. The great Ātman is comprehended only by the enlightened mind.

48. It is neither woman nor man nor an eunuch. It is neither above nor below nor in the sides. It is nowhere.

49. It remains unembodied in the unsteady bodies. It is stable and steady like a stump. It is unchanging. Only the sober, self-possessed and bold can perceive it by means of reflection.

50. Of what avail is much talk? The Puruṣa is separate from the body. Unwarranted is the vision of those who do not see it separate.

51. There is nothing more impure, uncontrolled, miserable and uncertain than the body of the Puruṣa.

52. The Puruṣa becomes happy, miserable or deluded on becoming associated with the body—the seed of all adversities caused by his own activities.

53. As the field flooded with water generates sprouts so also the action flooded with ignorance generates the man.

54. Thousands in number are his bodies both of the past and the future. These are mortals, abodes of excessive distress.

55. A perpetual stay in the bodies that successively

come to the embodied soul and get shattered, is never attained by any one.

56. Covered by and separated from these bodies this soul resembles the disc of the moon in the sky that is covered by and separated from the passing clouds.

57. The different activities of the soul in the different bodies resemble the motion of the die in the different squares in the chess-board.

58. None belongs to him. He does not belong to anyone. The contact with wives, sons and kinsmen is but a chance meeting on the way.

59. The mutual contact of living beings is like that of a piece of log with another log in the great ocean. The two meet together and get separated.[188]

60. He sees the body but the body does not see him. A certain other being, the great Ātman sees both but both of them do not see him.

61. All living beings beginning with Brahmā and ending with the immobile are termed Paśus. Examples cited relate to these Paśus.

62. These Paśus are bound with Pāśa (noose) and are fed upon joy and misery as their fodder. The wise say that these are but instruments of games and sports of lord Śiva.

63. The ignorant creature cannot effect and prevent his happiness and misery. Induced by the lord he goes up to the heaven or falls into the deep ditch.

Sūta said:—

64. On hearing these words of Vāyu, the sages were delighted in their minds. After bowing to him who was expert in the Śaivite Āgama they spoke:—

188. The Verse occurs in the ŚP of MB

CHAPTER SIX

(The Principle of Śiva cult)

The sages said:—

1. You have explained what is Paśu and what is Pāśa. Now mention what is their lord different in characteristics from the two?

Vāyu said:—

2. There is a certain releaser of Paśu from Pāśa. He is Pati, the creator of the universe. He is the abode of endless charming attributes.

3. In his absence how could the universe have been created, since Pāśa is insentient and the Paśu is ignorant?

4. Without an intelligent cause nothing has ever been seen anywhere created by Pradhāna, Paramāṇu or any such insentient being.

5. Since the universe is an effect possessing parts it is dependent on a creator. And creativity can be only in Pati and not in Paśu or Pāśa.

6. Creativity of Paśu without the knowledge of creation like the going of a blind man is due to the inducement of his lord.

7. Realising distinction between him and himself and being gratified after resorting to him Paśu can attain immortality.

8. The sphere of Pati is really greater than and beyond that of Paśu and Pāśa. The knower of Brahman becomes free from births by knowing him alone.

9. Lord the redeemer of the universe sustains the universe of Kṣara and Akṣara, the two in unison, the manifest and the unmanifest.

10. The enjoyer, the enjoyed and the instigator—the three alone shall be distinguished. There is nothing else to be known by the seekers of knowledge.

11-12. The man endowed with truth and penance sees in his Ātman the great Ātman like the oil in the gingelly seed or the ghee in the curd or water in the current or the fire in the Araṇi.

13. He is the lord born alone. Associated with Īśānīs, his Śaktis he creates the worlds and rules over them.

14. He is always alone. There is none second to him.[189] After creating the worlds he protects them and withdraws them.

15. He has eyes, faces and feet all round.[190]

16. The sole lord and creator of the heaven and earth is Maheśvara. He is the origin and the place of merger of all the gods.[191]

17. The Śruti says that Rudra the great sage is superior to all; he creates Hiraṇyagarbha the first among the deities.[192]

18. I know this great Puruṣa, the undying, steady, having the colour of the sun, the lord stationed beyond darkness.[193]

19. There is nothing greater, subtler and grosser than this. The universe is filled by him.

20. He has all faces, heads and necks. He lies in the cavity of the heart of all. He is all-pervading and present everywhere.

21. He has hands, feet, eyes, heads, ears and faces all around. He stands enveloping everything in the world.

22. He has all apparent attributes but is devoid of the sense-organs. The lord is the friend and refuge of all.

23. They call him the great Puruṣa—who sees without eyes, hears without ears and comprehends all and whom no one knows.

24. He is subtler than the atom, greater than the greatest.[194] He is the unchanging. He lies in the cavity of the heart of this Paśu.

189. TS 1. 8. 6.; N. 1. 15
190. VS 17. 19; MNU. 2. 2.
191. Ibid. 17.
192. MNU 10. 3.
193. Ibid 31. 18.
194. MNU. 8. 3.

25. By the grace of the creator, one devoid of sorrows perceives him who is endowed with the excellence of greatness and who does not possess intelligence but is intelligence itself.

26. I know the unaging ancient omnipresent lord whose birth is denied by those who can expound the knowledge of the Brahman.[195]

27. After annihilating in the end, the lord creates the universe again from the beginning in association with his manifold Śaktis.

28-29. The Māyā of Śiva is the unborn mother of the universe and has variegated colours and shapes. It is white, red and black. She, the unborn, gives birth to man. He, the unborn, resorts to it and gets involved in distress Another Aja, the liberated soul, eschews her after she has been enjoyed.[196]

30. Two birds resort to the same tree. One eats the sweet fruit, the other simply watches without eating.[197]

31-32. Sitting on this tree the deluded Puruṣa bewails. When he sees the lord, the ultimate cause, and realises his greatness he is freed from sorrow and becomes happy.

33. The great Ātman, the Māyin entering this, creates the universe by his Māyā. Māyā shall be known as Prakṛti and Maheśvara as Māyin.

34-35. The universe is permeated by his parts. The Puruṣa attains perpetual peace and calmness on realising lord Śiva the creator and enveloper of the universe and the subtler of the subtlest, from his very inception in the foetus.

36. He alone is Kāla, the protector, the lord of universe. On realising him one is released from the noose of death.

37. On realising the lord pervading all living beings like the subtle cream over the ghee, one is freed from sins.

38. He alone is the great god Śiva, the creator of the universe. Only on realising him one attains immortality.

39. When everything was neither existent nor non-

195. VS. 31. 18
196. TA. 10. 10. 1; MNU 9. 2.
197. RV. I. 164. 20

existent, when it was neither day nor night, Śiva alone existed from whom the ancient wisdom emanated.

40. None can grasp his top, sides or middle. There is nothing resembling him. His is the great fame.[198]

41. Those who are frightened of rebirths meditate on the unborn. For the sake of succour they resort to the front face of Rudra.

42. The two Vidyā and Avidyā lie hidden in the imperishable, infinite great Brahman.

43. Avidyā is perishable while Vidyā is imperishable. He who rules over the two is lord Śiva. He is other than the two.

44. It is he who spreads his net in various ways, creates all and rules all. He possesses such exploits.

45. He illuminates the quarters above, below and to the sides, shining himself. He is innately alone, foremost of all who presides over all.

46. Transforming the attributes, the expressions of nature and expressed ones into what is enjoyed and the one that enjoys, he occupies the universe.

47. The gods and the sages know him as hidden in the secret Upaniṣad, who is Brahman, greater than the greatest. the progenitor of Brahmā and the cause of the universe.

48. Those who knew the lord eschewed their bodies. The lord can be realised only through piety. He is wishless, the cause of positive and negative substances and the creator of Kalās.

49. It is the greatness of the lord whereby this universe revolves but the deluded people call it a natural occurrence or the power of time.

50. It is by him in the form of the annihilator of death that these are enveloped perpetually, the activities urged by him transform into worldly existence along with the elements.

51-53. The individual indulges in activities more and more and returns to the earth. He gets entangled in the tattvas. By means of the fourteen attributes of the Ātman he pursues worldly activities. When these activities cease even the results are quelled.

198. VS. 32. 3.

54. When these are quelled he goes to another world. This is the cause of union of the two—the enjoyer and the enjoyed.

55. Lord alone is beyond the three times. He is attributeless, the knower of all, the lord of the three attributes. He is brahman itself greater than the greatest.

56. We worship and meditate upon the lord of manifold forms, the unborn, lord of people, object of worship and meditation by the entire universe. He is stationed in our minds.

57. He is beyond Kāla. From him the whole cosmos originates. He is the repository of the universe and effects virtue and quells sins. He is the lord of enjoyment.

58. We know him as the greatest of lords, the greatest of deities, the lord of the worlds.

59. He has neither cause nor effect. Nowhere in the universe there is anyone equal or superior to him.

60. It is mentioned in the Vedas that his threefold power is great, manifold and innate, comprising knowledge, strength and activity. It is by these activities that the universe is created.

61. He has no lord, no sex and no ruler. He is the cause of causes and the lord of lords.

62. He has no progenitor nor does he take birth from anywhere. He has no causes of birth such as Dirt, Māyā etc.

63. He is the solitary lord hidden in all living beings.[199] Spread all round he is the innate soul of all living beings. He is mentioned as the presiding deity of all sacred rites.

64. He is the abode of all living beings, the cosmic witness, the provoker of thoughts, devoid of attributes and the sole lord with self-control, devoid of activities and helpless.

65. He is the most permanent among the permanent. He is the most sentient among the sentient.

66. On realising the lord of the universe, comprehensible through Sāṅkhya and Yoga, the cause of the universe the person gets released from all illusions.

67. He is the creator and the knower of the universe. He is the knower of his source, and the creator of time. He

199. Cp. Śveta 4. 6. 11

possesses attributes. He is the lord of Prakṛti and the individual soul; he presides over the Guṇas; he is the releaser of illusion.

68-69. After realising the lord who at the outset created Brahmā and taught him the Vedas, through the clarity of my intellect, I shall be desirous of salvation from this worldly existence. I take refuge in Śiva who is devoid of attributes and activities, who is quiescent, the undespicable and the unsullied.

70-71. After realising the great bridge that takes to immortality I shall be quiescent like the fire that has consumed fuel. When men wear the ether as they wear a hide they will realise the end of miseries before they have realised Śiva.

72-73 O sages, due to the power of penance, the grace of the lord and the result of my good fortune I secured the holy knowledge straight from the mouth of Brahmā, the knowledge that quells sins, lies hidden in the Upaniṣads and was enunciated in a previous Kalpa.

74. This excellent knowledge shall not be delivered to one who is not quiet, nor to a son who is not well behaved nor to one who is not one's own disciple.

75. These facts reveal to him who is of noble soul, who has great devotion to the lord and to the preceptor in the form of Śiva.

76. Hence listen to the gist. Śiva is greater than Prakṛti and Puruṣa and beyond it. At the time of creation he creates the universe and at the time of dissolution he withdraws everything.

CHAPTER SEVEN

The glory of Time

The sages said:—

1. Every thing originates from Kāla and is annihilated through Kāla. There is nothing independent of Kāla anywhere.

2. The whole universe caught in its mouth whirls like a wheel through the activities of creation and annihilation.

3. By his control, Brahmā, Viṣṇu, Rudra, gods and Asuras cannot transgress the laws of propriety.

4. It classifies itself in the factors of past, present and future and makes people grow old. Thus freely lording over all it is extremely terrible.

5. O skilful one, please tell us. Who is this lord Kāla ? Under whose control is he? Who does not come under his control ?

Vāyu said:—

6. It is the great splendour of lord Śiva named Kālātman. Kalā, Kāṣṭhā, Nimeṣa are the forms it embodies.

7. It is the power of the lord that controls the universe in the form of directives which are untransgressable to the universe consisting of the mobile and immobile beings.

8. The Energy in the form of Kāla consists of its various parts. It comes out of it and permeates it like the piece of steel that sheds sparks of fire.

9. The universe is under the control of Kāla. Kāla is not under the control of the universe. Kāla is under the control of Śiva. Śiva is not subject to its control.

10. Since the unobstructed splendour of Śiva is firmly fixed in Kāla the limit of Kāla is extensive and is untransgressable.

11. Who can go beyond Kāla with the help of intellect? None can go beyond Karman perpetrated by Kāla.

12. Even those who attack the earth and rule it under a single umbrella cannot step beyond Kāla like the oceans that do not overflow the shore.

13. Even those who restrain their sense-organs and conquer the universe cannot conquer Kāla. Kāla overwhelms them.

14. Physicians well-versed in medicines regularly taking in elixirs and aphrodisiacs do not thwart death. Indeed Kāla is untransgressable.

15. The individual soul proposes something on the basis of its glory, beauty, conduct, strength and pedigree but Kāla disposes it.

16. By means of pleasing, displeasing and unexpected contacts, Kāla unites and separates the living beings.

17. At the same time when some one is miserable another is very happy. Wonderful indeed is the unscrutable nature of Kāla.

18. A young man changes into a feeble aged man. A powerful man becomes weak. A rich man becomes deprived of prosperity. O brahmins, the ways of Kāla are wonderful.

19. Neither nobility of birth, nor good conduct nor strength nor skill is of any avail. Kāla is unthwartable.

20. Kāla is impartial in its activity over those who are well guarded donors attended upon by songs and musical instruments as well as those who are helpless, living on doles.

21. Even elixirs, panaceas and well administered medicines do not have any effect if the time is not opportune. Those very things brought into use at the proper time are efficacious and yield happiness.

22. No one dies or is born before time. No one flourishes well before the proper time. No one is happy or miserable before the time for it arrives. There is no object which is untimely.

23. At the proper time the cool wind blows, the rain falls; the heat subsides and every thing grows.

24. Kāla is the cause of all births. Plants grow and perish at the proper time. The living world too comes into life.

25. He who thus correctly understands the principle of Kāla goes beyond it and sees that which is beyond Kāla.

26. Obeisance to the great. Obeisance to Śiva of wonderful form who has no Kāla to influence him, no bondage and liberation and is identical neither with Puruṣa nor Prakṛti nor the universe.

CHAPTER EIGHT

(*The span of life of the trinity*)

The sages said:—

1. By what unit is the duration of life calculated in Kāla ? What is the upper limit of Kāla in the form of number ?

Vāyu said:—

2. The basic unit of life is Nimeṣa. The upper limit is Śāntyatīta.

3. The time taken for the winking of an eye is Nimeṣa. Fifteen such Nimeṣas constitute one Kāṣṭhā.

4. Thirty such Kāsthās make one Kalā. Thirty Kalās make one Muhūrta. Thirty Muhūrtas make one day.

5-6. Thirty days constitute one month of two fortnights. A month constituting the bright and dark halves is one day of the manes.

7-8. Six Māsas constitute one Ayana. Two Ayanas make a year. One human year constitutes one day and night for the celestials, Uttarāyana being the day and Daksināyana the night.

9. The divine month like the human month constitutes thirty days. The year of the gods constitutes twelve months.

10. Three hundred and sixty human years make one divine year.

11. The calculation of yugas is based on the divine unit of time. The wise understand that there are four Yugas in the land of Bhārata.

12. The first Yuga is Kṛta, then comes Tretā. Dvāpara and Kali are the other Yugas. These are the four Yugas.

13. Four thousand years constitute the Kṛtayuga. The period of four hundred years constitutes the intervening junction and a hundred year period constitutes Sandhyāṁśa (a subdivision of the junction).

14. In the three other yugas, their Sandhyās and

Sandhyāṁśas the thousands and the hundreds become reduced by one.

15. Thus the twelve thousand years and the surplus period constitute a Caturyuga. A thousand Caturyugas constitute a Kalpa

16. Seventyone Caturyugas constitute a Manvantara. In a Kalpa there are fourteen such Manvantaras.

17. In this order, hundreds and thousands of such Kalpas and Manvantaras have passed by this time.

18. They are innumerable and hard to be known precisely. It is impossible to mention them in detail in the precise order.

19. A Kalpa constitutes a day of Brahmā of unmanifest origin. A thousand Kalpas make a year of Brahmā.

20. Eight thousand Brahmā years make one Brahmā Yuga. A thousand Brahmā Yugas make one Savana of Brahmā.

21. Three thousand and three Savanas make the life time of Brahmā.

22-23. A day of Brahmā's life constitutes the life of fourteen Indras, a month of his life constitutes a four hundred and twenty Indras; a year of his life five thousand and forty Indras; his whole life five hundred and forty thousand Indras.

24-25. A day of Viṣṇu is the life-time of Brahmā. A day of Rudra is equal to the life-time of Viṣṇu. A day of Śiva is equal to the life-period of one Rudra. A day of Sadāśiva is the life-period of Śiva. A day of Sākṣāt Śiva is the life-period of Sadāśiva. The life-time of the latter is equal to the life-period of five hundred and forty thousand previous deities.

26. This Kāla functions as directed by Sākṣātśiva. O Brahmins, this is the period of time of creation as mentioned by me.

27. This Kālāntara shall be known as a day of Parameśvara. Parameśvara's night shall be known to extend so long.

28. His day is the period of creation. His night is

the period of dissolution. But understand that he has neither day nor night as we conceive them.

29-31. The dissolution is effected for the benefit of the world. The subjects, the Prajāpatis, the three deities, gods, Asuras, the sense-organs, the sensual objects, the five great elements, the subtle and gross elements, the cosmic Intellect, the deities, all these abide during the day of the self-possessed Parameśvara. They get dissolved at the end of the day. At the end of the night again begins the origin of the universe.

32. Obeisance to the great Śiva, the soul of the universe, whose energy in respect of activity, time and innate nature is untransgressable and under whose command the whole universe functions.

CHAPTER NINE

(*The creation and sustenance*)

The sages said:—

1. How does lord Śiva perform his great sport commanding all, creating the universe and placing it in position?

2. What is it that came into being at the outset? By what are all these pervaded? By which being of huge belly is this swallowed?

Vāyu said:—

3. Śakti came into being at the outset; with Śāntyatītapadā following. From Śiva in association with Śakti Māyā came into being and then the unmanifest from it.

4. Śāntyatītapada originated from Śakti and from it Śāntipada; then the Vidyāpada; from it the Pratiṣṭhāpada came into being.

5. Nivṛttipada originated from Pratiṣṭhāpada. Thus has been briefly described the creation induced by the lord.

6. The creation of these is in the inverse order; the anni-

hilation is in the reverse order. There is a creator apart from and greater than what is indicated by these five Padas.

7. Hence the entire universe is pervaded by the five Kalās. Avyakta is the cause there but activitised by the Ātman.

8-10. It is agreed that everything begins with intellect and ends with Viśeṣa but the makership is neither of the Avyakta nor of the Puruṣa since Prakṛti is insentient and Puruṣa ignorant. Without an intelligent cause nothing is created by the insentient beings—Pradhāna, Paramāṇu etc. But the universe is dependent on a maker since it is an effect composed of parts.

11-12. Hence the creator must be powerful, independent, omnipotent and omniscient with no beginning, no end and endowed with lordly qualities. He is the maker of the universe, Mahādeva, Mahesvara, the protector and annihilator of everything. He is separate from it.

13. The transformation of Pradhāna and the activities of the Puruṣa function at the bidding of the lord of truthful vow.

14. It is in the minds of the noble that this firm and permanent conviction finds a place. A being of meagre consciousness does not resort to this side.

15-17. Hundred Brahmā years constitute the span of Brahmā born of unmanifest It is termed Para. Its half is Parārdha. At the advent of Dissolution the Avyakta withdraws to itself all its effects and abides in Ātman.

18. When the Avyakta abides in Ātman, when the effects have been withdrawn, Pradhana and Puruṣa stand on an equal footing.

19. The two have the Guṇas of Tamas and Sattva, remaining on a par with each other. The two without the Guṇas being predominant are mutually interwoven.

20. In the equal and undivided state of Guṇas in the rise of darkness, when the wind was in lull and the water was calm, there was nothing to be seen.

21-22. When the universe was unmanifest the lord meditated upon the great Śakti throughout the night. When it dawned the lord in contact with Māya entered Pradhāna and Puruṣa and set them to motion.

23. Then at the bidding of Brahmā, the creation evolved out of the unmanifest that is the source of origin and the spot of merger for all living creatures.

24. Obeisance to him who is different from the worlds, in a fraction of whose Śakti everything terminates, whose will is ever variegated and wonderful far above that of the universe and whom those who know the path call the lord of the path —the Ātman.

CHAPTER TEN

(*The description of creation*)

Vāyu said:—

1. At the outset, at the bidding of Iśvara the secondary elements beginning with the cosmic intellect and ending with Viśeṣa came into being from the Avyakta presided over by Puruṣa.

2. Then from these, the three deities Rudra, Viṣṇu and Brahmā were born as the cause of all.

3-4. Maheśvara bestows on these the power to pervade all the worlds unobstructed anywhere, unequalled perfect wisdom, the perpetual Siddhis of Aṇimā etc; and the state of being the cause of activities of creation, sustenance and dissolution.

5. In another Kalpa he conferred on each the activities of creation, sustenance and dissolution in order that they may not have any mutual rivalry due to delusion of intellect.

6. These three are born from one another, sustain one another, flourish one another, respect and follow one another.

7. Somewhere Brahmā, somewhere Viṣṇu and somewhere Rudra are praised. However their glory does not diminish.

8. Only impetuous fools censure them. Undoubtedly they become demons and ghosts.

9. Lord Śiva who is beyond the three Guṇas, who is divided into four units, who is all-in-all and the support of all is the cause of creation.

10. The Ātman who has created the universe sportively remains as the lord of three deities as well as of Prakṛti and Puruṣa.

11. He alone is their support, he who is greater than all, who is supreme, eternal, devoid of attributes and is their Ātman and their presiding deity.

12. Hence he alone is Prakṛti, Puruṣa, Sadāśiva, Bhava, Viṣṇu and Brahmā. Everything is identical with Śiva.

13. In the beginning were born the cosmic intellect, the great principle. When it was agitated the ego was born. The ego was split into three.[200]

14. The ego split into the gross and subtle elements and the sense-organs. When the ego had the Śattva predominant the Sāttvika creation took place.

15-16. The secondary creation took place simultaneously. The five sense-organs, the five organs of activity and the eleventh the mind, originated. The mind is both an organ of knowledge and of activity. When the ego becomes associated with Tamas, the Bhūtatanmātras are born.

17· Since it is the cause of Bhūtas it is called Bhūtādi. From this is born the Śabdatanmātra, from this the ether.

18. From the ether the Sparśatanmātra, from it Vāyu, from Vāyu the Rūpatanmātra, from this the Tejas, from Tejas the Rasa tanmātra is born.

19. From Rasa the water ; from this the Gandha Tanmātra is born, from this the Pṛthivī, from these elements the mobile and immobile beings are created.

20. Since they are presided over by Puruṣa and blessed by Avyakta the principles beginning with Mahat and ending with Viśeṣa generate the cosmic egg.[201]

21. When thus the activities of Brahmā are fulfilled Brahmā becomes flourished in that Egg.

22. He is the first embodied soul, called Puruṣa. He is the first creator of living beings. Brahmā thus existed in the beginning.

23. From him was born the intellect, the cause of

200. On the scheme of creation see P. 1072 note.
201. See P. 246 note 208.

virtue and prosperity, with the characteristics of wisdom and detachment.

24-25. Whatever is wished for by the mind is born of Avyakta. He functions in the three worlds, dividing himself into three because he has all in his control, possesses all the attributes and is dependent on Avyakta. In these three forms he creates, supports and annihilates.

26. He is four-faced as creator; as destroyer he is Kāla and as Puruṣa he has thousand heads. The self-born has thus three states.

27. As Brahmā he has Sattva and Rajas, as Kāla Tamas and Rajas, as Viṣṇu he has Sattva alone. Thus the increase of Guṇas in the lord is threefold.

28. As Brahmā he creates the worlds, as Kāla he condenses; as Puruṣa he sustains; he is indifferent. Thus the activity of the lord is threefold.

29. Since he is divided into three he is called Triguṇa. Since he has split himself into four he is glorified as Caturvyūha.

30. Since he is the beginning he is called Ādideva; since he is unborn he is called Aja; since he protects the subjects he is called Prajāpati.

31. The golden Meru is the foetus of that great Ātman; the oceans constitute the water of the womb and the mountains constitute the outer skin of the womb.

32. All these worlds in this universe, the moon, sun, stars, planets and Vāyu are in this cosmic egg.

33. The egg is enveloped with waters ten times bigger than it. The waters are enveloped by Tejas ten times bigger.

34. The Tejas is enveloped by Vāyu ten times bigger. Vāyu is enveloped by Ākāśa and Ākāśa is enveloped by Bhūtādi.

35. The Bhūtādi is enveloped by the Mahat. The Mahat is enveloped by Avyakta. Thus the egg is enveloped by even coverings.

36. O excellent brahmins, eight Prakṛtis, the causes of creation, sustenance and destruction are stationed covering each of these.

37. Thus born of one another, the effects and their causes sustain one another supporting and being supported.

38. Just as the tortoise spreads its limbs first and then withdraws them, so the Avyakta creates the beings and then withdraws them.

39. Everything originating from Avyakta is born in this order. When the time of dissolution arrives it gets dissolved in the reverse order.

40. The Guṇas become equal and unequal due to Kāla. Dissolution takes place when there is equilibrium of the Guṇas. When this is upset, creation takes place.

41. Thus this egg, large and thick, is the source of origin of Brahmā. It is called Brahmā's sphere ; Brahmā is the lord of this.

42. There are thousands and crores of such eggs stationed at the sides, above and below since Pradhāna is present everywhere.

43. In the different places there are four-faced Brahmās, Viṣṇus and Rudras created by Pradhāna with the presence of Śiva.

44. The lord is beyond the manifest. The egg is born of the unmanifest. From that egg is born lord Brahmā and the worlds are created by him.

45. The primary creation of Pradhāna is without the intervention of the cosmic intellect. The ultimate dissolution is effected sportively by the lord alone at the end.

46. What is called as the unmanifest cause is Pradhāna. Brahmā is the progeny of Prakṛti. The Pradhāna has neither beginning nor middle nor end. Its prowess is infinite. It is white and deep red. It is associated with Puruṣa.

47. When the Rajas predominates it becomes generative. It creates the eight secondary tattvas in the beginning, which cause flourishing of the worlds. In the end it devours them.

48. The stability and the subsequent operation of the causes projected by Prakṛti take place by the thought of supreme lord whose prowess is not effected by Prakṛti.

CHAPTER ELEVEN

(The description of creation)

The sages said :—

1. Please narrate the Manvantaras, the Kalpas, the subsidiary creations and the re-creation after dissolution.

Vāyu said:—

2. The tenure of Brahmā who comes and goes according to the calculation of time is first a Parārdha and another Parārdha thereafter. At the end of the latter the re-creation takes place.

3. In each day in the life of Brahmā, the fourteen Manus come and go.

4. The Manvantaras and Kalpas have no beginning or end. Being unknowable they cannot be narrated separately.

5. Even if they be knowable, of what avail is it to you to know them. Hence I do not attempt to narrate them separately.

6. Among these Kalpas, I describe the creation and re-creation of this Kalpa.

7. The current Kalpa is named Vārāha. O excellent brahmins, in this Kalpa the Manus are fourteen in number.

8. Among the Manus, Svāyambhuva and others constitute the first seven Manus, Sāvarṇika and others constitute the next seven. Among them Vaivasvata Manu is the seventh.

9. It shall be known that in all the Manvantaras, the creation, sustenance and annihilation are more or less of the same nature.

10-13. When the previous Kalpa had ceased, the storm had burst, the forest and trees had been uprooted, the fire-god had consumed the worlds like dry grass, the earth had been drenched, oceans had overflowed their shores, the quarters had been sunk in deep sheet of water and the waters of dissolution had started their fierce devil dances with the waves for their arms showing movements of gestures by means of the water, Brahmā assumed the form of Visnu, slept soundly in that vast expanse of water.

14. One shall cite this mantra, a Śloka, regarding Nārāyaṇa. O excellent sages, listen to the mantra as well as the actual meaning of the words.

15. Waters are called 'Nārāḥ'. Waters are sons of Nara. He is called Nārāyaṇa because waters constitute his abode.[202]

16-17. With their palms joined in reverence the Siddha residents of Janaloka and the gods awakened the lord of gods who was in Yogic slumber, with hymns, in the morning as the Śrutis had done formerly at the beginning of creation.

18. The lord woke up, got up from his bed and came to the water. He looked all round at the quarters with the Yogic slumber still lingering in the eyes idly.

19. He did not see anything except himself. He sat up like a wonderstruck person and began to ponder deeply.

20. "Where is that charming goddess the great Earth, with her lofty mountains, rivers, cities and forests."

21. Thinking thus Brahmā could not locate the earth. Then he thought of his father, the three-eyed lord.

22. By meditating on the lord of gods, of immeasurable splendour, Brahmā understood that the earth had sunk under water.

23. Then Brahmā desirous of lifting up the Earth, thought of the divine Boar supporting about and diving into the waters.

24-29. He then assumed the form of a Boar and entered the nether worlds in order to lift up the Earth. His body was like a huge mountain. His snorting sound was like thunder. He had the lustre of a blue cloud. He was terrible with his snorting sound. His shoulders were thick, heavy and rounded. His buttocks were plump and raised. The tips of his calves were short and rounded. The hoofs were sharp. His eyes were round and terrible having the brilliance of rubies. The huge body was oval-shaped. The stiff ears shone brilliantly. Inhaling and exhaling his breath he stirred up the waters of dissolution. The shining manes covered his beautiful cheeks and shoulders. He was embellished in gemset

202. Manu. 1. 10

jewels of various sorts. He shone like clustering clouds with lightning.

30. Then the boar that resembled a mountain shone well as if he had reached the foot of the lord.

31. Then he lifted the Earth sunk under water and held it on his curved fangs. He rose up from the nether worlds.

32. On seeing him, the Siddhas, sages and other human beings rejoiced and danced. They scattered flowers on his head.

33. The body of the Boar covered up with flowers shone like the mountain of collyrium with glow-worms falling on it.

34. The Boar brought the earth to its own place. It then assumed his natural form and fixed it there.

35. He levelled the earth, fixed the mountains and set up the four worlds on the earth as before.

36. Thus after lifting the earth along with the mountains from the midst of the vast sea of dissolution the lord created the universe—the mobile and immobile beings.

CHAPTER TWELVE

(*The description of creation*)

Vāyu said:—

1. At the time of meditation while he was pondering intelligently, delusion in the form of darkness appeared before him.

2. Darkness, delusion, great delusion, blinding darkness and ignorance; the five appeared before the noble lord.

3. While he was meditating, the creation was ramified into five, enveloped all round by darkness as in a seed vessel (?)

4. Both within and without it was devoid of light benumed and unconscious. It had no intellect, faces and sense-organs.

5-6. Hence this creation became stationary consisting of trees and mountains. On seeing that this creation did not multiply Brahmā was dissatisfied. He began conceiving and meditating a second time. While he meditated, the lower animals came into being.

7. These animals had light within but not without. They had the form of animals and went a wrong path.

8. When this creation too proved ineffective the creation of the gods of the Sāttvika type took place.

9. Men had plenty of pleasure, were not concealed but had light within and light without. They had innate consciousness too.

10. Again he meditated and from the unmanifest evolved the human creation which had a downward trend. Though effective it was full of misery.

11-13. The human beings had light within and light without. They had Tamas and Rajas in abundance. The fifth creation appeared in four forms in respect of Viparyaya, Śakti, Tuṣṭi and Siddhi. These had no possessions, being of different species, prone to eating and drinking, were known as Bhūtas etc.

14. The first creation of Brahmā is that of Mahat; the second is that of subtle elements and is called Bhūtasarga; the third is known as organic.

15. The primary creation took place without the intervention of intellect. The fourth was the creation of immobile beings.

16-17. The fifth was the creation of animal kingdom; the sixth of gods; the seventh of human beings. The eighth is called Anugraha and the ninth Kumāra.

18. The first three creations are primary. They work without intelligence. The five secondary creations function intelligently.

19-20. Brahmā had in the beginning created four sons: Sanaka, Sananda, Sanātana and Sanatkumāra. These are known as yogins free from passion and jealousy.

21-22. They were not interested in the activity of creation because their minds were drawn towards the lord. When Sanaka and others disinterested in creation had left the world,

Brahmā, desirous of creation, performed penance. Though he performed penance nothing happened.

23. When a long time elapsed he was distressed and his distress turned into anger. From the eyes of the infuriated Brahmā drops of tears fell.

24. From these goblins and ghosts emerged. On seeing these born of tears Brahmā censured himself.

25. As a result of anger and annoyance he fell into swoon. Then the enraged Brahmā cast off his breath.

26. Then Rudra, the lord of vital breaths, appeared through the mouth of Brahmā in order to confer unequalled favour.

27. Lord Rudra divided himself into eleven Ātmans. When these appeared they were addressed by him.

28-29. O dear, you have been created by me for blessing the worlds. Hence endeavour assiduously for the establishment and benefit of the world and for its progeny. Thus spoken to, they cried and ran all round.

30. In view of their crying and flight they are called Rudras. Rudras are vital breaths and vital breaths are Rudras.

31. Then Rudra, the merciful son of Brahmā, bestowed vital breaths on Brahmā.

32. Rudra was delighted at the return of Brahmā to life. He spoke to Brahmā.

33. O Brahmā, preceptor of the worlds, do not be afraid. Your vital breaths have been resuscitated by me. O one of good rites, get up comfortably.

34-35 On hearing these words as if heard in dreams Brahmā glanced at Rudra, his eyes shedding lustre of lotuses, when the vital breath returned to him. With palms joined in reverence he spoke in pleasing but majestic tone.

36. "Indeed by your very vision you delight my mind. Who are you, sir, standing in cosmic form dividing yourself into eleven forms?"

37. On hearing his words, Śiva lord of the gods touched Brahmā with his pleasing hands and spoke.

38. Know me as the great Ātman, born as your son. The eleven Rudras have come to protect you well.

39. Hence shake off this lethargy through my blessing. Be wakeful. It behoves you to create beings as before.

40. When the lord spoke thus, Brahmā was pleased. He eulogised Rudra with the eight names.

Brahmā said:—

41-43. (i) Obeisance O lord Rudra, with the splendour of the sun; to lord Bhava the taste, of the form of water; to Śarva of the form of the earth, Nandin the bull; to Īśa, Vasu in the form of touch, to the lord of Paśus, to the fire-god of great brilliance, to Bhīma in the form of ether, the sound, the subtle element, to Ugra of terrible features in the form of the sacrificer, to Mahādeva with Umā and the moon. Obeisance to the lord of eight forms.

44. After eulogising Mahādeva, Brahmā, the grandfather of the worlds requested the lord after due homage.

45. O lord of the past and the future, O Rudra, my son, it was for the creation that you the destroyer of the cupid were born out of my limbs.

46. Hence, O lord of the universe, help me in this task. It behoves you to create beings everywhere.

47. Thus requested by him Rudra, the suppressor of the Tripuras, consented to his proposal.

48. Then Brahmā congratulated him. Permitted by him Brahmā created people.

49. He mentally created Marīci, Bhṛgu, Aṅgiras, Pulastya, Pulaha, Kratu, Dakṣa, Atri and Vasiṣṭha. He created Dharma and Saṁkalpa too.

50. These are the twelve sons of Brahmā including Rudra. They are the ancient householders.

51. Their families are twelve including the gods. Endowed with progeny and holy rites they are embellished by the sages.

52-53. Then he created the four—the gods, Asuras, Pitṛs and the human beings. Desirous of creating these,

Brahmā set himself to the task of creation along with Rudra. He created the gods from his face and the pitṛs from the sides.

54. From his loins he created the Asuras; from the organ of generation the human beings. The Rākṣasas overwhelmed by hunger were born of his privities.

55. Strong night-prowlers with Tamas and Rajas prominent were born as his sons. The serpents, Yakṣas, Bhūtas and Gandharvas were born.

56. The crows were created from the sides, birds from his chest, goats from the face and serpents from the sides.

57. From his feet were born the horses, elephants, Śarabhas, wild oxen, deer, camels, mules, stags and other animals.

58-62. Medicinal herbs, fruits and roots were born of his hairs. From his eastern face he created Gāyatrī, Ṛks, Trivṛtsāma, Rathantara, Agniṣṭoma and other sacrifices. From his southern face he created Yajus Traiṣṭubha Chandas, the fifteen Stomas, Bṛhatsāma and Uktha. From his western face he created Sāman, Jagati Chandas, the seventeen Stomas, Vairūpya and Atirātra mantras. From his northern face he created the Atharva Veda, the twentyone Āptorvāman, Anuṣṭubh Chandas and the Vairāja. High and low animals and living beings were born of his different limbs.

63. Yakṣas, Piśācas, Gandharvas, Apsaras, human beings, Kinnaras, Rākṣasas, birds, deer and other animals, serpents etc. were born.

64. The mobile and immobile beings which were perishable and imperishable attained their activities.

65. Created again and again the beings retain their previous nature, violent or non-violent, soft or ruthless, virtuous or evil, true or false.

66-70. They attain birth with the impressions of their previous traits. The creator himself has assigned the variety and diversity to the elements, the sensual objects etc. He himself has assigned them names and forms through the Vedic texts. He has bestowed the names of the sages and the functions prescribed in the Vedas on those who were born at the close of the night. When a new season arrives its nature appears itself. So also when the new yuga arrives its nature appears along with it. Thus creation manifests itself through the limbs of Brahmā.

71-73. Beginning with intellect and ending with Viśeṣa this secondary creation is derived from Prakṛti itself. There in the Brahmavana which has the light of the moon and the sun, which is embellished by planets, stars, rivers, oceans, mountains and abounds in beautiful cities and countries the unmanifest Brahmā, having his source in the seed of Avyakta and blessed with the benign favour of the lord, the knower of all, moves about.

74-75. The eternal tree in the form of Brahmā shall be resorted to by all. The cosmic intellect is its main stem as well as its branch; the sense-organs its inner hollows; the great elements characterize its size; the Viśeṣa is its tender sprout; Dharma and Adharma its good flowers; happiness and misery its fruits.

76. Wise men say that the heaven is his head; the sky his navel; the sun and the moon his eyes; the quarters his ears and the earth his feet. That unponderable soul is the maker of all living beings.

77. Brahmins are born of his mouth: the Kṣatriyas of his chest, the Vaiśyas of his thighs; the Śūdras of his feet. All the castes are born of his body.

CHAPTER THIRTEEN

(*The creation of Brahmā and Viṣṇu*)

The sages said:—

1. Sir, you have narrated the creation of the great Ātman through the mouth of the four-faced lord. There we have a doubt.

2-6. The Odd-eyed Śiva is the foremost among the gods. The trident-bearing Śiva is brilliant. Lord Rudra the Kālātman is Kapardin and Nīlalohita. When the end of the yuga arrives he becomes infuriated and annihilates this universe including Brahmā, Viṣṇu and the fire-god. He makes the worlds shrink. Brahmā and Viṣṇu are under his control. They make obeisance to him out of fright. He is the lord who formerly created Brahmā and Viṣṇu from his limbs. He alone is the cause of acquisition and retention. He is the primordial and ancient god. How did such a lord become the son of Brahmā who is born of Avyakta?

7. We have also heard that Brahmā and Viṣṇu were born of Rudra and created Rudra. Thus they mutually created each other.

8. How could the two, progenitors of the living beings, come out of each other thereby possessing both prominence or otherwise?

9. There is nothing unseen or unheard by you. Every thing is remembered by you who had been the disciple of the lord himself.

10. Please narrate how Brahmā became the lord of all sages. O dear, we are faithful and eager to hear the great glory of the lord.

Vāyu said:—

11. O Brahmins, this question has been well put by you, experts in the art of queries. I had put the same query to Brahmā who replied suitably.

12. I shall narrate how Rudra was born and how Brahmā and Viṣṇu were born from each other.

13-15. The three are the Ātmans as causes born of Maheśvara; they are the causes of creation, sustenance and annihilation of the universe consisting of the mobile and immobile beings. Endowed with great qualities they are sanctified by the great lord. Presided over by his Śakti they can always perform their activities. Brahmā can create; Viṣṇu can protect; Rudra can annihilate.

16-21. But they rivalled with one another. Desirous of excelling one another they propitiated their father, the supreme lord by means of penance. Attaining all round favour of the lord at the outset in a former Kalpa, Rudra created Brahmā and Viṣṇu. In another Kalpa, Brahma created Rudra and Viṣṇu. In another Kalpa Viṣṇu created Rudra and Brahmā. Thus in different Kalpas, Brahmā, Viṣṇu and Rudra desiring mutual benefit are born of one another. Based on the events in their respective Kalpas, their process in being the cause of origin of one another is extolled by the sages. Now listen to their holy and wonderful story that releases from sins.

22-26. Listen also to what happened to Brahmā in his Kalpa. In the Kalpa, Meghavāhana, Viṣṇu became a cloud and showered the earth for a thousand divine years. Seeing this, Śiva gave imperishable Śakti to Viṣṇu. Obtaining the Śakti from Śiva Viṣṇu created the universe along with Brahmā. On seeing that glory of Viṣṇu, Brahmā created by him was seized by jealousy and said derisively. Go you, O Viṣṇu. The cause of your origin is known to me. Rudra is superior to both of us. There is no doubt in this.

27. It is due to the grace of that lord that you, the sustainer, have become a creator today.

28. I too shall propitiate Rudra, the leader of gods, by means of penance and shall create the entire universe along with you. There is no doubt in this.

29. Slighting Viṣṇu thus, Brahmā attained Śiva by means of penance and submitted to him thus.

30. O lord of the gods, O lord of the universe, Viṣṇu is born of your left and I am born of your right side.

31. Still Viṣṇu created the universe along with me. Due to rivalry he was taunted by me depending on the strength of your support.

32. "O Viṣṇu, your piety towards the lord is not more than that of mine" (I told him) because our origin from you is on the same footing.

33. O Śiva, it behoves you to give all that to me also in the manner you bestowed on him before due to his devotion.

34. Thus implored by him the merciful lord Śiva gave all to him as justifiable.

35. Thus obtaining the state of being the Atman of all in a trice, from Śiva, Brahmā hastened to and saw Viṣṇu.

36-41. He saw Viṣṇu lying on Śeṣa[203] in his abode in the milk-ocean.[204] A white canopy resembling the sun was spread. It was created by him mentally. It was set with gold and gems. Lord Viṣṇu had eyes resembling lotus. He had splendid body with four arms. He was bedecked in ornaments. He was holding conch and discus. His face shone like the disc of the moon. The scar Śrīvatsa marked his chest. He was smiling sweetly. His lotus-like feet attained red hue due to the contact of the lotus-like Lakṣmī. In Yogic slumber he appeared lying in the nectarine milky ocean. By the Guṇa of Tamas he was Kālarudra; by that of Rajas he was Brahmā; by that of Sattva he was Viṣṇu. In Nirguṇa state he was lord Śiva. On seeing him Brahmā spoke seriously—"O Viṣṇu, I am going to devour you as you did me formerly."

42. On hearing this Viṣṇu woke up, saw Brahmā and smiled slightly.

43. In the meantime Viṣṇu was devoured by Brahmā and immediately created through the middle of the eyebrows.

44-47. In the meantime the moon-crested lord came to the place to test their Śakti. Though devoid of form he assumed a form in order to bless them as he had previously done. Both of them were delighted and frightened and so eulogised the lord and bowed to him with respect from a distance. The trident-bearing lord blessed them and vanished even as they watched him with respect.

203. The milky ocean is supposed to be identical with the Sea of Japan. See "geo. of the Purāṇas," PP. 42-44.

204. Skt texts abound in descriptions of Visnu reclining on Serpent Śeṣa. In this context, it may be noted that there is a vivid picture of Śeṣaśāyī Viṣṇu on the outer wall of the Dasāvatāra temple at Deogarh (c. 5th cent. A.D)

CHAPTER FOURTEEN

(*The manifestation of Rudras*)

Vāyu said:—

1. I shall expain the reasons for the manifestation of Rudra in every Kalpa whereby the broken series of Brahmā's creation is resumed.

2. After creating the subjects in every Kalpa, Brahmā born of the cosmic egg felt excessively distressed. He was deluded.

3-4. In order to pacify his misery and to multiply his subjects, in the various Kalpas, Rudra, Brahmā's younger brother, becomes the son of Brahmā and blesses him.

5. He alone is lord Īśa, a mass of splendour, free from ailment, devoid of beginning and end, the creator and the lord making all living beings shrink.

6. Endowed with lordly qualities, he is purified by Parameśvara. He is presided over by his Śakti and marked by his symbols.

7. He has the same name, the same form; he can perform his task; he has same function as he maintains and abides by his commands.

8. He resembles a thousand suns, he is bedecked in crescent moon. Serpents constitute his necklaces, shoulderlets and bangles.

9. He is brilliant holding the skulls of asura Jalandhara, Brahmā, and Indra, his tawny hair, moustache and beard are drenched in the surging waves of Gaṅgā.

10. His lips shine with the tips being hit by the sharp-pointed curved fangs; his ear-rings make a halo around his left ear.

11. He is seated on a great bull; his voice sounds like thunder. He is lustrous like fire, his strength and exploits are great.

12. He whose features are hideous in this manner and who is born as the son af Brahmā bestows wisdom on him and co-operates with him in the activity of creation.

13. It is due to his grace that the creation in every Kalpa functions as a perpetual series.

14. Once, when requested by Brahmā to create, he mentally created all beings exactly like himself.

15. All of them had matted hair; they were free from fear and distress, had blue necks and three eyes, were free from decaying age and death; they had shining tridents as their excellent weapons.

16. The fourteen worlds of the universe were filled up by them. On seeing these various Rudras, Brahmā spoke to Śiva.

17. "Obeisance to you, O lord of gods, do not create such subjects. Welfare to you. Create other subjects that may be endowed with death."

18. When told thus, the lord replied to Brahmā, "Such a creation is not my task. You alone create inauspicious beings.

19. The noble beings of great strength created by me mentally will walk about in my company. They will regulate the sacrifices."

20. After saying thus to the creator, Śiva the lord of living beings desisted from creation and remained in the company of Rudras.

21. From that time onwards the lord does not procreate auspicious beings. He stands in Yogic trance till the dissolution of the universe.

CHAPTER FIFTEEN

(*Song of Prayer addressed to Śiva and Śivā*)

Vāyu said:—

1. When the creation of Brahmā did not multiply Brahmā thought of creation by the process of sexual intercourse.

2. Since the race of women had not emanated from the lord formerly, Brahmā could not produce creation through sexual intercourse.

3. Then he finally resolved that the lord should be asked in respect of multiplying the subjects.

4. Thinking that without his grace the subjects will not increase, Brahmā began to perform penance.

5-7. His primordial eternal Śakti is subtle, pure, pleasant and intelligible only through piety; it is devoid of attributes, unsullied, unramified unruffled, perpetual and it ever remains with Īśvara. Thus Brahmā pondered over the lord and his great Śakti and performed penance.

8. Ere long the lord was pleased with Brahmā who was endowed with severe penance.

9. Becoming half-female[205] after introducing certain parts into a certain image, the lord himself came there.

10-15. On seeing the lord, Brahmā eulogised him as well as the goddess, with hymns full of subtle meaning—the lord who is beyond darkness, is eternal, without a second, incomprehensible, invisible to the libertine, the creator, overlord, endowed with the creative power, who is beyond arguments, has no fallacious appearance, is immeasurable, unaging, stable, unmoving, devoid of attributes, quiescent. possessed of infinity, omnipresent, bestower of boons, devoid of difference between the Existent and the non-Existent, incomparable, worthy of being sought refuge and permanent. He prostrated before him and then stood up with palms joined with reverence. He eulogised him with faith and humility by means of hymns of subtle, sweet, refined and pious meanings that explained the Vedic texts.

Brahmā said:—

16. O lord, be victorious. O Īśvara, O Maheśvara, splendid with attributes, be victorious.

17. O auspicious goddess, O heroine of Prakṛti and the one beyond Prakṛti and naturally beautiful, be victorious.

18. O lord of fruitful Māyā, of fruitful will, of great sports and of fruitful strength, be victorious.

19. O mother of the universe, O goddess identical with the universe, O creator and companion of the universe, be victorious.

205 See P. 1075 note

20. Be victorious, O lord of eternal prosperity and permanent abode. Be victorious, O lord of eternal form. Be victorious, O lord of permanent devotees.

21. Be victorious O creatress, protectress, annihilatress and the heroine of the three Ātmans.

22. Be victorious, O lord ready to survey, enlarge the universe. Be victorious, O lord from whose terrible glance rises the fire that consumes all the worlds.

23. Be victorious, O goddess incomprehensible to the gods and others, O goddess that shinest brilliantly with your subtle vision. Be victorious, O goddess the part of the gross Śakti of the Ātman. Be victorious, O goddess pervading the mobile and immobile beings.

24. Be victorious. O lord merging various principles of the universe into one. Be victorious, O lord the groups of whose followers have stepped on the heads of Asuras.

25. Be victorious, O goddess affording protection to those who resort to you. Be victorious, O goddess who uproot the spirits of the poisonous tree of worldly existence.

26. Be victorious, O lord enhancing prosperity, prowess and heroism. Be victorious, O lord, stationed beyond the universe, O lord who hast quelled the might of the enemies.

27. Be victorious, O immortal lord who hast laid the rite of "five objects." Be victorious, O goddess having the form of the hymn with the knowledge of the "five objects."

28. Be victorious, O lord, the physician par excellence for the great suffering of the terrible worldly existence. Be victorious, O goddess the moon-light for the layers of darkness of ignorance, the primordial dirt.

29. Be victorious, O black fire that consumed the Tripuras. Be victorious, O goddess Tripurabhairavī. Be victorious, O lord devoid of three attributes. Be victorious O goddess, the possessor of three attributes.

30. Be victorious, O omniscient one. Be victorious, O goddess enlightening every one. Be victorious O lord having prolific divine limbs. Be victorious, O goddess bestowing all desires.

31. O lord, where is your great splendour and where the worthless words of ours. Still O lord, forgive me that babble but with devotion.

32. After eulogising with these and similar hymns the four-faced lord, the creator of the universe bowed again and again to Rudra and Rudrāṇī.

33. This holy and excellent hymn "Ardhanārīśvara Stotra" uttered by Brahmā enhances the delight of Śiva and Śivā.

34. He who recites this with devotion or teaches to anyone whatsoever reaps the fruit thereof as a result of the pleasure of Śiva and Śivā.

35. I bow to Śiva and Śivā the sanctifiers of living beings in the entire universe; the couple whose bodies are devoid of birth and death and who have taken the bodies of an excellent man and a youthful maiden.

CHAPTER SIXTEEN

(*The manifestation of divine śakti*)

Vāyu said :—

1-3. Then the delighted god Śiva spoke to Brahmā with a benign and sweet smile. His voice sounded like thunder. All the letters were sweet, majestic, soft, clear, full and rich in meanings. They had royal qualities being pure and efficient in the protection of all subjects.

Lord Śiva said :—

4. Dear child, O fortunate one, the gravity of your statements has been understood by me.

5. It is for the increase in the number of the subjects that this penance has been performed by you. I am delighted with your penance. I shall grant you what you desire.

6. After this sweet and liberal speech the excellent lord created the goddess from a part of his body.

7. It is the goddess whom scholars of the Vedas call

the greatest Śakti endowed with the divine qualities of Śiva the great soul.

8. It was the goddess in whom there is neither birth, nor death nor old age nor other similar things. It was the goddess who manifested herself from the body of Śiva.

9. She from whom words recede along with the mind and the sense-organs,[206] appeared to be born of a part of the body of her husband.

10. The goddess who pervades everything through her greatness was seen like a wonderfully embodied being.

11. It is she who fascinates the entire universe with her Māyā. Really she is unborn but she appeared to be born of Śiva.

12. Her great form is not visible even to the gods. Such a great goddess of all the gods was divided in the body of her lord.

13-14. On seeing the great omniscient, omnipresent subtle goddess, devoid of the difference between Sat and Asat, the goddess who illuminates the universe with her brilliance, Brahmā bowed and prayed.

Brahmā said :—

15. O Goddess in the beginning I was created by the lord and employed in the activity of the creation. I create the universe.

16. O Goddess, the gods and others are mentally created by me. Though they are created again and again they do not increase in number.

17. Hereafter I wish to increase the number through copulation.

18. The race of women has not emerged from you. Hence I cannot create an everlasting race of women.[207]

19-22. Śaktis originate from you. Hence I worship you alone who bestow Śaktis upon everyone everywhere, who grant boons and who are Māyā and the goddess of the gods. O omnipresent goddess for the increase of the mobile

206 Cp. Vāyavīya S. 3. 1.

207 Cp. Ch. 15. V. 2.

and immobile beings, please be born with a part of yours, as the daughter of Dakṣa my son. Thus requested by Brahmā the goddess created a Śakti equal in splendour to herself from the middle of her eyebrows. Lord Śiva looked at her laughingly and spoke.

23-25. "After propitiating Brahmā with penance you shall carry out what he desires". The Śakti obeyed the lord. At the instance of Brahmā she became the daughter of Dakṣa. After giving the incomparable Śakti in the form of Brahman to Brahmā, the goddess re-entered the body of the lord. The lord vanished. Since that time the enjoyment of sexual pleasures in women was established.

26. O leading brahmins, procreation functions through copulation. O leading sages, Brahmā too was satisfied.

27. Thus the manifestation of Śakti has been narrated to you. It enhances merit. It shall be narrated with the story of creation.

28. He who recites this every day attains merits and obtains worthy sons.

CHAPTER SEVENTEEN

(*The Narrative of Creation*)

Vāyu said :—

1-2. Securing the great and eternal Śakti from the lord and desiring to initiate the process of procreation by copulation, Brahmā became a wondrous man in one half and a woman in one half. From the woman-half was born Śatarūpā.[208]

3. The man-half created Virāja, called Svāyambhuva Manu, the first creation.

4. Performing a difficult penance the gentle Śatarūpā got the Manu of bright fame as her husband.

208. Rudra S. I. 16. 11-12.

5. Śatarūpā bore him two sons, priyavrata and Uttānapāda.

6. She bore two daughters of great fortune from whom emanates all creation. They were Ākūti and Prasūti.

7. Lord Manu gave Prasūti to Dakṣa. Brahmā gave Ākūti to Ruci.

8. The mental son Ruci begot of Ākūti a son Yajña and a daughter Daksiṇā. The two make the universe whirl.

9. Lord Dakṣa begot of Prasūti, the daughter of Svāyambhuva, twentyfour daughters called the mothers of the world.

10-16. Lord Dharma took thirteen of his daughters as his wives. They were Śraddhā, Lakṣmī, Dhṛti, Puṣṭi, Tuṣṭi, Medhā, Kriyā, Buddhi, Lajjā, Vapu, Śānti, Siddhi and Kīrti the thirteenth. The other eleven were Khyāti, Satī, Asambhūti, Smṛti, Prīti, Kṣamā, Sannati, Anasūyā, Ūrjā, Svāhā and Svadhā. O sages, the sages Bhṛgu, Śarva, Marīci, Aṅgiras, Pulaha, Kratu, Pulastya, Atri, Vasiṣṭha, Pāvaka and the Pitṛs married them. Thirteen sons beginning with Kāma and ending with Yaśas were begotten by Dharma of Śraddhā and others happy and conducive to happiness. Nikṛti and others were begotten of Hiṁsā by Adharma. They bore the traits of Adharma and were conducive to unhappiness. They had no wives or sons. They practised no virtue.

17-21. The Tāmasa creation was controlled by Dharma. Dakṣa's daughter Satī, wife of Rudra cast off her body as daughter of Dakṣa in the context of the insult offered to her husband. She rebuked Dakṣa and Dakṣa's wife and their kinsmen. She was born as the daughter of Menā and Himavat. On seeing Satī how Rudra created many Rudras with lustres similar to his, has already been narrated. Bhṛgu begot of Khyāti the daughter Lakṣmī who became the wife of Viṣṇu.He begot two sons Dhātṛ and Vidhātṛ who became the founders of Manvantara. Their progeny is numerous, in hundreds and thousands.

22. The descendants of Bhṛgu lived in the Svāyambhuva Manvantara. Sambhūti, son of Marīci, gave birth to a son Paurṇamāsa.

23. He had four daughters and descendants large in number. In that family was born Kaśyapa who had many sons.

24-25. Smṛti, wife of Aṅgiras, bore two sons Āgnīdhra and Śarabha and four daughters. Their progeny continued in thousands. Dantogni was born as the son of Prīti the wife of Pulastya. He was Agastya in the previous birth in the Svāyambhuva Manvantara.

26-27. His descendants famous as Paulastyas were many. Kṣamā bore sons to Pulaha the Prajāpati. The three known as Kardama, Āsuri and Sahiṣṇu had the splendour of the sacrificial fires. Their race is well established.

28. Sannati, wife of Kratu, bore him sons who were equal to Kratu. They did not marry and hence were issueless.

29. They were sixty thousand in number and known as Vālakhilyas. They surround the sun and go ahead of his charioteer.

30. Atri's wife Anasūya bore five sons the Ātreyas and a daughter Śruti, the mother of Śaṅkhapada.

31. The glorified five Ātreyas are Satyanetra, Havya, Āpomūrti, Śanaiścara and Soma.

32. The sons and grandsons of the noble Ātreyas are in hundreds and thousands. They lived in the Svāyambhuva Manvantara.

33-34. Seven sons were born to Vasiṣṭha in Ūrjā and a daughter Puṇḍarīkā. They were Rajas, Gātra, Ūrdhvabāhu, Savana, Anaya, Sutapas and Śukra.

35. Their descendants with the names of Vasiṣṭha were in hundreds and hundred millions all in Svāyambhuva Manvantara.

36. This is the creation of the sages. It is impossible to mention this in detail.

37. Svāhā, wife of the fire-god the mental son of Brahmā in the form of Rudra, bore three sons of unmeasured splendour.

38. They are Pāvaka, Pavamāna and Śuci. Pavamāna is the fire kindled by attrition. Pāvaka is the fire produced by lightning.

39-40. The solar fire is called Śuci. Their sons in order are:—Havyavāha, Kavyavāha and Saharakṣas. They are the deities, manes and gods. Their sons and grandsons are fortynine.

41. They are propitiated in the three rites Kāmya, Naimittika and Nitya. They shall be known as saintly observing holy rites.

42-43. These are in the form of Rudra and devoted to him. Whatever is offered in fire by whomsoever it may be is the offering to Rudra. This is the decision in regard to the fires stated in order.

44-47. O Brahmins, I shall describe the manes now but not in detail. The manes preside over the seasons. Hence the Vedas declare "The seasons are the Pitṛs". The mobile and immobile beings are created in the seasons. Hence it is mentioned in the Śruti, "The things produced in the seasons are the Pitṛs."[209] Noble persons derive prosperity from the Pitṛs who preside over the seasons. They stand in contact with the clouds. The Pitṛs are of two types : Agniṣvāttas and Barhisads.

48-49. Householders are also of two types : Non-sacrificers, and Sacrificers. Svadhā bore the Pitṛs two daughters : Menā and Dharaṇī who uphold the universe. Menā was the daughter of Agniṣvāttas and Dharaṇī the daughter of Barhiṣads.

50. Menā, wife of Himavat, gave birth to Maināka, Krauñca, Gaṅgā and Gaurī sanctified by the embrace of Śiva's body.

51. Dharaṇī, wife of Meru, gave birth to Mandara abounding in divine herbs and beautiful peaks of variegated forms.

52. Mandara the glorious son of Meru became the abode of Śiva due to the strength of penance.

53. Dharaṇī gave birth to three famous daughters Velā, Niyati and Āyati.

54. Āyati and Niyati became the wives of the sons of Bhṛgu. I have mentioned to you about their race in Svāyambhuva Manvantara.

209. VS. 17.3

55. Velā bore Sāgara the holy daughter Savarṇā who became the wife of Prācīnabarhiṣ.

56. Sāmudrī bore Prācīnabarhiṣ ten sons who were called Prācetasas. They were the masters of the science of archery.

57. Dakṣa in Svāyambhuva Manvantara became the son of the Prācetasas in the Cākṣuṣa Manvantara due to the curse of Śiva.

58-59. Thus the divine families, attended upon by the devas, of the noble-souled sons of Brahmā, Dharma and others, have been described by me, O Brahmins. They observed holy rites. They had progenies and were embellished by great prosperity.

60. This creation born of the Prajāpatis cannot be enumerated even in hundreds of crores of years.

61. Holy royal families function in two different lines viz. the solar and the lunar.

62. Iksvāku, Ambarīṣa, Yayāti, Nahuṣa and others belong to those families well known and reputed.

63. There are several other saintly kings of different exploits. Of what avail is their detailed enuneration. ?

64. Moreover, in the context of the story of lord Śiva, the eulogy of royal families is not approved of by good men. Thus I do not attempt to speak much.

65. Being relevant so far as it implies the greatness of lord Śiva, I have mentioned creation. Enough of those details too.

CHAPTER EIGHTEEN

(*The abandonment of the body by Satī*)

The sages said :—

1. How did the goddess, daughter of Dakṣa become the daughter of Himavat and Menā after abandoning the body born of Dakṣa ?

2. How was Rudra censured by Dakṣa the noble soul? What could be the cause whereby Śiva was censured?

3. O wind-god, formerly in the Cākṣuṣa Manvantara how was Dakṣa born due to the curse of Śiva? Please narrate.

Vayū said :—

4. Please listen. I shall narrate the activity of the mean Dakṣa resulting in his insult to all gods due to his sinful blunder.

5. Once formerly, all the gods, Asuras, Siddhas and the sages went to the summit of Himavat in order to see the lord.

6. O Brahmins, the lord and the goddess were seated on a divine seat as they granted interview to the gods and others.

7. At the same time Dakṣa too had accompanied the gods in order to see Śiva his son-in-law and the goddess his own daughter.

8. In view of their dignity, the lord and the Goddess did not give any special preferential treatment to Dakṣa.

9. But deluded that he was, Dakṣa did not realise the greatness of the lord and the goddess. Thinking her to be his daughter he began to nurse a grudge and hatred against her.

10. Due to this enmity and further incited by Brahmā, Dakṣa after initiation did not invite them in the sacrifice.

11. He invited the other sons-in-law and honoured them severally.

12. On hearing from Nārada that they had assembled there, Satī went to her father's abode after informing Rudra.

13-19. She stepped into the aeroplane along with her dear friends. It was a divine plane with doors on all sides; had good conditions; could be easily mounted. It was very charming. It shed golden lustre. It was studded with jewels of various sorts and had a canopy covered with pearls. It was decorated with stringed flower garlands. It had been wrought in molten gold; hundreds of be-jewelled pillars supported it all round. The adamantine steps were neatly built. The columns and festoons were decorated with corals. The chief seat therein was studded with gems and covered with a silken cloth with flower-designs. Through every aperture rays of diamonds were diffused; a good gemset platform without dents shone. A flagstaff as pure as cloud decorated its front with the sign of the great Bull. It was studded with jewels. The main door was guarded by invincible Gaṇeśvaras wearing jewel-studded bodices and wielding canes in their hands. Many women, experts in playing on Mṛdaṅgas, flutes, Vīṇās and in music were seated there richly dressed and bedecked in ornaments.

20-21. Two Rudra virgins held the auspicious chowries and fans beautiful in their handles set with diamonds, and fanned the goddess. In the middle of the chowries the face of the goddess shone like a lotus in the midst of two fighting swans.

22-23. Sumālinī held over her head a pearl-stringed umbrella as white as the moon. The splendid umbrella shone above the face of the goddess as the moon s disc above the vessel of nectar.

24-25. Śubhāvatī of sweet smiling face sat in front of Satī and delighted her by playing at the game of dice. Suyaśas held the auspicious sandals of the goddess, studded with gems, in the middle of her breasts and served the goddess.

26-27. Another lady held the glistening mirror. Another held the fan. Another held the betelbox. Another held the charming parrot.

28. A certain lady held charming fragrant flowers. Another lotus-eyed lady held the repository of ornaments.

29-30. A certain lady held the unguent, good flowers and the auspicious collyrium. Other ladies did their respective duties. They sat around serving her. In their midst the goddess shone like the moon in the Autumn in the midst of a galaxy of stars.

31-32. Then after the blowing of the conch the great wardrum was sounded indicating the time of departure. Then hundreds of bugles and sweet-toned instruments sounded without being beaten (obstructed) along with the sounds of clapping the hands.

33-34. Then eight hundred groups of the thousand strong-armed Gaṇeśas equal in brilliance to lord Śiva went ahead. In their midst, the glorious chief of Gaṇas, honoured by the moon and Nandīśvara sat on the Bull like Bṛhaspati on an elephant.

35-37. The divine drums were sounded in heaven. Clouds were divinely pleasing. The sages danced. Siddhas and Yogins rejoiced. Everywhere on the way the clouds in association with the gods and others made showers of flowers above the canopy. The goddess entered her father's house as if in a moment.

38. On seeing her Dakṣa became infuriated which subsequently became the cause of his destruction. He worshipped her younger sisters too in an insulting manner(?)

39. Then the goddess spoke to her father in the midst of the assembly, relevantly unexcitedly and undemeaningly.

The goddess said:—

40. O father, the lord at whose bidding everyone from Brahmā to the Piśācas becomes subservient has not been duly worshipped.

41. Let that alone. Why did you slight me your eldest daughter in a despicable manner?

42. Thus addressed, the infuriated Dakṣa replied angrily "The younger daughters are better than you. They deserve my special reverence.

43. Their husbands evoke my respect and joy, for they are superior to your husband lord Śiva.

44. He is stiff-souled and you have resorted to him. So I dishonour you. He is antagonistic to me."

45. Thus insulted the infuriated goddess spoke to her father within the hearing of all present there.

46. O Dakṣa, you insult my husband the lord of the world, whose insult no one has hitherto made.

47. The Śruti says that these are great sinners—viz. a stealer of learning, a traitor to the preceptor and an insulter of the Vedas and of the god. They deserve to be punished.

48. Therefore a terrible punishment befitting the great sin shall be meted out to you by divine intercession.

49. Since the lord of gods has not been worshipped by you, know that your family is defiled and ruined.

50. After saying thus to her father Satī abandoned her body and without fear went to mountain Himavat.

51. The glorious leader of mountains attained the fruit of his merits. It was for her that he had performed penance for a long time.

52. The goddess blessed the lord of mountains. Through her Yogic Māyā and at her own will, she made him her father.

53. When Satī rebuked Dakṣa and went away, the frightened and agitated Mantras too vanished. The sacrifice became hindered.

54. On hearing about the departure of the goddess, Śiva was angry with Dakṣa and the sages and cursed them.

55-57. O Dakṣa, since for my sake the sinless Satī had been dishonoured and the other daughters worshipped along with their husbands, these sons-in-law of yours will be born but not of a womb in the sacrifices of Brahmā in the Vaivasvata Manvantara. In the Cākṣuṣa Manvantara you will become a king as the grandson of Prācinabarhiṣ and the son of Pracetas.

58. O wicked one, there also I shall put up obstacles before you in all activities regarding virtue, wealth and love.

59. Thus addressed by Rudra of unmeasured splendour, Dakṣa abandoned the body and fell on the ground.

60. Then in the Cāksusa Manvantara Daksa was born as the grandson of Prācinabarhiṣ and the son of Pracetas.

61. Bhṛgu and others were born in the Vaivasvata Manvantara in the sacrifice of Brahmā bearing the bodies of Varuṇa.

62. Then in the Vaivasvata Manvantara in the virtuous sacrifice of the wicked Dakṣa the lord created obstacles

CHAPTER NINETEEN

(The origin of Vīrabhadra)

The sages said:—

1. How did the lord create obstacles before the wicked Dakṣa who performed a sacrifice for virtue's sake? We wish to know this.

Vāyu said:—

2-4. When Himavat was delighted by becoming the father of the mother of the universe by the strength of his penance, when Śiva married her and sported with her in his abode on the peak of Himavat when a long time elapsed, in the Vaivasvata Manvantara Dakṣa as the son of Pracetas wanted to perform a horse-sacrifice.

5. On the top of Himavat in an auspicious spot at the source of Gaṅgā, frequented by the sages and the Siddhas Dakṣa began his sacrifice.

6. All the gods Indra and others gathered there and thought of going to attend the sacrifice.

7-8. The Ādityas, Vasus, Rudras, Sādhyas, Maruts, Ūṣmapās, Somapās, Ājyapās, Dhūmapās, Aśvins, Pitṛs, and the other sages came there along with Viṣṇu to take part in the sacrifice.

9. On seeing all the gods assembled there without Śiva, Dadhīca became angry. He spoke to Dakṣa thus.

Dadhīca said:—

10. Indeed that man incurs great sin who does not worship those who deserve worship and worships those who do not befit it.

11. Lord's terrible punishment[210] falls where the wicked are honoured and the good are dishonoured.

12. After saying this the sage spoke again to Dakṣa

210. The statement is reminiscent of the concept of Divine origin of punishment well expounded in the Bhīṣma-Yudhiṣṭhira dialogue in the ŚP of the MB.

"Why don't you worship the lord deserving worship, the lord of souls?"

Dakṣa said:—

13. I see eleven Rudras armed with tridents and having matted hair. I do not know anyone else as the lord.

Dadhīca said:—

14. What avails worshipping the gods in the sacrifice if the king of sacrifice, Rudra, is not worshipped by you?

15. He is unchanging, the creator of Brahmā, Viṣṇu and Rudra, to whom all from Brahmā to Piśācas, say "What shall we do?"

16. He is beyond all Prakṛtis and Puruṣa. He is meditated upon by Yogic scholars, sages and the seers of truthful principles.

17. He is the imperishable great Brahman, the Sat-Asat and Asat; devoid of beginning, middle and end, incomprehensible and eternal.

18. He is the creator, sustainer, and annihilator. I do not see any one else in the form of Śiva in the sacrifice.

Dakṣa said:—

19. I offer this Caru in the golden vessel, sanctified by mantras, after assigning the share to Viṣṇu the lord of sacrifice.

Dadhīca said:—

20. "O Dakṣa, since Rudra the lord of the chief of the gods is not propitiated your sacrifice will not be efficacious."

21. After saying this, the infuriated sage Dadhīca left for his hermitage.

22. Even when the sage walked out, the gods did not leave Dakṣa in view of the inevitability of the disaster that was to take place.

23. O brahmins, in the meantime knowing about all this from Śiva the goddess urged the lord to destroy the sacrifice of Dakṣa.

24. Urged by the goddess the lord created the heroic Vīrabhadra the chief of Gaṇas, intending to destroy the sacrifice.

25-33. He had a thousand faces, a thousand lotus-like eyes. He was holding a thousand iron clubs, thousands of arrows, spear, axe, mace, bow, discus and the thunderbolt. He looked fierce and terrible. The crescent moon adorned his crest; the thunderbolt illuminated his hands. His hair shone like lightning. He had a huge mouth terrible with the curved fangs and a huge belly. His tongue was like lightnings His lips hung down. His voice sounded like the cloud and th. ocean. He wore the tiger's hide dripping with blood. He ear-rings formed circles close to his cheeks. He had adorned his crest with the garlands from the heads of leading gods. He was bedecked in golden shoulderlets and jingling anklets. He was shining with heaps of gems. His chest was covered by necklaces. He was equal in exploit to the great fabulous animal Śarabha, tigers and lions. His gait was gentle and majestic as that of a stately elephant in rut. His lustre was white like conch, chowrie, Kunda flower, moon and the lotus-stalk. He was like the snow-capped lord of mountains who had become mobile. Flames surrounded him. Wearing pearl ornaments he shone brilliantly as the fire at the dissolution of the world.

34. That chief of Gaṇas knelt and bowed. With palms joined in reverence he stood beside the lord of gods.

35. With his anger he created Bhadrā the goddess Kālī as a witness of his activities and his companion.

36. On seeing Vīrabhadra standing like deadly fire in the company of Bhadrā, Śiva said "Welfare be to you."

37. He submitted to the lord in the company of the goddess. "Please command what task shall I carry out?"

38. Then with a desire to please Pārvatī, Śiva spoke to the huge-armed Vīrabhadra in raised sound.

The lord of gods said :—

39. O chief of Gaṇas, accompanied by Bhadrakālī, destroy the sacrifice of Dakṣa the son of Pracetas.

40. O chief of Gaṇas, I shall witness your exploit staying near Raibhya's[211] hermitage along with the goddess.

211. This sage, friend of Bharadvāja, had his hermitage on the Himālayas on the Ganges.

41-42. In the place Kanakhala[212] there are huge trees near Gaṅgādvāra[213] resembling the mountain with the golden peaks like Meru[214] and Mandara.[215] Dakṣa is holding sacrifice there. Immediately create obstacles in that sacrifice too. Do not delay.

43-44. When this was mentioned by the lord, the goddess, daughter of Himavat looked at Vīrabhadra and Bhadrakālī as does a cow at her calf Embracing him and sniffing at his head as at the head of Subrahmaṇya[216] she smiled and spoke in sweet voice

The goddess said :—

45. O dear Bhadra, O blessed one, of great strength and exploit, you are born to carry out the task that pleases me. Wipe off my anger and sorrow.

46. In view of his enmity Daksa is performing a sacrifice without inviting the lord of sacrifice. O chief of Ganas, split that sacrifice.

47. At my bidding O dear. inflict violence in the company of Bhadrā. Kill the sacrificer. Let the holy sacrifice be turned into non-sacrifice.

48. At the behest of Śiva and Śivā of wonderful activities, with bent head, as if it was their blessing, Bhadra bowed to them and left.

49-50. The infuriated lord Vīrabhadra, fond of cremation ground, created from his skin-pores chiefs of Gaṇas, and from his right hand hundred crores others.

51. He also created these from his feet, thighs, back,

212. It is a holy place of pilgrimage near Haradvāra. Here the patriarch Dakṣa is said to have performed the great sacrifice where Sati immolated herself.

213. Gaṅgādvāra, identical with Haradvāra is known by various names—Mokṣadvāra, Māyādvāra etc. See P. 1082 note, P. 1362 note.

214. See PP. 310 note, 623 note.

215. It is a mythical mountain but identified by some with the mountain of that name to the south of Bhagalpur in Bihar (ASR Vol. VIII. P. 130).

216. Kārttikeya is called six-faced, for he was fostered by the six Pleiads (Krittikas) as their offspring.

sides, mouth, throat, privities, heels, middle of the head, neck, face and belly.

52. Then the universe with all its open spaces and crevices was covered with the chiefs of gaṇas equal in exploit to Bhadra.

53. These had thousand hands holding thousands of weapons and had the lustre of Rudra.

54. They had spears, tridents and maces, axes, stones and rocks. They resembled deadly fire and Rudra. They had three eyes and matted hair.

55. They flew in hundreds and seated on lions roared loudly like clouds.

56. Lord Bhadra surrounded by the Bhadras shone like Kālabhairava surrounded by hundreds of deadly fires at the time of dissolution.

57. In their midst, mounted on a lordly bull and with a bull-emblem, lord Bhadra went ahead like Śiva seated on Nandin.

58. When Bhadra was seated on the bull, Bhasitaprabha held the pearl umbrella and the white chowries.

59. Bhasita shone by the side of Bhadra like the lord of mountains by the side of Śiva.

60. Bhadra too shone in his company as he held the white chowries like the lord with the trident weapon and the crescent moon.

61. Bhānukampa of great splendour bedecked in gold and jewels blew on the auspicious white conch Bhadra in front of Bhadra.

62. The divine drums were sounded with divine tumultuous tone. The clouds in hundreds made showers of flowers on his head.

63. Winds taking up the fragrance of full blown flowers pregnant with honey blew favourbly on their way.

64. Then the elated chiefs proud of their strength danced, rejoiced, cried, laughed, spoke and sang.

65. Then Bhadra stationed in the midst of the Bhadraganas in the company of Bhadrā shone like Śiva in the midst of Rudraganas in the company of Pārvatī.

66. In a moment the strong Vīrabhadra with his

followers entered the golden gate of the sacrificial altar.

67. Then the chief of Gaṇas Bhadra entered like Rudra desirous of burning the worlds at the time of dissolution.

CHAPTER TWENTY

(*The destruction of Dakṣa's sacrifice*)

Vāyu said :—

1. Then he saw the great Satra of the gods of great splendour the chief of whom was Visnu. The satra had all the paraphernalia—the flags of various colours etc.

2. Good grass was scattered in straight lines. The sacrificial fire was well-kindled. It was embellished with glittering sacrificial vessels of gold.

3. The rites were performed neatly in accordance with the rules found in the Vedas by the sages who were experts in sacrifices and who performed the rites properly.

4. Thousands of celestial damsels were there. The Satra was attended by the Apsaras. The sweet sound of flutes and lutes spread and was enhanced by the sound of Vedic hymns.

5. On seeing all this, the heroic Vīrabhadra of great exploits roared like a lion or a majestic rumbling cloud.

6. Then a hurrah of joy, filling the sky and superseding the sound of the ocean was produced by the lords of gaṇas.

7. Overwhelmed by the great sound the frightened heaven-dwellers ran helter-skelter dropping their garments and ornaments.

8. "Has the great Meru been burst ? Is the earth pierced through ? What is this ?" the gods began to scream and shout.

9. Some abandoned their lives due to fear like lordly elephants in a thick forest on hearing the roar of the lion.

10. Mountains crumbled. The earth quaked. Winds rolled and reeled. The ocean was agitated.

11. Fires did not blaze. The sun did not shine. Neither the planets nor the stars nor the other luminary bodies shone.

12. In the meantime lord Bhadra in the company of Bhadras and the goddess Bhadrā reached the brilliant sacrificial altar.

13. On seeing him, Dakṣa stood steady and firm though he was frightened. He spoke angrily "Who are you? What do you wish?"

14-15. On hearing the words of the wicked Dakṣa, Vīrabhadra of great splendour and of majestically rumbling sound like the cloud smilingly looked at Dakṣa, the gods and the Ṛtviks. He spoke the relevent words full of meaning without the least excitement.

Vīrabhadra said :—

16. We are the followers of lord Śiva of great splendour. We have come for our share. May that be given to us.

17. If the share has not been allotted to us in the sacrifice let the reason be mentioned or let the gods fight with me.

18. When they were told thus by the chief of Gaṇas the gods headed by Dakṣa said—"The mantras are our authorities. We are not the lords."

19. The Mantras said—"O gods, your minds are oppressed by Tamas. Hence you do not deserve the first share. Worship lord Śiva."

20. Though advised by the Mantras the gods with deluded minds did not offer the share to Bhadra. They desired to drop him out.

21. When their truthful and wholesome words went in vain the Mantras turned away from that place and went to the eternal Brahmaloka.

22-23. Then the chief of Gaṇas spoke to the gods headed by Viṣṇu, "You have not accepted the mantras being proud of your strength. Since we have been dishonoured by the gods thus in this sacrifice, I will drive out your arrogance along with your lives."

24. After saying thus the infuriated lord burnt the sacrificial altar with the fire of his eyes as Śiva had burnt the three Puras.[217]

25-26. Then the lords of gaṇas of mountain-like huge bodies uprooted the sacrificial posts and tied them to the necks of the Hotṛ priests by means of ropes. They broke and powdered the sacrificial vessels of various shapes and sizes dissolved them in water and hurled all the appendages of the sacrifice in the currents of the Gaṅgā river.

27-28. There were heaps of foodstuffs and beverages; milk flowed like rivers exuding nectar; curds formed smooth slimy slush. Sweet smelling meat and foodstuffs lay in heaps high and low. There were juicy beverages, and foodstuffs to be lapped up. The heroes ate, chewed and scattered them.

29-30. The heroic Bhadras born of Vīrabhadra's body hit and split the haughty gods including the guardians of the quarters by means of discus, thunderbolts, spears, Śaktis, nooses, iron clubs, iron rods, swords, axes, Bhindipalas and huge battle-axes

31-32. "Chop off and split" "Hurl quickly" "Let him be killed" "Take away and strike" "Peel and tear off" such ruthless words full of excitement, usual in wars and jarring to the ears arose from the lords of Gaṇas.

33-36. Some rolled their eyes, gnashed their fanglike teeth and bit their lips and palates. They pulled out the sages in the hermitages and killed them. They took away sacrificial ladles and spoons and hurled them into fire and water. They broke domes, gemset platforms. They sang, shouted and laughed again and again drinking blood-like wine. The leading Gaṇas danced.

37. Pounding up the gods including Indra, the leading Gaṇas, strong like lordly bulls, elephants and lions, of unrivalled glory, perpetrated hair-raising deeds of destruction.

217. The three cities or castles of the Asuras Tāraka, Vidyunmālī and Maya were received as gifts from Brahmā pleased by their penance. These were destroyed with a single shaft by Śiva who was annoyed at their savage activities. Prof Agrawal considers the burnings of Tripuras as historical event.

38. The Pramathas rejoiced, struck, ran, prattled, danced, laughed and jumped about.

39. Some of them evinced a desire to seize the watery clouds, some jumped up to seize the sun; others wished to blow along with the wind.

40. Some wielded weapons and rushed through the sky like peaks of mountains; tossed the gods like the Garuḍa tossing huge pythons.

41. Some looking like the black clouds uprooted the houses, windows, daises, hurled them into water and roared.

42. The doors, door-frames and walls of the sacrificial mansion were upset; the windows, ceiling frames, the halls were destroyed utterly. The complete edifice of sacrifice crumbled helplessly like a statement without foundation.

43. While houses were being dismantled, the women shrieked and cried helplessly "O husband" "O child" "O father" "O brother" "O mother" "O uncle."

CHAPTER TWENTYONE

(*The punishment of the gods*)

Vāyu said :—

1. The chiefs of gods headed by Viṣṇu and Indra were terribly afraid. They fled in excessive fright.

2. Seeing that the gods had fled uninjured and thinking that those who deserved to be punished remained unpunished the leading Gaṇa became angry.

3-4. He took up the all-destroying trident and looked up. He vomitted flames from his mouth, chased the gods as the lion chases the elephants. His gait as he pursued them resembled that of an elephant in its rut.

5-7. Then he agitated the army of the gods as the lord of elephants in rut stirs up a lake, shedding different hues blue, grey and red. He wore a tiger's skin as his cloth which was inlaid with excellent gold and pearls. Cutting, piercing, moistening, tearing and pounding, Bhadra moved among the hosts of the gods like fire consuming dry grass.

8-9. As he walked about speedily armed with a spear all alone, the gods thought him to be numbering a thousand. The infuriated Bhadrakālī excited by the fight pierced through the gods in the war holding spears shedding flames.

10-11. Bhadra born of Rudra's anger shone in her company as the fire at the time of dissolution with a lustre pale and smoky due to smoke. Pursuing the gods in the course of war, Bhadrakālī shone as the flame of fire at the end of the Kalpa that burns the universe.

12-15. Bhadra the leader of Rudragaṇas angrily kicked the sun and his horse on the head sportively with his left leg. The heroic Gaṇeśvara, Bhadra with self-control hit Pāvaka with his swords, Yama with iron-clubs, Rudras with his spear and Varuṇa with iron clubs. Holding the axe he hit Vāyu with it and Nirṛti with big clubs. The war was a sportive game for him. He attacked the gods and the sages antagonistic to Śiva.

16. Then the lord cut off the tip of the nose of Sarasvatī as well as of the mother of the gods with the tip of his nail.

17. With a dagger he chopped off an arm of Vibhāvasu, and the tongue up to two inches from the tip, of the mother of the gods.

18. The lord nipped off the right nostril and the nipple of the left breast of Svāhā with his nail-end.

19. The impetuous Bhadra uprooted the eyes of Bhaga large and lustrous like the lotus.

20. With the end of his bow he hit Puṣan's pearl like row of teeth. Thereafter Puṣan could not utter words clearly.

21. Then the lord stamped the moon with his toe, as though he was only a worm and ground him on the ground.

22. The infuriated Bhadra cut off the head of Dakṣa and handed it over to Bhad-akālī even as Viriṇī, wife of Daksa was lamenting.

23. Taking up the head resembling the fruit of a

palmyra the goddess played with it like a ball in the battle-field.

24. Then the sacrifice itself was hit and smashed with feet and hands like fallen women hit by their husbands.

25-26. Catching hold of by the neck, Ariṣṭanemi, Soma, Dharma, Prajāpati Aṅgiras, father of many sons, Kṛśāśva and Kaśyapa, the powerful chiefs of Gaṇas of leonine exploits rebuked and hit them on the heads with fists.

27. Just as in Kaliyuga women of noble families are molested and defiled by paramours forcibly so also the women and the daughters-in-law were molested by Bhūtas and Vetālas.

28-30. Thus the sacrificial spot appeared like a desolate forest. The domes were smashed. The posts were broken. The festivities ended. The hall was burnt. The portals and festoons had crumbled. The army of the gods was uprooted. The sages were killed. The Vedic chant had subsided. The population had dwindled. The distressed women shrieked The appendages were spoiled.

31. The excellent gods fell on the ground with their arms, thighs and chests pierced, with the heads cut off with the trident.

32. When thousands of gods were killed and their bodies lay sprawled on the ground, the chief of Ganas entered the place of sacrificial fires.

33. On seeing that Bhadra resembling the deadly fire had come the sacrifice was afraid of death and fled assuming the form of a deer.

34. Bhadra pursued him drawing his great bow, terrible due to the twanging sound of the firm bow-string, and discharging the arrows.

35. He sounded the bow by drawing the string to the ears like the thundering cloud. The bowstring, heaven, sky and earth reverberated.

36-37. The sacrifice was terrified on hearing the sound. 'O I am doomed', he thought. He was trembling with the legs shaking. His lustre disappeared. He ran in the form of a deer. The heroic Bhadra, with a half curved arrow, decapitated him.

38. On seeing the sacrifice thus insulted, Viṣṇu was infuriated and got ready for a fight.

39-41. Garuḍa the devourer of serpents and the king of birds bore him speedily over his shoulders. The god Indra and others who had escaped helped him as if ready to abandon their lives. Seeing them along with Viṣṇu like the lion viewing the jackals the lord of Bhūtas laughed. He looked like a lion without distress.

CHAPTER TWENTYTWO

(*The destruction of Dakṣa's sacrifice*)

Vāyu said :—

1. At that time a chariot resembling a thousand suns and with the emblem of a bull on the banner cloth appeared in the sky.

2. The splendid chariot had two horses and four wheels. Several divine weapons and missiles had been kept ready therein. It was embellished with jewels.

3. It was driven by the same charioteer who drove Śiva's chariot in the latter's war with the Tripuras.

4. At the bidding of Śiva, Brahmā brought the excellent chariot to Vīrabhadra and spoke with palms joined in reverence.

5. "O lord Vīrabhadra the eternal moon-crested lord commands you to mount the chariot.

6. O great-armed one, Śiva, stationed near the hermitage of Raibhya along with Śivā, is witnessing your unbearable exploit.

7. On hearing his words and blessing Brahmā, the heroic leading Gaṇa mounted the divine chariot.

8. In the excellent chariot where Brahmā sat as the charioteer the splendour of Bhadra increased like that of Rudra, the enemy of the Tripuras.

9. Then keeping an excellent conch shining like the

full moon, in his mouth, the powerful Bhānukampa blew on it.

10. At the sound of the conch resembling that of the swan, the fire in the belly of the gods blazed with fear.

11. In an instant the quarters including open spaces and crevices were filled up and thronged with leading Yakṣas Vidyādharas, serpents and Siddhas who desired to witness the battle.

12. Then Nārāyaṇa as the cloud inflicted pain on the Gaṇas as the cattle, through a great shower of arrows from his bow.

13. On seeing Viṣṇu coming and discharging arrows Bhadra took up his bow and showered thousands of arrows.

14. He took up the divine bow and slowly drew it like Śiva who drew the bow Meru.

15. As the bow was drawn a loud report was produced shaking the earth.

16. Then the chief of Gaṇas, of fierce valour and glory took an excellent arrow blazing like a serpent.

17. His hand in contact with the opening of the quiver for taking up the arrows appeared like a serpent wishing to enter an anthill.

18. The arrow lifted and held in the hand shone like the young one of a serpent held within the mouth of a great serpent.

19. With his stout and sharp arrow, the infuriated Bhadra who resembled Rudra, hit the unchanging Visnu on his forehead.

20. Viṣṇu thus insulted and hit on the forehead became angry with the chief of Ganas like a cow or bull becoming angry with the lion.

21. Then he hit the serpent like arm of the chief of Gaṇas, with a cruel, pointed great arrow resembling the thunderbolt.

22. The powerful Vīrabhadra too, with a great velocity discharged an arrow brilliant like ten thousand suns again at his arm.

23. Viṣṇu hit Bhadra. Bhadra hit Viṣṇu. O brahmins both of them hit each other.

24. The tumultuous hair-raising fight between the two discharging the arrows on each other in quick succession then ensued.

25. On seeing their mutual noisy battle the sounds of 'Hā-Hā' raised by the aerial wanderers rose in the sky.

26. Then Bhadra hit in the broad chest of Viṣṇu with an arrow that shone like the sun and the tip of which blazed like fire.

27. Acutely hit by the arrow that fell sharply, Viṣṇu suffered great pain and fell into swoon.

28. He regained consciousness instantaneously and got up. He discharged his weapons against Bhadra.

29. The chief of the army of Śiva stopped all the missiles discharged from Viṣṇu's bow by means of terrible anti-missiles.

30. Then Viṣṇu with eyes reddened by anger discharged an arrow in which his name had been engraved and which had never been obstructed anywhere, against the Gaṇa chief. Showering arrows, lord Bhadra split the arrow into pieces on the way before it reached him.

31-33. Then within an instant he split the bow with a single arrow and the wings of Garuḍa with the two arrows. This was a wonderful feat. Then by his Yogic powers Viṣṇu let loose from his body thousands of terrific gods holding conch, discus and the club. But the mighty Bhadra burnt all of them instantaneously by means of the fire of his eyes like Śiva who burnt the Tripuras.

34-36. Thus infuriated Viṣṇu raised his discus in a hurry and attempted to hurl it on the hero. On seeing him in front with the discus lifted up, the chief of the Gaṇas smiled and without any strain made his hand stiff and benumbed. With his limbs turned numb, Viṣṇu became incapable though he was desirous of hurling the unequalled and terrible discus.

37-39. Gasping for breath with a hand holding the discus he stood idly, immobile like a stone, like the soul without a body, like a bull without a horn or like a lion without its fangs. So stood Viṣṇu. On seeing Viṣṇu in a miserable plight the infuriated Indra and other gods took up their weapons. They hastened to fight with the chief of Gaṇas like cows or bulls attempting to fight with a lion.

40-41. On glancing at them as a lion glances at the deer, Bhadra of Rudra's body, the hero surrounded by excellent heroes, benumbed them with a boisterous laugh.

42. The right hand of Indra who desired to release the thunderbolt it held remained steady as painted in a picture.

43. The hands of others too became fixed, as the activities of idle men at the start remain unprogressive.

44. Thus the gods with their efficacy thwarted in the battle were rendered incapable of standing in front of him.

45. Frightened by the splendour of Vīrabhadra they could not stay further in the battle. In that fierce battle they fled even with their benumbed limbs.

46. The mighty Vīrabhadra hit the fleeing warriors, with sharp arrows like the cloud hitting the mountains with sharp showers.

47. The multitudinous arms of Vīrabhadra, resembling iron clubs, shone with their various shining weapons like serpents with fiery flames.

48. The hero discharging weapons and missiles shone like Brahmā discharging (creating) all living beings.

49. Just as the sun covers the earth by his rays so the hero enveloped the quarters by means of his arrows.

50. The arrows of the Gaṇa chieftains embellished with gold and flying in the firmament like lightning became the standard of comparison.

51. The great arrows took away the lives of the gods even as the water snakes squeeze the lives out of the frogs. They drank their blood as though that were wine.

52. The hands of some had been cut off. The faces of some had been split. Some gods fell on the ground with their sides lacerated and bruised.

53-54. With their limbs shattered by the arrows, joints severed and eyes dislocated they fell dead on the ground. Some desired to enter the earth and some wished to go up to the sky. Being unobstructed they merged into one another. Some entered the earth. Others entered the caves of mountains. Others went up to the sky. Still others entered the water.

55-56. With the gods with their limbs cut off, the hero shone like Bhairava who had seized people and like Śiva who had burnt the three cities.

57. Thus the entire army of the gods was dejected and looked hideous. They had their bodies mutilated by the Gaṇeśvara.

58. Then a terrible stream of flood from the bodies of the warriors began to flow striking terror in the living beings.

59. The ground of the sacrificial rites drenched with the blood shone like the goddess Kauśikī who had killed Śumbha with her garments wet with the blood.

60 When the extremely terrible battle had concluded the earth quaked as though frightened terribly.

61. The ocean was agitated with the surging waves, foams and whirlpools. Meteors fell portending great evil. Trees shed down their branches.

62-64. The quarters looked gloomy. Inauspicious wind blew. Ah, the adverse working of the fate. This is a horse-sacrifice. The sacrificer is Dakṣa himself. Dharma and others are the councillors. The Garuḍa-bannered deity is the patron. Indra and other gods take their shares directly. Still the sacrificer, the sacrifice and the priests are beheaded immediately.

65. Hence no such action shall be performed that is not indicated in the Vedas, and that which excludes Śiva and is taken up by the wicked.

66. A person devoid of devotion to Śiva does not attain the fruit of any rite even though he may perform holy rites and sacrifices.

67. Even after committing great sin, if any one worships Śiva with devotion he is liberated from the sin. No hesitation need be made in this respect.

68. Of what avail is much talk ? If any one censures Śiva, the charitable gifts he makes, the penance, the sacrifice, the homa, everything goes in vain.

69. Then the gods including Viṣṇu and the guardians of the quarters pierced by the arrows discharged from the bow of the chief of Gaṇas and overwhelmed by great pain fled from the battle.

70. The warriors of the gods with their hair dishevelled

moved about. Some sat exhausted with their huge bodies. Some fell with their faces cut and some perished.

71. Some fell in adversity with their garments, ornaments, weapons and missiles scattered. Eschewing their pride, arrogance and strength they fell evincing signs of dejection.

72. Destroying Dakṣa's sacrifice, performed in the wrong way, by means of weapons the invincible lord of Gaṇas shone amidst the leading Gaṇas like the lion in the midst of bulls.

CHAPTER TWENTYTHREE

(*Śiva's Fury*)

Vāyu said :—

1. Thus the gods headed by Viṣṇu with their bodies split and mutilated attained a miserable plight and trembled. Only a few of them servived.

2-3. The excessively infuriated Pramathas and Gaṇas urged by Vīrabhadra seized the warriors frightened of the battle tying their hands, feet, shoulders and bellies by means of strong iron fetters.

4. In the meantime Brahmā who had secured his favour due to his charioteership, implored Bhadra, the devotee of the daughter of Himavat.

5. "O lord, enough of this fury. The gods are ruined. Please forgive their faults. O you of auspicious rites."

6. Implored thus by Brahmā the delighted chief of Gaṇas became calm.

7. Getting the opportunity through Brahmā the gods joined their palms in reverence above their heads and eulogised him by various hymns.

The gods said :—

8. Obeisance to Śiva the quiescent. Obeisance to the trident-bearing destroyer of sacrifice. Obeisance to Bhadra, the lord of Rudras, the wealth and prosperity of Rudras.

9. Obeisance to Rudra the deity of deadly fire; to the slayer of death and Kāma; the remover of the heads of the gods and of the wicked-souled Dakṣa.

10. O hero, incensurable though we are we have been chastised by you in the war due to our association with this sinner Dakṣa.

11. We have been burnt. O lord, we are afraid of you. You alone are our goal. Save us who have sought refuge in you.

Vāyu said :—

12. Thus eulogised the lord was satisfied. He set gods free from fetters. He took them to the presence of lord Śiva.

13. Śiva, the omnipresent lord of the worlds, was standing in the firmament along with the Gaṇas.

14. On seeing him the gods headed by Viṣṇu were pleased and awe-struck. They bowed to him.

15. Seeing them frightened, Śiva the destroyer of the distress of his devotees said laughingly after glancing at Pārvatī.

Lord Śiva said :—

16. O gods, do not be afraid. You are my own subjects. It is only to bless you that the punishment has been meted out to you by the merciful lord.

17. The transgression of you the gods has been forgiven by us. When we are infuriated you have neither sustenance nor life.

Vāyu said :—

18. Thus spoken to by Śiva of unmeasured splendour the gods immediately had their doubts cleared. The gods danced joyously.

19. Becoming delighted and excited in their minds with bliss, the gods began to eulogise Śiva.

The gods said:—

20. O lord assuming the forms of Brahmā, Viṣṇu and Rudra through Rajas, Tamas and Sattva you are the creator, protector and the annihilator of the worlds.

21. O omniformed, O conceiver of the universe, O sanctifier. O formless, O bestower of happiness you take up forms only for the sake of devotees.

22. O Śiva, O lord of gods, it is due to your favour that the moon became free from ailment, when dead she plunged into Yamunā and regained life and happiness.

23. Sīmantinī whose husband had died, O lord, attained unequalled marital bliss by worshipping you. By performing the holy rites on Mondays she bore sons.

24. The lord gave excellent region to Śrīkara. You protected Sudarśana from the fear of danger from the hosts of kings.

25. The storehouse of mercy enabled Medura to cross the ocean of worldly existence. By your miraculous activity you enlivened the husband of Śāradā.

26. Destroying the calamity of Bhadrāyus you conferred happiness on him. By serving you Sauminī became free from worldly bondage.

Viṣṇu said :—

27. O Śiva you are Brahmā, Viṣṇu and Śiva by means of the Guṇas Rajas, Sattva and Tamas. With the desire to bless the people you became the creator, sustainer and the annihilator.

28. You are the destroyer of the arrogance and the brilliance of everyone. You are the hidden secret of all lores, the cause of blessings for all.

29. O lord, everything originates from you. You are all. Everything is in you. Save us again Please be merciful on me.

30. In the meantime, getting the opportunity Brahmā bowed to him with palms joined in reverence and informed the trident-bearing lord.

Brahmā said:—

31. O lord, be victorious. O destroyer of the distress of your devotees, who else other than you becomes pleased when offences are of this nature ?

32. Those who are killed in battle will regain their souls. When the lord is delighted who will not revive ?

33. The fault in the offences committed by the gods, O lord, is actually a blessing because of the weightiness of your acceptance. I consider so.

34-35. When Brahmā implored thus, the lord smiled and glanced at the face of the goddess. As a result of his affection to Brahmā who was like a son unto him, the lord revived the gods to life.

36. He restored the goddesses—mothers of the gods who had been punished by the Pramathas and others.

37. Lord Brahmā made the face of Dakṣa look like the the face of an old goat as a befitting punishment for his sins.

38. He was resuscitated and endowed with good intellect. On seeing Śiva he was afraid. With palms joined in reverence he eulogised Śiva.

Dakṣa said:—

39. O lord of the universe, O cause of the blessing for the worlds, O lord, be merciful. Forgive my guilt.

40. You are the creator, protector and the annihilator of the worlds. This has been known by me particularly. You are the lord of Viṣṇu and all others.

41. Everything is spread and pervaded by you alone, created and destroyed by you alone. Viṣṇu and other lords are not superior to you.

Vāyu said :—

42. The lord, the storehouse of mercy glanced at the guilty one who was emotionally distressed and smilingly said "Do not fear".

43. Saying so and with a desire to please his father Brahmā, the lord bestowed on Dakṣa the imperishable chieftancy of the Gaṇas.

44. Then Brahmā and other gods saluted the lord with palms joined in reverence. In words of humility they eulogised the lord.

Brahmā and others said :—

45. O Śiva, O lord of the gods of the distressed and the helpless, O great lord, be merciful, forgive our guilt.

46. O protector of sacrifices, O lord of sacrifices, O destroyer of sacrifices, O Maheśāna, forgive our guilt.

47. O lord of the gods, O great lord, O nourisher of the vital breath of your devotees, O lord, bestower of punishment on the wicked, be merciful. Obeisance be to you.

48. O lord, you remove the arrogance of the wicked who do not know you. You are the protector of the good whose minds are devoted to you.

49. Certainly due to your kindness your conduct is wonderful. O lord, forgive us for our fault. Lords are favourably disposed towards the distressed.

Vāyu said:—

50. Thus eulogised by Brahmā and other gods lord Śiva, the ocean of mercy, favourably disposed towards the devotees was pleased.

51. Śiva favourably disposed to the distressed blessed Brahmā and other gods and delightedly granted them boons.

52. Then the merciful lord who made their fear subside addressed the gods who had sought refuge in him, with words characterised by smile.

Śiva said :—

53. On seeing you all seeking refuge in me your entire guilt and sin committed as if urged by fate, has been excused by us.

54. O gods headed by Visnu, Brahmā and Indra return happily to Devapura[218] unmindful of the present suppression and without the sense of shame in your minds.

55. Saying this to the gods lord Śiva the destroyer of the sacrifice performed by Dakṣa, along with Śivā, his attendants and followers disappeared even as he stood in the firmament.

56. The gods too returned through the aerial path, free

218. Devapura, 'city of the gods' is identical with Amarāvatī, the capital of Indra's heaven, renowned for its greatness and splendour. It is situated somewhere in the vicinity of Meru.

from worries. Discussing about the heroic exploits of Bhadra, Indra and others went in different directions.

CHAPTER TWENTYFOUR

(*Śiva's sports on the Mandara mountain*)

The sages said :—

1. Where did Śiva who vanished along with the goddess and his attendants go ? Where did he stay ? What did he do and not do ?

Vāyu said :—

2. The excellent mountain Mandara[219] with different caves became the pleasing spot of penance for lord Śiva.

3. He had performed a great penance for the previlege to support Śiva and Śivā on his head. After a long time he felt the pleasure of contact with their lotus like feet.

4. The beauty of the mountain cannot be mentioned in detail by persons with thousand faces even in hundreds of crores of years.

5. Even if it is possible to describe I do not attempt to describe its beauty lest it should stand comparison with the other beautiful mountains.

6. This is possible to mention that it has the beauty of being qualified to be the residence of the lord through some supernatural magnificence.

7. That was why the lord made this mountain as his harem with a desire to do what was pleasing to the goddess.

8. The slopes of the mountain abounding in rocks and trees humiliate the universe due to the perpetual presence of Śiva and Śivā.

9-10. The mountain renders help to the parents of the worlds with light and clean waters of the streams cool to

219. See P. 1839 note 215

the touch for bath as well as drinking. Due to these merits he is coronated as the king of mountains with the very waters spreading here and there.

11. During the nights when the moon remains at the outskirts of its peaks the mountain shines with the imperial umbrella in the form of the moon.

12. When the tresses of the womenfolk of the gods shake, he appears as being fanned by the chowries signifying his Emperorship.

13. In the morning when the sun rises, the mountain embellished with jewels and gems appears to be eager for observing the beauty of his body in a mirror.

14-15. This king of mountains appears to be honoured with benedictions of victory by the trees that seem to be sages with the twining growths of creepers for the matted hair; through the chirping of vociferous birds, by extending their arms in the form of creepers shaken by the breeze and shedding flowers and tender sprouts.

16-19. With the various peaks some facing down, some shooting up and some projecting sideways he appears to jump into the nether worlds, jump up from the ground, fly through the sky in all directions. Through the vast caves he appears to have kept his mouth gaping. He appears to see the universe and dance continuously. His beauty never fades nor wears out. He appears to stretch himself to devour the universe, to drink the ocean; to vomit the darkness within and to cover up the sky with clouds.

20. The different abodes have mirror-like surface. The tall shady trees in the hermitages set the blazing sunshine at nought.

21. The breezes made cool by their contact with the rivers, tanks and lakes are rendered fruitful by Śiva and Śivā who roam here and there and enjoy them.

22. It was to this excellent mountain that Śiva accompanied by Śivā while staying in the hermitage of Raibhya[220] was attracted and proceeded.

220. See P. 1838 note

23. Reaching the garden there along with the goddess, lord Śiva sported about in the divine harem grounds.

24. As time elapsed and population increased, two demons were born. They were two brothers Śumbha and Niśumbha.

25. As a result of the power of their penance Brahmā granted them the boon that they would not be killed by any man in the universe.

26-27. Brahmā was requested by them thus—"Our death may take place in a battle with the lady with whom we fall passionately in love. She shall be a virgin born of Śiva's part, not from any womb. She should not have experienced the sexual contact with any man. Her exploit shall be unthwartable." Brahmā had consented to their request.

28. Ever since, the two demons wrought havoc in the universe. They defeated Indra and other gods in war. They abolished the study of the Vedas and offering to the gods.

29-30. Then Brahmā requested Śiva, the lord of the gods for killing them—"It behoves you to bestow on the gods the goddess who will kill Śumbha and Niśumbha. She shall be the Śakti born of the sheath of Śiva's colour. She shall be in the form of a virgin devoid of passion. By rebuking her secretly or by infuriating her this shall be arranged.

31-32. Thus requested by Brahmā, the lord Nīlalohita called Kālī in secret outwardly rebuking her while smiling within. The goddess Kālī was angry by her allusion to the colour. Derisively and forcibly she spoke to her husband thus.

The goddess said :—

33. "If my lord has no pleasure in my complexion how is it that I have been held up here so long.

34. If you are displeased with me why do you sport with me? There is nothing in this universe which is unachievable for my lord, the lord of the universe.

35. To my lord taking delight in the soul, happiness is not derivable from sexual indulgence; for the very reason Kāma was reduced to ashes.

36. The life of the lady most beautiful in limbs is in vain though she may possess all other qualities if her husband is not delighted with her.

37. The creation of women rests solely in the enjoyment of her husband. That being the case, where can a woman who is contrary to that be used?

38. Hence, eschewing this colour censured by you in secret I shall attain another colour or I shall cease to exist myself."

39. After saying this she stood up from the bed. Bent upon penance she requested for the permission of her lord in words choked with emotion.

40. Then lord Śiva, afraid of a rupture in love, replied to her falling at her feet.

Lord Śiva said :—

41. "O beloved, why are you angry with me, not knowing that this was only a jocular remark of mine. If I am not delighted with you, where else can I seek delight?

42. If I am not delighted with you how can it be proper since you are mother of this universe and I am its father and lord?

43. Is our mutual love generated by Kāma? Even before the birth of Kāma the universe existed.

44. The deity Kāma was formulated by me for the sexual pleasure of men and women. Then why did you taunt me for having burnt Kāma?

45. The mind-born Kāma considered me on a par with the gods. While he attempted to tease me I reduced him to ashes.

46. Even our sport and pastime is meant for the universe. For that very purpose I have made this jocular remark.

47. That purpose ere long will be revealed to you." On hearing this the goddess, remembered the remark that caused her annoyance and said.

The goddess said :—

48. O lord, your jocular remarks I have heard before whereby I have been deceived though I am very bold.

49. Even an auspicious lady of a noble family who does not abandon her life incurs the displeasure of her husband and is held despicable by good men.

50. Your displeasure is very great because I am not fair. How is the remark "Kālī" relevant otherwise though it be a jocular remark?

51. Dark complexion is hated by good men. You too disapprove of it. Without wiping it off by dint of penance I am not inclined to stay here.

Śiva said :—

52. If your distress is such, of what avail is penance? You can assume any other colour at my will or at your choice.

The goddess said :—

53. I do not wish to have any other colour either at your will or at my choice. I shall propitiate Brahmā by penance and become Gaurī.

Śiva said :—

54. O goddess, Brahmā attained his status formerly by my grace. What will you do by invoking him through your penance?

The goddess said :—

55-56. True that Brahmā and other gods acquired their status only from you. Still at your bidding I propitiated Brahmā formerly and in the name of Satī I became Dakṣa's daughter and attained you, the lord of the worlds, as my husband.

57. So now also by propitiating him by penance I wish to become Gaurī. What is the harm therein?

58. Thus replied to by the goddess, Śiva did not insist on his point as he desired to carry out the task of the gods.

CHAPTER TWENTYFIVE

(*The goddess attains fair complexion*)

Vāyu said:—

1. Then circumambulating the lord and restraining the pangs of separation she went to the mountain Himavat.

2. Out of love she selected the same spot for her penance where she had formerly performed the same along with her friends.

3-7. She visited her parents at their house and bowed to them. Informing them of her intention and securing their permission she went to the penance-grove and discarded her ornaments. She took her bath and assumed the holy dress and features of ascetics. She performed the very difficult penance. She meditated upon the lotus-like feet of her lord. She conceived the same in Śiva's external phallic emblem in accordance with the injunctions. In the three junctions of time every day she worshipped the same with the flowers and fruits of the forest. Thinking thus—"He alone, after assuming the form of Brahmā, will grant me the fruit of this penance", she conducted the penance.

8. After some time had elapsed, seeing her performing the penance a huge tiger approached her with wicked intention.

9. The body of that animal of wicked soul became stiff and benumbed when he approached her.

10. Even after seeing the tiger that approached her with wicked intention the goddess did not turn away from her pious thoughts like ordinary people.

11-12. The animal with his body stunned and overwhelmed with hunger, stood there in front of her glancing perpetually at the goddess and thought, "My prey is nothing else." Virtually this became his cherished goal.

13. Mercy was generated in the heart of the goddess who thought, "He is the perpetual performer of contemplation on me and my protector from the wicked animals."

14. By this feeling of mercy the threefold dirt of the tiger perished and he realised the goddess.

15. His hunger receded. The benumbed stiffness subsided. His congenital wickedness disappeared. Contentment set in.

16. Realising his contentment with great piety he waited upon the goddess as a sudden devotee.

17. He roamed about the penance-grove as a router of wicked animals and wicked souls.

18. The penance of the goddess increased and became gradually acute. Meanwhile the gods sought refuge in Brahmā due to the pressure of the Daityas.

19. The gods submitted to him how Śumbha and Niśumbha inflicted pain on them due to their strength derived from the boons.

20-21. On hearing the distress of the gods Brahmā grew merciful. He knew how Daityas could be destroyed. On being requested he went to the penance-grove of the goddess along with the gods reflecting in his mind that the liberation of the gods from misery could be achieved through his effort.

22-23. Brahmā saw the goddess, the mother of this universe, the mother of Trinity, the daughter of the lord of mountains, the foundation of the universe, firmly engaged in penance. On seeing her he was delighted.

24. On seeing that Brahmā had come along with the gods, the goddess offered him Arghya and received him with words of welcome.

25. Replying suitably and congratulating her the lotus-born Brahmā asked her the purpose of her penance as though he did not know.

Brahmā Said :—

26. What is being striven for, O goddess, by means of this penance ? The benefits of penances are under your control.

27. The fruit of the penance has been obtained by you in having obtained lord Śiva as your husband, who alone is the lord of all worlds.

28. Or all this is only a form of your divine sport. But this is surprising how you can bear separation from the lord.

The Goddess said :—

29. When at the beginning of creation as mentioned in the Vedas you are born of lord Śiva you are the first of my creation, my first-born son.

30. When for multiplying the subjects, Śiva was born of your forehead you became my father-in-law and so elder to me.

31. When the lord of mountains, my father became your son you became my grandfather, O grandfather of the worlds !

32. How can I inform you, the arranger of worldly existence what happened at the harem with my husband ?

33. Of what avail is this talk ? I wish to get rid of my dark complexion through legitimate remedies and obtain white colour.

Brahmā said :—

34. O goddess, why did you perform a severe penance for this purpose ? Was not your wish alone sufficient for that ? Indeed this is only your sport

35. O mother of the universe, your play too benefits the worlds. Hence some benefit pleasing to me may be sought through it.

36. Two Daityas, Śumbha and Niśumbha to whom I had granted boons have turned arrogant. They are harassing the gods. Their destruction is only through you.

37. Do not delay. For a short while be steady. The Śakti that is to be released now shall be their death.

38. Thus requested by Brahmā, the goddess, daughter of the mountain, cast off her outer skin and became white.

39. The outer sheath thus cast off became Kauśikī who is known as Kālī, the virgin with the lustre of the black cloud.

40. She is the Śakti in the form of Māyā, the Yogic slumber of Viṣṇu. She held the weapons, conch, discus, trident in her eight great arms.

41. She had three traits: gentle, terrible and a mixture of the two. She had three eyes. She was moon-crested. She

had not experienced the sexual contact of any man. She was invincible and beautiful.

42. This eternal Śakti was given to Brahmā by the goddess as the would-be destroyer of Śumbha and Niśumbha, the leonine Daityas.

43. A very powerful lion that came there, was given to her as vehicle by the delighted Brahmā.

44. He fixed her abode on the Vindhya mountain. He ordained her worship by the gift of meat, fish, pies and wine.

45-46. That Śakti, approved of by Brahmā, the creator of the universe, bowed to her mother Gaurī and Brahmā in due order. Surrounded by many Śaktis equal to her and born of her she proceeded to the Vindhya[221] ready to slay the leading Daityas.

47-48. The leading Daityas were killed by her in battle, the Daityas whom the arrows of Kāma pierced in the minds and her own arrows split and pierced in the bodies. That battle is not described here as it has been described elsewhere. It can be guessed through other sources as well. I shall resume the present description.

CHAPTER TWENTYSIX

(*The attainment of higher status by the tiger*)

Vāyu said:—

1. After creating Kauśikī and handing her over to Brahmā, Gaurī spoke to Brahmā demanding the recompense.

The goddess said:—

2. Is this tiger that has resorted to me seen by you ? He has guarded my penance grove from wicked animals.

3. Dedicating his mind to me he worships me without thinking of anything else. There is nothing more pleasing to me than his protection.

221 See P. 623 note 69

4. He shall be appointed as an official in my harem. Out of pleasure Śiva will grant him the post of Ganeśvara.

5. I wish to return with my friends keeping him ahead. I seek permission from you the lord of the subjects.

6. Thus addressed, Brahmā smiled and told the goddess describing the lion's wicked antecedents as though the goddess was unaware.

Brahmā said:—

7. O Goddess, animals are cruel. How can your blissful thought be directed to these ? Why do you sprinkle nectar in the mouth of the serpent ?

8. This is a certain night-prowling wicked demon in the garb of a tiger. Cows, Brahmins and saints have been devoured by him.

9. He is roaming about assuming forms as he pleases, pleasing and propitiating them. The fruit of a sinful action must of necessity be reaped by him.

10. Why shall mercy be shown to wicked souls like this ? What is the purpose served by one innately sinful ?

The goddess said:—

11. What you have said is entirely true. Let him be like this. Still he has resorted to me. One who has sought refuge in me shall not be abandoned.

Brahmā said :—

12. I narrated his antecedents without realising his devotion. If there be devotion, sins are not effective ? Your devotee never perishes.

13. What can a man of virtuous rites achieve without depending on your behest ? You alone are the unborn, intelligent, ancient goddess.

14. Bondage and liberation depend on you. There is no greater Śakti than you. Without you rites cannot achieve results.

15. You alone constitute Śakti of living beings. Himself incompetent to do anything what will a mere agent do ?

16. It is only your behest that is the cause of acquisi-

tion of prosperity and glory by Viṣṇu, by me or by any of these—gods, Dānavas or Rākṣasas.

17. Innumerable Brahmās, Viṣṇus and Śivas have passed by. Such innumerable ones are yet to be born, these carry out your behests.

18. O goddess of the gods without propitiating you the fourfold arms of life cannot be acquired by all of us.

19. Since merit and evil have been established by you the mobile and immobile may even be inter-changed.

20. You are the primordial and eternal Śakti of Śiva the great soul, the lord of the universe, the Śakti without beginning, middle or death.

21. For the functioning of the universe you assume some form or other and play about in different aspects. Who knows you factually ?

22. Hence let this wicked tiger too attain the great Siddhi by your blessings. Nothing can prevent it ?"

23. Thus requested by Brahmā after duly reminding her of her great aspect the goddess ceased from her penance.

24-29. Then taking leave of the goddess Brahmā vanished. The goddess visited her parents Menā, Himavat. She bowed to them and alleviated the pangs of her parents due to her absence. The goddess then proceeded to Mandara talking to her friends about the trees in the penance-grove who had been her loving companions. "They are shedding tears due to their grief at separation, by their scattering flowers, they are crying in distress by the chirping sound of birds seated on their boughs." The goddess was impatient to see her lord. She kept the tiger ahead thinking him as son born of herself, out of affection. With the brilliant lustre of her body she illuminated the quarters. Thus Gaurī reached Mandara where lord Śiva was staying—the lord who is the creator, protector and annihilator of the worlds.

CHAPTER TWENTYSEVEN

(*Gaurī's embellishment*)

The sages said:—

1. After assuming fair complexion how did the goddess, the daughter of the excellent mountain look at her husband on entering the mansion ?

2. What was done by the Gaṇeśas at the portals at her entry ? What did the lord do ?

Vāyu said:—

3. It is impossible to narrate adequately such an exquisite sentiment couched in love whereby the imagination of all sentimental people has been captured.

4. She was received by the doorkeepers in full flutter and agitation. The lord was eagerly awaiting her arrival. Entering within the mansion she hesitatingly glanced at the lord.

5. She was welcomed by the inmates of the mansion with loving feelings. She was saluted by the Gaṇa chiefs with words of welcome. She bowed to lord Śiva.

6-8. After bowing no sooner did she get up than the lord seized her with his hands, embraced her and joyously walked her round. Even when he attempted to make her sit on his lap she sat on the couch. Smilingly he seized her from the couch and made her sit on his lap. Smilingly gazing at her with his wide open eyes as if he would drink her in, the lord initiated the conversation with her by speaking himself first.

The lord of the gods said :—

9. O lady, exquisitely beautiful in every limb, has that condition of yours passed wherein no means of pacification is fruitful due to your anger ?

10-11. O lovely lady, I do not mind whether you are Kālī or of any other complexion. My mind is attracted by your innermost feeling. How did this concept escape your memory ? Out of our will we have accepted physical bodies. Causes dirtying up the mind do not crop up there.

12. Should there be any cause for our mutual displeasure as in the case of ignorant fellows, the whole world consisting of the mobile and immobile beings would cease to exist.

13. I am stationed on the head of Agni. You are stationed on the head of Soma. This universe in the form of "Agniṣoma" is presided over by us both.

14. We move about for the welfare of the universe. We have taken up physical bodies out of our free will. At our separation the universe is left without support.

15-16. There is another reason based on Scriptural texts and independent arguments. The universe comprising the mobile and immobile beings is integrated as words to their meaning. You are the nectarine word. I am the nectarine meaning. How can the two nectars become disjointed?

17. You are the lore that makes my conviction possible. I am the object of knowledge on the basis of your conviction. How can we separate in asmuch as we are in the forms of knowledge and object of knowledge ?

18. I am not creating and re-creating this universe merely by my activity since everything gets evolved through command or behest. You are the great command.

19. Lordship has behest as its core because it is the symbol of freedom. How can there be lordship in me if I am deprived of command ?

20. We can never stay apart from each other. It was for accomplishing the task of the gods that I made that joke.

21. It was not unknown to you that you got angry ? It was for the protection of the worlds that you feigned anger towards me.

22-24. What is harmful to the living beings does not find room in you. When lord himself spoke thus the goddess, the natural source of love, smiled but did not reply to her husband. Out of bashfulness she did not say anything but gave an accormt of Kauśikī.

The goddess said:—

25. Was not Kauśikī, created by me seen by my lord ? Such a girl has never been before in the world nor will ever be.

26-27. Brahmā will tell you about her prowess, strength, residence on the Vindhya, her victory in the battle with Śumbha and Niśumbha, their death, her blessing to the devotees and her protection of the worlds.

28. At the behest of the goddess who spoke thus her friends brought the tiger in their presence.

29. On seeing him the goddess spoke again—"O lord, see this tiger. There is no other devotee of mine like him.

30-32. My penance-grove was guarded by him from wicked hosts. He is greatly devoted to me. In view of his protecting me he is trustworthy. He has left his native place and come here for your favour. If you are pleased with him and if you love me, O god, let him stay at the door of the harem along with the other guards and under the charge of Nandin himself."

Vāyu said:—

33-34. On hearing the auspicious, loving and sweet words of the goddess the lord said to him "I am pleased". Immediately he was seen like Gaṇeśa wearing the dress and features of a watchman, holding the cane made of gold and a dagger of serpentine lustre and wearing a bodice set with various gems.

35. He was named Somanandin because Soma means Śiva and this tiger pleased Soma as well as Nandin.

36. After carrying out this task pleasing to the goddess the lord with the circular moon on his crest embellished him with divine ornaments set with gems.

37. Then lord Śiva with the moon as his ornament made the majestic beautiful Gaurī the daughter of the lord of Himavat sit on the conch and embellished her with ornaments.

CHAPTER TWENTYEIGHT

(*The glory of Bhasma*)

The sages said:—

1-2. We wish to hear these things in the proper order. What was it mentioned by the lord while pacifying the goddess ? He had said that the universe is in the form of Agnīṣoma. He had said that it was in the form of words and their meanings. He also mentioned lordship has command as its core. You are that command.

Vāyu said:—

3. The body of Rudra which is fiery and terrible is called fire. The moon pertains to Śakti. It is nectarine and is the body of Śakti that causes calmness.

4. What is called Amṛta is Pratiṣṭhā. Tejas is Vidyā and Kalā itself. In all the subtle elements the two are predominant, viz, Rasa and Tejas.

5. Tejas functions in two ways, in the form of the sun and of fire. Rasa too functions in the form of the moon and of water.

6. Tejas is lightning etc. Rasa is sweet etc. The universe of the mobile and immobile beings, is sustained by Tejas and Rasa.

7. Amṛta issues from Agni. Agni increases through Amṛta. The powerful Agnīṣoma is beneficent to the universe.

8. The luxuriant growth of Vegetation is for the Havis. The rain contributes to the flourishing growth of vegetation. So Havis is the outcome of rain, the universe is sustained by Agnīṣoma.

9. The Agni blazes upwards as far as the great Amṛta of Soma. The Amṛta of Soma flows as far as the support of Agni.

10. That is why the Kālāgni stays below and the Śakti upwards. The upward blazing is till burning and the downward flow is till complete drenching.

11. The Kālāgni supported by Ādhāra Śakti proceeds upwards. Similarly Soma having its region in Śiva-Śakti flows downwards.

12. Sivā sustains Śakti from below and Śiva is Śaktidhara (upholder of Śakti) above. Thus there is nothing not pervaded by Śiva and Śakti.

13. Frequently the world consumed by fire is reduced to ashes. They call it Agnivīrya because Bhasma constitutes the powerful part of the same.

14. He who dusts himself with Bhasma repeating the mantra "Agniriti"[222] etc., if bound becomes free from bondage.

15. Bhasma which is Agnivīrya when drenched with Soma is conducive to the lordship of Prakṛti without having recourse to Yogic union.

16. But being drenched all round by having recourse to Yogic union the Bhasma may turn one back from lordship by the shower of Amṛta belonging to Śakti.

17. Hence for the conquest of death the drenching with Amṛta shall be perpetual. How and wherefore shall one die if the nectarine contact of Śiva and Śakti is acquired ?

18. He who knows the secret of burning and drenching as mentioned is never reborn after leaving the world, the region of Agnīṣoma.

19. He who burns his body with Śaivite fire and drenches it with the nectar of Śakti and Soma attains immortality.

20. It was after keeping this in mind that the lord had said—"The universe is in the form of Agnīṣoma."

CHAPTER TWENTYNINE

(*The analysis of Vāg Artha*)

Vāyu said:—

1. I shall mention briefly how the universe in the form of 'Vāg-Artha' can be known through the six pathways.

2. There is nothing that is not the meaning of a word.

222. See P. 1730 note 157

There is no word without meaning. Therefore all words make all meanings known in their proper time.

3. The two words and their meanings are the transformations of Prakṛti which is form of Śiva and Śivā.

4. The magnificence in the form of word is mentioned as threefold by scholars—gross, subtle and the great. The gross one is what we hear with our ears.

5-8. The subtle one is in the form of thought, the one beyond is devoid of thought. The Śakti based on the principle of Śiva is Parāśakti. In the name of "Śakti Tattva" it is the root cause of all effects. It is the composite unit (Samaṣṭi) of all Śaktis because it is in association with Jñāna Śakti and is supported by Icchāśakti. The same is called Kuṇḍalinī Māyā and Śuddhādhvaparamā. This Śakti is ramified into six paths. The three paths pertain to words and the three pertain to their meanings.

9-10. The capacity for merging and enjoyment is possessed by all men in accordance with their purity based on the divisions of all Principles. The principles are pervaded by Kalās suitably as in the beginning the great Prakṛti is transformed into five. They are Kalā, Nivṛtti and others.

11-12. The three paths based on words are : the path of mantras, the path of words, the path of letters. The three paths based on meanings are the path of universe, the path of principles, the path of Kalās. These are mutually pervaded and pervading.

13. The mantras are pervaded by the words constituting the statement. The words are pervaded by letters. Learned men call the group of letters a word.

14-17. The letters are pervaded by the words because they are obtained there. The words are pervaded by the Tattvas because of their origin from within and without. They are effected by the Tattvas in various ways. Some of the words have cropped up from the middle, some from the Śaiva Āgamas. Some of Tattvas are those famous in the Sāṅkhya and Yoga systems of Philosophy. Others are famous in the sacred texts of Śiva. The Tattvas are duly pervaded by Kalās.

18. Since in the beginning the primordial Prakṛti is

transformed into five Kalās, Nivṛtti and others pervaded by each other.

19. The undivided Śakti pervades the six paths. She is pervaded by Śivatattva.

20. Everything from Śakti to Earth is born of Śivatattva and pervaded by it alone just as pot etc. are pervaded by clay.

21. The great abode of Śiva is attainable through six paths. The non-pervading Śakti becomes pervasive by the purification by five Tattvas.

22. The situation of the cosmic egg upto Rudra is purified by Nivṛtti. Above that upto the sphere of Avyakta It is purified by Pratiṣṭhā.

23. Above that upto Viśveśvara it is purified by Vidyā in the middle. Above that it is purified by Śānti. At the end of the path the purification is through Śāntyatīta.

24. It is this they call the greatest firmament in view of the contact with Parāprakṛti. These are the five Tattvas whereby the entire universe is pervaded.

25-26. All this could be seen only there by the aspirants. He who wishes to purify without realising the mode of pervasion of the paths is a deceiver of purity. He cannot achieve the fruit. His effort is wasted and leads him to hell.

27. It is not possible to know the Tattvas factually nor their pervasiveness nor increase without the union of Śakti and the individual soul.

28. Śakti is the order of Śiva in the form of cit. With that as the cause Śiva presides over everything.

29. It is not of the nature of the Ātman nor of Māyā nor of secondary nature. It is neither bondage nor liberation but it causes bondage and liberation.

30. She is the acme of Śiva's lordship never swerving. By means of sensations she is of the same traits as he.

31. With her alone he is a householder and with him alone she is a housewife always. As a result of their union the universe is the offspring.

32. Their difference is specified in this that he is the

maker and she is the cause. The single Śiva himself stands two-fold.[223]

33-34. Some declare that their difference consists in their genders: man and woman. Others say that she is undetachably associated with him as the light of the sun. But in the form of cit she is different. The arrangement is that Śiva is the great cause and his behest is the great goddess.

35-36. Urged by his behest the original unchanging Prakṛti becomes threefold in accordance with the three types of effects. It is called Mahāmāyā, Māyā and Triguṇā Prakṛti. It produces the six paths in the form of words and their meanings. The entire universe is thus sixfold. The whole collection of scriptural text is only an extension of this.

CHAPTER THIRTY

(The principle of Śiva)

The sages said:—

1. The activities of deities of domestic nature are curious, dense and inscrutable, even to the gods. They delude our minds.

2. In the union of the principles of Śiva and Śivā no defect is noticeable. However in their activities the Prākṛta feeling is rather prominent.

3. Brahmā and others the causes of creation, sustenance and annihilation attain restraint and blessing from Śiva and are subservient to him.

4. Śiva is not subject to anyone's Nigraha and Anugraha. Surely his lordship is not dependent on any one else.

5. If his lordship is like this, characterised by freedom, it can be either innate or subject to his embodied state

223. Matsya P. 3. 31· स्त्रीरूपमर्धमकरोदर्धं पुरुषरूपवत् । In the half male and half female form (अर्धनारीश्वर रूप) Śiva symbolises the progenitive principle.

6. But a physical form does not fit in with a free being for this basic reason. But the form is an effect of some cause. Lordship has no cause for its being.

7. Everywhere the greater and the lower Bhāvas are mentioned. How can these two be relevant in one place?

8. Indeed the great Ātman is devoid of attributes. How can he become possessed of attributes. Svabhāva is unrevertible.

9. If you say that his innate nature is reverted by his own wish he being free, why does not Īśāna make an interchange in permanent and non-permanent things?

10. The wise have said that the embodied Ātman is Sakala; the unembodied Śiva is Niṣkala. The embodied Ātman is presided over by Śiva.

11. If it is contended that the embodied Ātman is the form of Śiva, the dependence of the embodied on the form becomes certain. How can we explain that?.

12. Otherwise how is the form adopted by the non-dependant? The adoption of form is with a purpose to get the fruit of his desire.

13. The assuming of physical bodies out of wish is not consistent with freedom. Such a wish too follows the activities of men.

14. Even beings including Brahmā and Piśācas can assume or cast off their bodies out of their wish. But don't they come under the scope of Karmans?

15. They consider the assumption of bodies at one's choice on a par with jugglery. It is not beyond the achievements derived from Aṇimā and other powers.

16. While Viṣṇu who had assumed the cosmic form was fighting with Dadhīca the latter assumed the cosmic form of Viṣṇu.[224]

17. Although Śiva is the great Ātman and superior to all, his similarity with other beings is observed by us because he has a body.

224 See RS II. Ch. 39

18. They say that Śiva the supreme cause blesses us all. He curbs and kills the gods. How can he be a blesser of all?

19. The lord cut off the fifth head[225] of Brahmā who stubbornly and repeatedly censured Śiva calling him "O son."

20. In the form of a Śarabha he forcefully attacked Viṣṇu the man-lion. Pressing him with his feet he tore off his heart by his sharp claws.

21. With the sacrifice of Dakṣa for a pretext none among the gods or their womenfolk was spared from punishment by the heroic Vīrabhadra.

22. The three cities[226] along with the Daityas, their womenfolk and children were made the fuel for the fire from his eyes in an instant by him.

23. Kāma the husband of Rati, the cause of the sexual pleasure of the people was consigned to the fire from his eyes even as the gods were lamenting.

24. Angrily glancing at some cows walking along the sky and shedding milk over his head he reduced them to ashes immediately.

25. The demon Jalandhara who bound Viṣṇu and his Serpent and hurled them a hundred Yojanas, was pierced after evolving a discus by making a circle in water with the foot [227]

26. He then killed him with his trident in the water (?). By performing penance Viṣṇu secured the discus and became powerful.

27. The family of cruel demons who desired to kill him was scorched in fire. The chest of Andhaka was pierced with the trident.

28-29. After creating a dark woman from his neck he killed Dāraka. After creating Kauśikī out of the outer skin of Gaurī, Śumbha and Niśumbha were killed.[228] The narrative on Skanda is found in the Skanda Purāṇa.

225. See P. 58 note
226 See Linga P. ch. 72
227. The details of this episode remain untraced.
228. See Mārkaṇḍeya P.

30. The lord, requested by Brahmā for the destruction of the leading Daitya Tāraka[229] the enemy of Indra, went to his harem on the Mandara mountion.

31-32. The lord indulged in sexual dalliance with the goddess for a long time. Due to the excessive sport the earth appeared to sink into the nether worlds. He deceived his own name and the goddess by withholding the discharge of semen in her. The unbearable semen was discharged into the fire like nectar or the sanctified Havis.

33-34. The fire cast it off into Gaṅgā and other places. Svāhā who assumed the form of the Kṛttikās and sported with her husband gathered the parts and deposited them in the Śara plants somewhere on the Meru. Svāhā was turned into gold in the process.

35. After some time her lustre illuminated quarters and the mountains. Meru itself was turned into gold.

36. After a long time the splendour grew into a boy of beautiful and tender limbs, a model for all boys.

37. On seeing him of charming features, the world of the gods, Asuras and mankind was surprised and fascinated.

38-40. The lord himself came there along with the goddess to see his son. He took the boy on his lap. The gods and the sages though averse to worldly pleasures glanced at his smiling face. The lord made him play on his chest and enjoyed the fun. The lord and the goddess congratulated each other

41-45 He asked the goddess to feed him on her breast-milk. He blessed him saying "your incarnation is for the welfare of the world." The lord and the goddess were not satiated. Indra who was afraid of the demon Tāraka joined in alliance and performed the coronation of the infant as the commander-in-chief of the gods. The lord vanished himself keeping him in the protection of Indra and the gods. Tāraka's head along with Indra's fear was chopped off by his trident in battle, the trident that resembled the deadly fire and pierced the Asura Krauñca. Viṣṇu Brahmā and other gods particularly eulogised him.

229. RS iv. chs. 1-10

46-47 Rāvaṇa, king of Rākṣasas, arrogant of his prowess lifted up Kailāsa with his long arms. Śiva, the trident-bearing lord of the gods could not brook that sin. He pressed it with his big toe and the demon sank under the pressure.

48. For a brahmin boy whose life came to an end and who sought refuge in him, the lord came there hurriedly and kicked Yama with his foot.

49. The submarine fire, not knowing the bull as the lord's vehicle swallowed him. Thereafter the universe became a vast sheet of water.

50. By means of different activities blissfully beautiful and unknown to the people, the universe has been set to motion frequently.

51. If Śiva is calm and blesses all, he shall fulfil all desires. Being competent why does he not liberate?

52. The variety of beginningless Karmans cannot be the restraining factor here. The Karman that is the cause is also effected by the lord.

53. Of what avail is much talk? O Māruta, please explain in detail so that the arguments of atheism may be refuted quickly.

CHAPTER THIRTYONE

(*Instruction in perfect wisdom*)

Vāyu said:—

1. O brahmins, it is but proper that you have had your doubts prompted by sufficient reasons. Mere desire to know does not bring about atheism in those with good intellects.

2. I shall mention authoritative testimonies in this context quelling your delusions. The wickedness of the wicked is due to the absence of the grace of the lord.

3. It is clear and certain that nothing can be done without the grace of Śiva, the perfect and supreme soul.

4. Innate good nature alone is the sufficient ground for the lord's benediction; nothing can be blessed without innate good nature.

5. The universe in the form of Paśu and Pāśa, has to be blessed. The lord endowed with the authority blesses the universe.

6. The lord, the commander blesses everything always. If a means is adopted for that, how does Siva become dependant?

7. No blessing can be independent of one that is blessed. Hence the meaning of the word freedom is not characterised by 'not depending on another'.

8. That which is to be blessed is accepted as 'depending on another'. Without blessing, the enjoyment of pleasures or liberation cannot take place.

9. Embodied Ātmans too stand in the category of those who are to be blessed. Śiva's blessing is construed in the form of driving out their ignorance. There is nothing in Siva influenced by ignorance.

10. Śiva in the form of the idol, whereby despite its being Saguṇa the Niṣkala is realised, is called Śaivamūrti only in a figurative use.

11. Actually in the Niṣkala form Śiva is not the cause of the universe. In the Sakala form too he has not been seen by any.

12. The state of being understood through the testimonies alone indicates his nature. Merely on account of this it should not be treated with indifference without the implication.

13. Some form, intense with the similarity of Ātman, is Śiva's idol. The other, the great one, the Ātman of the Mūrti is its implication.

14. Just as fire cannot be obtained without its being mounted in the twigs so also Śiva is not known or understood without its being superimposed in the idol.

15. If some one says "Bring fire," only the burning twig is brought. The fire by itself is not brought. In the same way Śiva is to be worshipped in the form of the idol.

16. That is why an idol is used in the worship of Śiva,

for what is done unto the idol is what is done unto Śiva himself.

17. In the form of different idols, phallic etc. and particularly in Arcā (offerings of flowers etc.) Śiva is worshipped by us.

18. Just as the Ātman of the idol is blessed by the great Ātman so also we, the paśus, are blessed by Śiva stationed in the Mūrtyātman.

19. The Mūrtyātmans, Sadāśiva and others are presided over by Śiva for blessing the worlds.

20. It is for the enjoyment of pleasures and for salvation in particular, that Śiva's connection with the Mūrtyātmans in the form of Tattva and Atattva is accepted.

21. Enjoyment of pleasures is in the nature of the ultimate transformation of the Karmans either by way of happiness or by way of misery. There is no Karman in Śiva and hence of what nature can his enjoyment be?

22. Śiva blessess every one. He does not curb any. It is impossible to attribute to Śiva those faults which are usually present in those who kill.

23. The instances of killing and curbing pointed out with regard to Brahmā and others are those of the activities of Śrikaṇṭhamūrti performed for the welfare of the worlds.

24. Surely Śrikaṇṭha has the overlordship of the universe. Śiva presides over the Mūrti Śrikaṇṭha in the course of his divine sport.

25. Only the gods and others who were faulty were restrained or slain by him as described above. Thereby the gods became sinners and the people free from ailments.

26. Restraining or killing as such is not declared despicable by the learned. That is why the punishment meted out by kings to those who deserve it, is commended.

27. If he does not have that which is achieved through the suzerainty of the whole class of effects how can he rule over the universe?

28. The wish of the lord comprises the establishment of rules and conditions. Brahmā is the commandment. His order is the mode of direction such as, "This shall be done. This shall not be done."

29. The characteristic of a man of good nature is the strict adherence to his directives; the opposite thereof is that of the non-saintly one.

30. If good nature is to be preserved the evil one is to be eschewed. It is quelled by the expedients of Sāma etc. If other means fail punishment alone is the means.

31. This is the characteristic of what is beneficent viz. chastisement ending with disciplinary measures. What is contrary to this is called maleficent.

32. The lord is the standard example of those who perpetually abide by what is beneficent. How can he be condemned by good men for curbing and killing the evil ones alone.

33. Perpetrators of improper actions are to be decried and despised by a judicious person. Improper action is that which afflicts and harasses the world.

34. Every act of curbing and restraining is not attended with hatred. A father who trains his son even by curbing and restraining him does not hate him.

35. There is bound to be some ruthlessness in him who curbs or slays those worthy of it even by standing detached.

36. The lord does not injure others though guilty, otherwise. Of course, he injures the ignorant by adopting neutrality.

37. Hence we shall say that he who inflicts injury ultimately painful is ruthless. Thus a few insist upon this condition. Others do not.

38. Ruthlessness cannot be attributed to the surgeon who operates upon the patient. The inducing factor is kindness alone.

39. Even kindness to violent enemies is not conducive to ultimate good. He who is kind to such persons is ruthless though his ruthlessness is concealed by an illusory kindness.

40. Even neglect and indifference for the opponents who ought to be protected, results in default. He who ought to be protected perishes immediately if neglected despite the capacity of the protector.

41. He who neglects the man worthy of being protected

on considering the apparent defaults though he observes his plight is in effect ruthless.

42. Hence it is not generally agreed that kindliness is conducive to good in every respect. What is admitted is the performance of what is befitting. Everything else is unapproved.

43-45. In reality there are the defects of passion, etc., in the Mūrtyātmans (Sadāśiva, Brahmā and others). Still the defects belong to them alone and not to Śiva. There may be flaw in the copper put in fire but due to its contact fire does not fade. If impure things are consigned to fire they do not make the fire impure. Some impure things become pure due to their contact with fire. Similarly Śiva does not become impure due to the contact with the Ātmans that are to be purified.

46. The Ātman alone is purified through the contact with Śiva. If the iron-rod is put in fire and heated, the burning is that of the fire, not of the iron-rod.

47. The prosperity, glory etc. of the Mūrtyātmans is really that of lord Śiva and not of the Ātmans. It is the fire, not the fuel, that blazes upwards.

48-50. The state of being the coal belongs to the wood and not to the fire. Similarly Śivatva is imposed on wood, stone and clay. But the attributes Maitrī, etc., are secondary and they act differently. They are conducive to both good and evil to those who are endowed with qualities. What is both secondary and non-secondary is not wholly conducive to good or evil.

51. Learned men do not say that the meaning of Anugraha is secondary. But the liberation from worldly existence is in the form of Ājñā and is beneficent.

52. Carrying out his Ājñā is beneficent. What is beneficent is Blessing. He who employs everything in what is beneficent is the cause of blessing to all.

53. The sense of the word Upakāra (benevolence) is also Anughraha. Since that too is of beneficent nature Śiva is all-benevolent.

54-55. Everything in the form of sentient and nonsentient is engaged in what is beneficent? But obstructed by their innate nature all do not get the benefit simultaneously. The sun spreads his rays on all the lotuses impartially. But all the flowers do not bloom simultaneously; they do so in accordance with their innate nature.

56-57. Even the innate nature of the entities is the cause of what is destined to be. The innate nature does not transform that what perishes. The contact with fire melts only gold and not the coal. Śiva liberates those whose ignorance is ripe and not the others.

58. What is capable of becoming does not become so by itself without conception. But the maker needs no such conception and is free perpetually.

59. Śiva the blesser is innately pure but the Ātmans (individual souls) are naturally impure.

60. Otherwise how is it that they invariably undergo worldly existence and do not merge into Śiva? Being infested by Karman and Māyā is called worldly existence by the learned.

61. There is sufficient cause for this that this infestation is for individual souls and not for Śiva. That cause is the personal but not extraneous dirt.

62. Should it be extraneous it may happen to anyone through any cause. But this cause is single due to its nature not being variegated.

63-64. Though the Ātman-hood is common some are bound and some liberated. Among those in bondage some have differing degrees of knowledge and eminence due to their being inclined towards abstinence and enjoyment. Some attain the status of identicality with the lord. Some attain the state of nearness.

65. Among those who have attained identicality, some are Śivas. They are stationed on the top of the Adhvas (pathways). Maheśvaras are stationed in the middle; Rudras in the lower region.

66-67. In the vicinity too the three are stationed beyond Māyā: the Ātman is stationed below; the Antarātman is stationed n the middle and the Paramātman is stationed beyond. They are Brahmā, Viṣṇu and Maheśvara. Some Vasus too are stationed in the region of Paramātman.

68. Some are stationed in the region of Antarātman, some in the region of Ātman. In the region of Śāntyatīta Śaivas are stationed and in the Śānta region the Māheśvaras are stationed.

69. Just as Raudras are stationed in Vidyā and the Vaiṣṇavas in Pratiṣṭhā, so also the Ātmans. Brahmā and Brahmā-born are stationed in Nivṛtti.

70. The eight groups of Deva-Beings are the chief ones. The human beings constitute the middling. The five Beings birdes etc. constitute the lower ones. Thus there are fourteen Beings.

71-72. The state of being chief or subsidiary shall be known as the dirt of the worldly being. Just as the food we take in has two states, the undigested and the digested, so the dirt too. When it is undigested the men go lower down; when it is digested they go up. Thus the dirt plays its part in the worldly existence.

73. The individual souls are threefold : those with single dirt, with two dirts and with three dirts. Those with single dirt are the higher ones, those with two dirts the middlings and those with three dirts shall be known as the meanest. Thus they are stationed in order.

74. Those with three dirts are presided over by those with two dirts and those in turn are presided over by those with single dirt. Thus is the conditioned difference in the universe.

75. Śiva presides over all these, those with single, two and three dirts. Though they are of non-Śiva nature they are presided over by Śiva.

76. Similarly the universe which is not in the nature of Rudra is presided over by Rudras. The Mahābhūmi, ending with the cosmic Egg, is presided over by Śatarudra etc.

77. The atmosphere ending with Māyā is pervaded in order by the lords of gods of the size of the thumb all round.

78. The heaven ending with Mahāmāyā is presided over by the lords of worlds, Vāyu, etc., which are stationed within the Adhvas and whose ends are not resorted to. (?)

79. They are the squatters in heaven, atmosphere and earth. They are the gods observing the rites of the gods.

80. Thus functions the ailment of worldly existence with the three dirts and their pathological reasons separately, whether ripe or unripe.

81. The medicine for this ailment is the perfect knowledge of Śiva and nothing else. The physician is the lord Śiva himself who heals the sufferer.

82. In this regard no doubt need be entertained—"Śiva can liberate the souls without subjecting them to misery. Why does he then subject them to misery?"

83. It is certain that the entire worldly existence is misery itself. How can misery be non-misery? The innate nature cannot be otherwise.

84. A patient does not become non-patient merely because the physician administers medicine. The physician redeems the patient from the sickness through the medicines.

85. Similarly, through the administration of the medicine in the form of his Ājñā, Śiva liberates the souls from misery—the souls innately dirty and innately miserable.

86. This inequality like the physician is not the cause of the ailment. So Śiva is the cause of worldly existence need not be a symbol of defect.

87. When misery is innately acquired how can Śiva be its cause? The dirt is inborn in men. It is that which makes them undergo the sufferings of worldly existence.

88. The dirt which is the cause of worldly existence, the insentient Māyā, etc., cannot function by itself without the proximity of Śiva.

89. The wise say just as the magnetic stone causes the movement of the iron filings by its mere proximity, so also Śiva causes the movement of the world.

90. It is not possible to avoid the proximity of Sat without its cause. Moreover the presiding deity Śiva is even unknown to the universe.

91. Nothing functions without Śiva. Everything is induced by him. Still he is not deluded.

92. His Śakti in the form of Ājñā is the all-round restraining factor. This universe is perpetually covered over by it. Still he is not defiled.

93. This is ruled over even from the beginning. He is the lord. His ruling is his Ājñā. Still he is not defiled.

94. He who considers otherwise due to delusion is evil-minded. He perishes and that too due to the power of his Śakti. Still he is not defiled.

95. In the meantime an unembodied voice was heard from the sky. "Satyam (Truth), Amṛtam (nectar), Saumyam" (gentle), Om Amen. This sound came out clearly.

96. Then the sages were surprised and delighted; their doubts were quelled. They bowed to the lord, the wind-god.

97. Although he had cleared their doubts he thought that their knowledge was not firmly established. So he said:

Vāyu said:—

98. Knowledge is of two types: indirect and direct. They say that the former is unsteady and the latter is stable.

99. What is acquired by reasoning and instructions is the indirect knowledge. The direct knowledge results from the practice of rites.

100. Coming to the conclusion that salvation is not possible without direct knowledge, strive assiduously for the acquisition of practice.

CHAPTER THIRTYTWO

(*The description of excellent practice*)

The sages said :—

1. What is that excellent practice of holy rites, whereby salvation is directly acquired? O Māruta, it behoves you to explain it as well as its means.

Vāyu said:—

2. What is termed excellent practice is the great cult of Śiva wherein Śiva the bestower of salvation is directly perceived.

3. It is fivefold divided into five sections, holy rites, penance, japa, meditation and knowledge

4. The five activities along with attendant virtuous rites constitute the greatest Dharma. Thereby one attains the direct and indirect knowledge that bestows salvation.

5. The two Dharmas the higher and secondary are mentioned in the Vedas. In the matter of Dharma the Vedas constitute the final authority for us.

6. The higher dharma upto the practice of Yoga is mentioned in the Vedantic section of the Vedas. The secondary Dharma is mentioned in the Karmakāṇḍa section of the same.

7. The Ātmans freed from Pāśa are authorised in the higher Dharma and in the other one, every one is authorised.

8. This higher Dharma is the means for achieving the greatest virtue of Śiva. It shall be supplemented in all parts by Dhasmaśāstras and other holy treatises.

9. The greatest Dharma of Śiva termed the excellent practice is explained in the Itihāsas and the Purāṇas.

10. In the Śaiva Āgamas a detailed explanation of every thing including the consecratory rites is given.

11. The Śaiva āgama is of two varieties : Śrauta and Aśrauta. The Śrauta consists of condensed Vedic texts; the other one consists of independent texts but well consecrated.

12. The independent texts were originally ten but supplemented subsequently by eight more so as to constitute eighteen texts. They are called Kāmika etc., and the entire literature is called "Śaiva Siddhānta"

13. The Śrauta literature consists of a billion verses. In it the Pāśupata Vrata and Jñāna are explained.

14. In every circle of Yugas, Śiva incarnates as Yogācārya in different places and propagates yoga.

15. The four great sages Ruru, Dadhīca, Agastya and the renowned Upamanyu have condensed these principles and propagated them.

16. They are all Pāśupatas and exponents of the Saṁhitās. Hundreds and thousands of their descendants have been the preceptors of their principles.

17. The great virtue of Śiva mentioned before is four-

fold with regular performance and observance as the basic Ātman for them. Among them the Pāśupata yoga facilitates the direct perception of Śiva.

18. Hence the excellent practice is this Pāśupata Yoga. The mode of it as practised by Brahmā shall now be mentioned.

19. This is Nāmāṣṭakayoga prescribed by Śiva himself. By means of this Yoga the discernment of Śiva is generated.

20. Through this discernment the stable and perfect knowledge is attained ere long. Śiva is delighted with him whose knowledge is well-founded.

21. Thanks to his grace the great Yoga is attained which facilitates the direct perception of Śiva. By perceiving Śiva directly the cause of worldly existence is quelled.

22. Then the devotee is liberated from worldly existence and being liberated he becomes identical with Śiva. The means mentioned by Brahmā is now separately mentioned here.

23-24. Śiva, Maheśvara, Rudra, Viṣṇu, Pitāmaha, Saṁsāravaidya, Sarvajña and Paramātman—these eight names mainly indicate Śiva. The first five are the names of the deities presiding over the Kalās, Śāntyatīta etc.[230]

25 28. The five names of Sadāśiva originate from the conditioning factors. When the conditioning factors cease to exist they too recede. The region is eternal and the Ātmans who occupy them are non-eternal. When the Padas are changed the Padins are released. In another evolution they attain the same region. But the first five Ātmans undergo the change of names. The last three names are due to the adoption of the three conditioning factors. They indicate only Śiva.

29-30. He who is naturally pure is called Śiva. He has the antecedent non-existence of the contact of the primordial dirt. Or, he who is full of good attributes and is Īśvara is called Śiva by good men who propound the Śaivite principles.

31-35. The name Maheśvara is explained thus: Prakṛti is greater than the twenty-three principles. Puruṣa the twenty fifth principle is greater than Prakṛti.[231] Puruṣa is Praṇava the

230. The twentytwo verses (23-44) of this chapter are the same as the verses 1-22 of Kailāsa S. Ch. 9.

231. See P. 1072 note

first Svara in the Vedas. Since his real nature is comprehensible only through the Vedas he is established in the Vedānta. He who is beyond this Puruṣa, who is associated with Prakṛti is Maheśvara because both the Prakṛti and Puruṣa function in subservience to him. Or, Maheśvara is the wielder of Māyā. Māyā is Prakṛti the principle with the three Guṇas. It is unchanging. He who makes this Māyā energetic is Maheśvara. He is glorified as Kālātman, Paramātman, the primordial, the gross and the subtle.

36. The explanation of the word Rudra:— 'Rud' means misery and 'Drāvayati' means 'routs'. Since the lord quells our misery he is called Rudra.[232] He is Śiva, the great cause.

37. Śiva pervades all living beings, the principles and elements. He is wakefully present in the bodies and presides over them. Hence he is called Viṣṇu.

38. Śiva is the progenitor of the souls that have attained the status of fathers. He is therefore called the grandfather.

39-40. Śiva is called the physician of the universe. Just as the physician who is conversant with the pathology diagnoses and cures the ailment with medicines so also the lord annihilates the worldly existence along with its roots. He is so called by all those who understand the nature of principles.

41-43. Even when they have the sense-organs for comprehending the ten objects of sensual perception, the atoms do not know the beings gross and subtle, present in the three periods of time, in their entirety because they are hidden by the particles of dirt in the form of Māyā, whereas Sadāśiva has not these causes of perception. Even when they are not present, he knows without any strain every object as it is. Hence, he is Sarvajña (omniscient).

44. Śiva is the Ātman of all. He perpetually possesses all these qualities. There is no greater Ātman than Śiva. Śiva is Paramātman.

45-47. By the grace of the preceptor the eight names shall be acquired. The knots of the Kalā, Nivṛtti and others shall be cut off with the five names of Śiva and purified by repetitions, strokes and non-restraints. By means of the Suṣu-

232. For another interpretation, see Vāyavīya S. ch. 12 v. 29.

mṇā, the *Puryaṣṭaka* alone with the chest, neck, palate, middle of the eyebrows and the hole on the top of the head, shall be cut off.

48-49. The Ātman shall be taken above to the splendour of Śiva beyond the moon stationed in the twelve-petalled lotus of the heart. The mouth is shrunk in size. The body is drenched with the shower of the nectar of the Śakti and merged in their reasons. The Ātman is then let down into the heart.

50-52. The devotee then meditates on the great god Śiva, favourably disposed to his devotees who is conceived as sitting in the white twelve-petalled lotus beyond the moon, who in the sweet crystal-pure, delighted, cool, lustrous form of Ardhanārīśvara, shall be meditated upon. The devotee shall have the mind in normal state. He shall then worship the lord with the eight names of Śiva and the sacred flowers.

53. At the end of the worship the devotee shall perform Prāṇāyāma and concentrate the mind well. He shall perform the japa of the eight names of Śiva.

54-56. He shall perform eight Āhutis in the navel and repeat "Namaḥ" alone with the Pūrṇāhūti, offering eight flowers and conclude worship. With a palmful of water he shall dedicate his Ātman. By doing this, ere long, the auspicious knowledge of Pāśupata cult is obtained. He acquires its magnificent status and the excellent conduct. Then securing the great Yoga he is liberated. There is no doubt in this.

CHAPTER THIRTYTHREE

(*Rules governing Paśupativrata*)

The sages said :—

1. O holy lord, we wish to hear of the great Pāśupata vrata on performing which Brahmā and others have become Pāśupatas.

Vāyu said:—

2. I shall tell you the great secret, Pāśupata vrata

that quells all sins. It is mentioned in the upaniṣad Atharvaśiras.

3. The time is the month of Chaitra and the full-moon-day therein. The place is anywhere acceptable to Śiva having good characteristics. It shall be auspicious, say, the garden in a holy centre or a forest.

4-9. There, first of all, on the thirteenth day he shall perform the special worship after taking his bath and performing the daily rites. He shall take the formal permission of the preceptor after bowing to him and honouring him. He shall wear pure white cloths. The sacred thread shall be white. He shall wear a garland of white flowers. White unguent shall be measured over the body. He shall be seated on Darbha grass. He shall hold a handful of Darbha grass, sit facing east or the north. After performing the Prāṇāyāma three times he shall meditate on the lord and the goddess. By way of submitting to them he shall perform the Saṅkalpa saying, "I am performing this Vrata (of Pāśupata)". The time limit for this Vrata is till death, or twelve years or six years, or three years or twelve months, or six months or three months or a month or twelve days or six days or three days or one day.

10-11. He shall arrange the sacrificial fire duly as in the Virajāhoma. He shall make the offerings of ghee, sacrificial twigs and caru and perform homa. After the Pūrṇāhūti, deserving the purity of the Tattvas, he shall perform the homa with the five-syllabled mantra and the sacrificial twigs.

12-15. In the course of the sacrifice he shall think thus—"Let the Tattvas in my body be purified." The Tattvas are:—The five elements, the five Tanmātras, the five sense-organs of knowledge, the five organs of activity, the seven Dhātus beginning with the skin, the five vital airs beginning with Prāṇa, mind, intellect, ego, the three Guṇas, Prakṛti, Puruṣa, Rāga (passion), Vidyā, Kalā, Niyati, Time, Mayā, pure Vidyā, Maheśvara, Sadāśiva, Śakti and Śiva Tattva.

16. After performing the Homa with the Viraja

mantras he is freed from sin. Attaining Śiva's blessing he is endowed with perfect knowledge.

17. He shall collect cowdung and roll it into balls and repeat the mantras over them. He shall place these into the fire and sprinkle with water. That day he shall take in only the cooked rice soaked in ghee.

18. On the morning of the fourteenth day he shall perform everything as mentioned before. On that day he shall observe fast and thus spend the latter part of the day.

19. On the full moon day also he shall perform similar rites. At the conclusion of the sacrifice the sacred fire shall be extinguished and the ashes gathered assiduously.

20. Thereafter he shall keep matted hair or shave off the hair completely or keep one matted tuft of hair. He shall take bath then. If he is not extremely bashful he shall remain naked thereafter.

21. Or he can wear ochre robes, hide or barks of trees. Only a single cloth or a single bark garment shall be worn. He shall have the staff and the girdle.

22-23. He shall wash the feet and perform Ācamana twice. He shall apply the ashes taken out of the Viraja fire all over his body from head to foot repeating the six mantras beginning with "Agniriti"[233] from the Ātharvaṇa texts.

24. Then in the same way he shall dust the body entirely repeating the Praṇava Oṁ and 'Śiva'.

25. Then repeating the mantra 'Triyāyuṣam' he shall wear Tripuṇḍra marks. He shall realise his own Śiva-hood and perform 'Śivayoga'.

26. He shall act thus during all the three Sandhyās. This Pāśupata Vrata yields worldly pleasures and salvation dispelling Paśu-hood.

7. Freed from Paśu-hood, the devotee shall worship the phallic image of Śiva.

28-29. If capacity permits, an eight-petalled Padma shall be made in gold embellished with the nine precious gems. The pericarp and the filaments shall be furnished.

233. Śiras. U. 5

If the capacity does not permit, a red or a white lotus shall be used. If that is not available, an imaginary lotus shall be conceiv d.

30. In the middle of the pericarp a small crystal phallic image along with its pedestal shall be kept and worshipped.

31. After installing the phallic image in accordance with the rules with due consecrations the pedestal shall be conceived along with the idol of five faces.

32. The ablution shall be performed with golden vessels, filled with Pañcagavya[234] collected in accordance with one's capacity.

33-35. The vessels shall contain scents along with camphor, sandal and saffron and these shall be smeared over the phallic image bedecked in ornaments. He shall worship it with Bilva leaves, red, white and blue lotuses, other fragrant flowers, holy and auspicious leaves, Dūrvā grass of various types, in accordance with their availability and the rules of worship.

36. Showing of lights, incense and the food offerings shall be made to the deity. After offering it to the deity the devotee shall be engaged in auspicious activities.

37. In this Vrata exquisite and pleasing things acquired legitimately, whatever they may be, shall be offered to the deity.

38. The number of lotuses to be offered is a thousand. O brahmins, with regard to the other flowers it shall be a hundred and eight for each.

39-40. The leaf of the Bilva tree shall never be excluded. A gold lotus is greater than a thousand lotuses. The case of blue lotuses is also on a par with that of Bilva leaves. With regard to the other flowers there is no restriction. They shall be offered just as they are available.

41-43. The Arghya with eight materials of worship as constituents is highly commended. So also the incense and the unguent. To the deity Vāmadevasandal paste is recommended. To the Pauruṣa deity yellow orpiment shall be

234. The milk, curd, butter, urine and excrement of the cow constitute the Pañcagavya.

offered; to Īśāna the ashes. In regard to the incense the procedure is different. To Aghora white and black Aguru in the mouth. To Pauruṣa fragrant gum-resin in the left; to Saumya scents in the mouth. To Īśāna, Uśīra shall be offered as Dhūpa.

44. Sandal, Aguru, etc., along with sugar candy, honey, camphor and the ghee of a tawny-coloured cow can be offered to all.

45. Thereafter series of lights with camphor and wick soaked in ghee shall be offered. Arghya and Ācamana shall be offered to every face.

46. In the first (outer column of the mystic diagram) Gaṇeśa and Kārttikeya shall be worshipped. Brahmā's body shall also be worshipped.

47. In the second Āvaraṇa shall be worshipped Vighneśas the Cakravartins. The eight deities[235] Bhava and others shall be worshipped in the third Āvaraṇa.

48. There the eleven deities[236] Mahādeva and others shall be worshipped. All the Gaṇeśvaras shall be worshipped in the fourth Āvaraṇa.

49-52. Outside the lotus the mystic diagram and in the fifth Āvaraṇa shall be worshipped the lords of the ten quarters along with their weapons and followers, the mental sons of Brahmā, the luminary bodies, the goddesses and gods, the heaven-walkers, the residents of the netherworlds, the other sages, Yogins, the sacrifices, the birds, the mothers, the Kṣetrapālas with their Gaṇas and the universe including the mobile and immobile beings. These shall be worshipped, as they are possessed of Śiva's pre-eminence. They shall be worshipped for the pleasure of Śiva.

53. Then at the end of the worship of the Āvaraṇas, after worshipping the supreme lord, delicious Havis shall be offered as Naivedya along with ghee and side-dishes.

54-55. The betel with something to chew with to render the mouth fragrant shall be given. After bedecking once again with different flowers and ornaments the detailed

235. For the eight forms of Śiva, see ŚRS. Ch. 2

236. In regard to the names of the eleven forms, the Purāṇas differ. See ŚRS. Ch. 28. V. 26; Matsya P. 5. 29-30

worship shall be concluded with the waving of lights. The drinking bowl with the complements and bedding shall be offered.

56-57. A moon-like necklace shall be dedicated to the bedding. Everything done or caused to be done shall be royal in its quality, very pleasing and befitting. The contrary worship shall be avoided. After reciting the Vyapohana hymns the Japa of the five-syllabled Mantra shall be performed.

58. After circumambulation and obeisance the devotee shall dedicate himself. Then in front of lord he shall worship two brahmin preceptors.

59-64. After offering Arghya and eight flowers the lord shall be ritualistically dismissed from the phallic idol. After restraining the fire from the fire and ritualistically removing that also, the devotee shall perform the service everyday. Then he shall hand over the phallic idol with the insignia and lotuses to the preceptor. Or he shall install it in the temple of Śiva After worshipping the elders, brahmins, Vrata-performers in particular, he shall propitiate brahmin devotees and if possible poor and helpless people also. If he is competent he shall observe fast or take to a diet of fruits and roots. Or he shall have milk for his diet, or live on alms or take single meal everyday only in the night. He shall be pure in body and mind and lie on the bare ground or ashes or grass. He shall wear deerskin or bark garment and observe celibacy. Thus he shall perform the holy rite.

65. If he is strong enough he shall observe fast on sundays on Ardrā star days, on full moon and new moon days and on the eighth and fourteenth days.

66. Mentally, verbally and physically he shall avoid contact with heretics, fallen men, poluted women in their menses and Śūdras, by all means.

67. He shall always practise forgiveness, charity, mercy non-violence to all living beings. He shall remain content, calm and engaged in meditation and Japa.

68. He shall bathe thrice a day or he shall dust with the ashes instead. He shall perform special worship mentally, verbally and physically.

69-70. Of what avail is much talk? A performer of the rite shall not commit any misdeed. If inadvertently he does commit, he shall consider its seriousness or otherwise and perform adequate expiatory rites in the form of worship, sacrifice, Japas etc. Till the conclusion of the Vrata he shall not repeat the mistake.

71. He shall make charitable gifts of cows and oxen, perform worship in accordance with his wealth and capacity devoutly and free from any specific desire, for the pleasure of Śiva.

72. The common features of this Vrata have been narrated briefly. I shall now explain the special features for every month in the manner I have heard.

73-76. In Vaiśākha the phallic idol of adamant, in Jyeṣṭha that of an emerald, in Āṣāḍha that of pearl, in Śrāvaṇa that of Sapphire, in Bhādrapada that of ruby, in Āśvina that of onyx, in Kārttika that of a coral, in Mārgaśirṣa that of lapis lazuli, in Pauṣa that of topaz in Māgha that of the sun-stone; in Phālguna that of the moon-stone and in Caitra that of sun-tone is auspicious. If gems are not available gold shall be substituted in every month.

77. If gold is not available silver, copper, rock or clay shall be used for making the phallic idol whichever is available. Even lac can be used.

78-82. Or he can make the idol as he pleases having all types of flowers. At the conclusion of Vrata after performing the daily rites he shall perform the special worship and sacrifice as before. After worshipping the preceptor and the Vratins in particular he shall take the permission from his instructor. Sitting facing the east or the north on a Darbha seat holding Darbha grass in the hands he shall restrain Prāṇa and Apāna. He shall make the Japa of the Mūla mantra to the extent of his ability; he shall meditate on Śiva and Śivā. Taking permission and bowing as before he shall say with palms joined in reverence: "O lord, at your behest, I am concluding this Vrata." After saying thus he shall cast off the Darbhas at the root of the idol towards the north.

83. Then he shall eschew the staff, the matted hair,

the bark garment and the girdle too. After performing Ācamana he shall repeat the five-syllabled mantra.

84. He who has resolved to perform this Vrata till death and takes the initiation accordingly and performs the Vrata undistressedly is a Naiṣṭhika.

85. He is an Atyāśramin, a Mahāpāśupata, the most excellent of all austere persons and a great Vratin.

86. Among those desirous of salvation there is none like him who is so content. The Naiṣṭhika who becomes an ascetic is called the excellent Naiṣṭhika.

87. He who performs this rite for twelve days or every day is on a par with the Naiṣṭhika, his Vrata being too severe.

88. A person who applies ghee over his body and performs the rite with devout feelings even for two or three days is also a Naiṣṭhika.

89. He who performs the excellent Vrata without a desire for the fruit feeling that it is his duty, always dedicating his Ātman to Śiva has no one equal to him.

90. A scholarly brahmin covered with ashes is immediately liberated from the terrible effects of even the great deadly sins.

91. The great virility of the Rudra fire is what is glorified as the ashes. Hence a person possessing the ashes is a virile and powerful person at all times

92. A person who has bathed with the ashes is called Bhasmaniṣṭha. His faults perish due to the contact of Bhasma fire.

93. He who has smeared his body with the ashes, wears Tripuṇḍraka with Bhasma and has a Bhasma bath is Bhasmaniṣṭha.

94. Surely the evil spirits, ghosts and goblins and repugnant diseases flee at the very proximity of a Bhasmaniṣṭha

95. It is called Bhasita because it shines; Bhasma because it devours sins; Bhūti because it causes prosperity and Rakṣā because it protects.

96. What else need be cited to indicate the glory of

Bhasma? The Vratin who has had the Bhasma-bath is lord Śiva himself.

97. This Bhasma is a great weapon of the devotees of Śiva. It is a divine missile whereby the mishaps of the elder brother of Dhaumya in the course of his penance had been removed.

98. Hence one should endeavour in all possible ways to collect Bhasma like wealth after performing the Pāśupata vrata and be engaged in Bhasma-bath.

CHAPTER THIRTYFOUR

(*The penance of Upamanyu*)[237]

The sages said:—

1. It was for obtaining milk that penance was performed by the boy Upamanyu, the elder brother of Dhaumya. So an ocean of milk was granted to him by lord Śiva.

2. How could that infant attain power to propound the sacred doctrine of Śiva? How could he realise the existence of Śiva and perform the penance?

3. How could he attain the perfect knowledge in the course of his observance of penance? How did he secure the protective ashes the virile element of the Rudra fire.

Vāyu said :—

4. It was not an ignorant common infant who performed the penance. He was the son of a great, wise and the learned sage Vyāghrapāda.[238]

5. He was a great Siddha in his former birth who had fallen from his position for some reason. Fortunately he was born as the son of a sage.

6. His penance for the sake of obtaining milk became the gateway to the future grace of lord Śiva obtained due to good luck.

237. For the similarity of expression and contents of this and the following chapter, see Liṅga P. 1. 107

The Upamanyu, episode of the Liṅga P. is concise and condensed; that of ŚP is detailed and comprehensive. The former seems to be the abridged version of the latter.

238. Liṅga P. omits to mention Vyāghrapāda, father of Upamanyu.

7. Śiva granted him perpetual bachelorhood, lordship of all the Gaṇas along with an ocean of milk.

8. The acquisition of Śiva's knowledge is due to Śiva's grace alone. He acquired the knowledge of Śakti even as a boy.

9. His ability to propound the Śivaśāstra was also derived from the lord. He rejoiced in attaining the ocean of knowledge from the sage.

10. There was an apparent reason for his acquisition of Śiva-jñāna. These were his mother's words full of sorrow for the milk.

11-12. Once the boy had tasted some quantity of milk in the hermi age of his uncle. His uncle's son had drunk ample milk to his satiety. The jealous Upamanyu affectionately told his mother thus.

Upamanyu said :—

13. O mother, my blessed mother, O saintly woman, please give me sweet cow's milk. I shall drink it very hot.

Vāyu said:—

14. On hearing the words of her son, the saintly mother, the wife of Vyāghrapāda, was very much distressed.

15. With love and affection she embraced the son and fondled him. Considering her poverty she became dejected and lamented.

16. The boy Upamanyu could not forget the milk he wanted. He the innocent child of great splendour cried frequently pressing his mother to give him milk.

17. Realising that the boy was tenacious the saintly brahmin lady thought of a plan to quieten his stubbornnes

18-19. She had gleaned a few grains which the swe voiced lady ground into a paste with water. "Come on, s dear," she addressed her son and though she was distress at heart she gave him the improvised milk.

20. On drinking that watery stuff offered as milk, th excited boy shouted. 'O mother, this is no milk.'

21. The distressed mother when she saw the boy thus

in misery caught hold of him, kissed on his head, wiped his lotus-like eyes with her hand and said:—

The mother said:—

22. Rivers full of gems whether in heaven or in the nether worlds are never seen by unlucky people and those devoid of devotion to Śiva.

23. If Śiva is not pleased with them, they do not get those pleasing things viz. kingdom. heaven, salvation or a milk diet.

24. Everything is the result of Śiva's grace and not that of any other lord. Those who are devoted to other lords wander in distress.

25. Whence can we have milk, we who stay in the forest for ever ? O dear, where the sources of milk and where we the forest-dwellers?

26. Wanting everything and overwhelmed by poverty I, your unfortunate mother, have given you this improvised milk grinding the fried grains into paste with water.

27-28. You tasted the boiled milk at your uncle's. So when you drank this 'sour stuff you found out on comparison that what I gave you was not milk. When you cry out saying so you make me miserable. Without the grace of Lord Śiva you cannot have milk.

29. What is dedicated with devotion at the lotus-like feet of the lord accompanied by Śivā and his Gaṇas is the cause of all riches.

30. The great lord who is the bestower of wealth and befitting benefits to those who desire them, has not been worshipped by us now.

31. Aiming at riches we have not worshipped Śiva hitherto. So we are poor. Hence you do not get milk.

32. O son, nothing else is obtained by us except what has been given by us in respect of lord Śiva or Viṣṇu.

Vāyu said:—

33. On hearing the words of his mother, true but

expressive of her grief, the boy, though distressed within spoke thus in a mature way.

Upamanyu said : —

34. O mother, do not feel unhappy ; if there is Śiva and Śivā everything good will result. O blessed lady, eschew your grief.

35. O mother, listen now to my words. If there is lord Śiva anywhere sooner or later I shall get an ocean of milk.

Vāyu said: —

36. On hearing the words of her highly intelligent son the delighted noble mother replied.

The mother said: —

37. O dear, what you have thought of is auspicious. It increases my pleasure. Do not delay. Worship Sadāśiva and the goddess Śivā.

38. Definitely there is Śiva superior to all, the great cause. The entire universe in created by him. Brahmā and and others are his servants.

39. If we have any prosperity it is created by his grace. We are only the slaves of the lord. Except Śiva, the benefactor of the worlds we do not know anyone else.

40. Eschewing other gods physically, mentally and verbally, worship him alone, with Śivā with due devotion.

41. "Namaḥ Śivāya", this mantra is directly expressive of Śiva, the overlord of the gods, the bestower of boons.

42. The seven crores of mantras including the Praṇava Om merge into this mantra and come out again.

43. Those Mantras are also beneficent with regard to those who are authorized therein. At the behest of the lord every one is authorized in this Mantra.

44. Just as Śiva, this mantra too is capable of protecting all Ātmans base or excellent.

45. This mantra is stronger than any other mantra. Only this and no other mantra is capable of protecting all.

46. Hence eschew all the other Mantras and devote yourself to this five-syllabled mantra. When that is in the mouth nothing is inaccessible here.

47. The excellent Aghora missile affording protection to the devotees of Śiva originates from this mantra. Considering this, be devoted to it and not otherwise.

48. This Bhasma produced in the Viraja fire was obtained by me from your father. It is excellent and it averts great mishaps.

49. Accept the Mantra bestowed on you by me. If the Japa of this mantra is performed your protection will be assured.

Vāyu said:—

50-51. The mother directed him thus saying, "May it be auspicious" and allowed him to go. The sage accepted her words with his bent head. Bowing to her he made preparations for performing penance. Then the mother said to him, "May the gods do everything auspicious for yo ."

52. Permitted by her he went to the mountain Himavat and performed penance with purity of minds. He took in only wind (no food).

53-54. With eight bricks he built an altar and installed Śiva's phallic image of clay. He invoked the unchanging lord Śiva accompanied by the Gaṇas and Pārvatī. He worshipped him with the leaves and flowers available in the forest repeating the five-syllabled Mantra with devotion. He performed penance for a long time.

55-56. Assuming the forms of Rākṣasa certain ghosts of sages cursed formerly by Marīci harassed the lonely, lean boy Upamanyu performing penance though he was an excellent brahmin devotee of Śiva. Thus they caused obstacles to his penance.

57. Though harassed by them he somehow maintained his penance. He uttered "Namaḥ Śivāya" like one in great distress.

58. At the very hearing of that sound the sages who hindered the penance left off that boy and began to serve him.

59. O sages, the whole universe including the mobile and immobile beings became ignited due to the penance of that brahmin, the noble Upamanyu.

CHAPTER THIRTYFIVE

(The story of Upamanyu)

Vāyu said:—

1. Then the excellent gods with their bodies illuminated hastened to Vaikuṇṭha. After bowing they mentioned everything to Viṣṇu.

2-3. On hearing them, lord Viṣṇu thought "What is this?" After understanding the reason he immediately went to the Mandara mountain with a desire to see lord Śiva. On seeing the lord and bowing to him with palms joined in reverence he said:—

Viṣṇu said:—

4. O lord, a certain brahmin well known as Upamanyu has burnt everything by his penance for obtaining the milk.

Vāyu said:—

5. On hearing the words of Viṣṇu, lord Śiva said:— "I shall prevent the boy. You may please go back to your abodes".

6. On hearing the words of lord Śiva, Viṣṇu the favourite of the gods went to his abode after consoling the gods and others.

7. In the meantime, the trident-bearing lord Śiva resolved to go there assuming the form of Indra.

8. Taking up the physical form as the king of gods, accompanied by gods, Asuras, Siddhas and serpents, and seated on a white elephant Sadāśiva went to the hermitage of the sage.

9. The elephant fanned the lord with the chowrie and held the white umbrella with the left hand while bearing the lord of gods accompanied by Śacī.

10. Lord Sadāśiva accompanied by Umā and assuming the form of Indra, shone with that umbrella like the Mandara mountain with the disc of the moon.

11. Assuming the form of Indra, lord Śiva went to the hermitage of Upamanyu in order to bless him.

12. On seeing lord Śiva, in the form of Indra, the sage bowed his head and spoke.

Upamanyu said :—

13. O lord of gods, O lord of the universe, O excellent god, my hermitage is sanctified since you have come here.

Vāyu said :—

14. Glancing at the brahmin who stood steady after saying thus, with palms joined in reverence, Śiva in the guise of Indra spoke majestically.

Indra said :—

15. O sage of good rites, O elder brother of Dhaumya, I am delighted with your penance. Mention the boon you wish to have. I shall grant you whatever you desire.

Vāyu said :—

16. The leading sage when urged thus by Indra spoke with palms joined in reverence—'I request you to grant me the boon of devotion to Śiva'.

17-19. On hearing that Indra said:—"you do not know me the lord of gods the overlord of the three worlds, Indra, saluted by the gods. O brahminical sage, be my devotee. Always worship only me. Welfare be to you. I shall give you everything. Abandon Rudra who is devoid of attributes. What purpose of yours can be served by Rudra who without attributes has become a ghost ostracised from the midst of the gods."

Vāyu said :—

20. On hearing that, the sage began to repeat the

five-syllabled Mantra. He thought that Indra had come there to put obstacles in his holy rites and so said.

Upamanyu said :—

21. You have said all these things in your eagerness to disparage Śiva. In that context you have mentioned the Nirguṇatva of the great lord.

22. You do not know Rudra the lord of the chiefs of the gods, the progenitor of Brahmā, Viṣṇu and Śiva and who is greater than Prakṛti.

23. I desire to get my boon granted by the lord who is separate from Sat and Asat, who is the unmanifest, as mentioned by the propounders of Brahman and who is eternal, single and multifarious

24. I desire to secure the boon from that lord whom the knowers of truth meditate upon, who bestows the goal of Sāṁkhya and Yoga, viz. release.

25. There is no higher truth than Śiva who is the cause of all causes, the creator of Brahmā, Viṣṇu and other gods and who is the lord beyond attributes.

26. Of what avail is such talk? I infer that in the previous birth I committed a great sin because a disparaging remark about Śiva was heard by me.

27. On hearing the censure of Śiva, one shall immediately abandon one's life and slay that person too. He then attains Śiva's region.[239]

28. O base god, let my desire for milk wait. After killing you with Śiva's missile I shall abandon this body of mine.

Vāyu said:—

29. After saying this, Upamanyu, ready to die himself eschewed his desire for milk and got ready to kill Indra.

30-31. He took the ash and reinvigorated it with the Aghorāstra mantra. Aiming it at Indra he cast it off and

239. Liṅga P. adds after this Verse

यो वा चोत्पाटयेज्जिह्वां शिवनिन्दारतस्य तु ।
त्रिः सप्तकुलमुद्धृत्य शिवलोकं स गच्छति ॥

shouted loudly. Remembering the feet of Śiva he attempted to burn off his body. Upamanyu held the fiery missile ready for discharge.

32. When the brahmin attempted this, lord Śiva disguised as Śiva who destroyed the eyes of Bhaga prevented the missile of the Yogin gently.

33. At the behest of the lord, Nandin the favourite of Śiva caught in the middle the Aghorāstra hurled by him.

34. Assuming his own form with the crescent moon for his crest, Lord Śiva revealed himself to the brahmin.

35-36. The Lord showed to him a thousand oceans of milk, nectar, curds, ghee, fruits, foodstuffs and a mountain of sweet pies.

37. The lord appeared thus seated on the bull along with the goddess and surrounded by the lords of Gaṇas and holding the divine missiles, trident etc.

38. The Dundubhi drums were sounded in the heaven. There was a shower of flowers; the ten quarters were filled with the gods, chiefs of whom were Viṣṇu, Brahmā and Indra.

39. Then Upamanyu enveloped by the waves of bliss fell at his feet, his mind made humble with devotion.

40. Then the smiling lord Śiva called him nearer, kissed him on the head and granted him boons.

Śiva said:—

41. Partake of various foodstuffs as you please along with your kinsmen, for ever. Be happy always, free from misery. Be my devotee.

42. O fortunate Upamanyu, this goddess Pārvatī is your mother. You have been adopted as my son. The milk ocean is given to you.

43. So also the ocean of honey, of rice with curds and ghee and of fruits etc.

44. O sage, mountains of sweet pies, the ocean of food stuffs, these are given to you. Please take them.

45. Your father is lord Śiva. Your mother is Pārvatī, the mother of the universe. I give you the status of a god; the eternal chieftainship of the Gaṇas.

46. Choose boons as you please. I am delighted. I shall grant you boons. You need not hesitate at all.

Vāyu said:—

47. Saying thus lord Śiva caught him with his hands, kissed him on the head and handed him over to the goddess saying, "This is your son."

48. The goddess received him with pleasure like Guha, placed her hand on his head, granted him the unchangings status of a Bachelor.

49. The milk ocean came in an embodied form holding sweet milk in his hands. Approaching the saintly boy he gave him imperishable condensed milk.

50. The goddess, out of delight, gave him the Yogic prosperity, perpetual contentment, imperishable Brahma-Vidyā and the greatest affluence.

51. The delighted Śiva saw the splendour of his penance, granted boons again to the sage Upamanyu.

52. He gave him the Pāśupata rite, the Pāśupata knowledge and the perpetual ability to propound and discourse.

53. Obtaining the divine boons and the perpetual bachelorhood from Śivā and Śiva he became joyous.

54. Delighted in his mind he bowed with palms joined in reverence. The brahmin then requested lord Śiva for a boon and said.

55. "O lord of the chiefs of the gods, be pleased. Please grant me devotion to you, great, divine and unflinching.

56. O great lord, grant me an abiding faith in persons devoted to you. Grant me the great slavery and the perpetual proximity to you.

57. After saying this, Upamanyu the excellent brahmin eulogised the lord in the words choked with delight.

58. "O great lord, O lord of gods, favourably disposed to those who seek refuge in you. O ocean of mercy, be pleased always, O Śiva, accompanied by Pārvatī.

Vāyu said:—

59. Thus requested lord Śiva, the granter of boons

replied with delighted mind to Upamanyu the excellent sage.

Śiva said:—

60. O dear Upamanyu, I am delighted. Indeed everything has been granted by me to you. O brahminical sage, you are of steady devotion. I wanted to test you.

61. Be free from old age, death and misery. Be glorious and endowed with splendour and divine knowledge.

62. Your kinsmen, your family and spiritual lineage shall be everlasting. O excellent brahmin, your devotion to me shall be permanent.

63. O excellent brahmin, I shall always be present in your hermitage. Near me you shall always blissfully sport about.

64. Thus granting him the boons lord Śiva who had the lustre of a crore suns, vanished there itself.

65. Securing the boons from the lord, Upamanyu, delighted in his mind, went to his mother's abode and attained the supreme bliss.

VĀYAVĪYASAMHITĀ

Section II

CHAPTER ONE

(Acquisition of sons by Śrīkṛṣṇa)

1. Obeisance to the lord whose chest is marked by the saffron from the plump pair of breasts of Gaurī and who causes the entire world whirl like a wheel.

Sūta said:—

2-4. After narrating how Upamanyu attained favours from the lord, Vāyu got up for the routine observances when the sun reached the middle of the sky. All the sages, the residents of the Naimiṣa forest, resolved within themselves what topic should be asked. After performing their duties as usual, they saw that the lord Vāyu was coming and so sat waiting for him.

5. At the end of the observance of the daily routine lord Vāyu occupied his assigned seat in the middle of the assembly of the sages.

6. Vāyu, saluted by all the worlds, comfortably seated himself in the seat. Keeping well in his mind the glorious prosperity of the lord, he spoke thus.

7. "I resort to that great lord, the unvanquished and the omniscient whose prosperity and glory constitute the universe consisting of the mobile and immobile beings.

8. On hearing the auspicious statement the sages of quelled sins spoke these words in order to hear further the details of the lord's glory.

The sages said:—

9-11. O lord, you have already mentioned the details of Upamanyu of noble soul, how he attained various favours from the supreme lord by means of the penance performed for the sake of milk. Formerly, we had heard that this elder brother of Dhaumya was met by Śrīkṛsna of unstrained activities, son of Vasudeva. Then Kṛṣṇa performed the Pāśupatavrata and attained perfect knowledge. How did lord Kṛṣṇa attain the perfect knowledge of Pasupati?

Vāyu said:—

12. Vāsudeva, the eternal god, had taken his incarnation out of his own free will. Still he performed the purificatory rites for his body thereby indicating that the human body is worthy of censure.

13. He went to the great sage's hermitage resorted to by other sages, in order to perform a penance for the sake of sons. There he saw the sage Upamanyu.

14-15. The sage had great splendour all over his body being rendered white due to the Bhasma smeared over. His forehead was marked with Tripuṇḍras. He was bedecked in resories of stringed Rudrākṣa beads. The clustered matted hair embellished him. He was surrounded by sages who were his disciples, just as the Veda is surrounded by the scriptural texts. He was calm and engaged in meditation on Śiva.

16. On seeing him hairs stood on their ends in the body of Kṛṣṇa due to delight. Respectfully he circumambulated him thrice and knelt before him. With shoulders drooping and palms joined in reverence he delightfully eulogised him.

17. At the mere vision of the sage, all dirt born of Māyā and Karman of Kṛṣṇa was quelled.

18-19. When the dirt of Kṛṣṇa had been quelled, Upamanyu dusted him with Bhasma repeating the Mantras "Agniriti"[240] etc. He was then made to perform the Pāśupata Vrata lasting for twelve months. Then the sage imparted to him the excellent knowledge.

20. Since then the divine Pāśupata sages of duly completed rites surrounded him.

21. Then at the behest of his preceptor, Kṛṣṇa of great prowess performed penance for the attainment of a son with Śiva and Pārvatī as the deity aimed at.

22. Due to that penance, at the end of a year, lord

240. Śirás Up. 5

Śiva, equipped with great splendour and accompanied by his Gaṇas and Pārvatī appeared there.

23. After bowing to Śiva of handsome features, who appeared before him for granting boons, Kṛṣṇa eulogised him with palms joined in reverence.

24. Kṛṣṇa of composed mind obtained his son Sāmba of good qualities bequeathed by Śiva who was delighted by his penance.

25. Since it was Śiva accompanied by Ambā, who blessed him with a son, he named Jāmbavatī's son Sāmba.

26. Thus I have narrated to you how Kṛṣṇa of wide activities attained knowledge from the great sage and a son from Śiva.

27. He who recites this everyday, listens to it or narrates it to others attains Viṣṇu's wisdom and rejoices with him.

CHAPTER TWO

(*The glory of lord Śiva*)

The sages said:—

1. What is the Pāśupata knowledge? How is Śiva the lord of Paśus? Why was Dhaumya's elder brother asked by Kṛṣṇa of unstrained activities.

2. O lord Vāyu, of the form of Śiva, please explain all these things. In the whole of the three worlds there is no other person competent to explain it like you.

Sūta said:—

3. On hearing the words of the sages, Vāyu thought upon Śiva, and began to explain.

Vāyu said:—

4. This excellent and exalted Pāśupata knowledge was mentioned to the goddess by lord Śiva on the mountain Mandara.

5. The same question was asked by Kṛṣṇa, the cause of the universe about the animal nature of the gods and others and the overlordship of Śiva.

6. I shall explain it succinctly as imparted to Kṛṣṇa by Upamanyu. Please hear attentively.

7. Formerly Viṣṇu in the form of Kṛṣṇa bowed to Upamanyu sitting in his hermitage and spoke courteously.

Lord Kṛṣṇa said:—

8. O lord, I wish to hear about the divine Pāśupata knowledge as mentioned to the goddess by the lord. I wish to hear about his prosperity and glory entirely.

9. How is the lord known as Paśupati, lord of Paśus? Who are the Paśus? What are those Pāśas (strings) with which they are bound? How are they released?

10. Thus implored by the noble Kṛṣṇa the glorious Upamanyu bowed to the lord and the goddess and spoke as follows.

Upamanyu said:—

11. Every being beginning with Brahmā and ending with immobile beings is called Paśu in relation to the lord of gods. Every being is subject to worldly existence.

12. Śiva, lord of the gods, is known as Paśupati in view of his being the lord of the Paśus. The Pati binds the Paśus through the Pāśas (strings) of dirt.

13-14. He alone releases when he is meditated upon and worshipped with devotion. The twentyfour principles, Māyā, Karman and the three Guṇas are called Viṣayas. These are the Pāśas that bind the Paśus. After binding the Paśus, from Brahmā to the grass, by means of these Pāśas, lord Śiva makes them do their respective duties.

15-20. At his behest Prakṛti generates Buddhi befitting the Puruṣa. Buddhi (cosmic intellect) generates Ahaṅkāra (Ego). The ego generates the eleven sense-organs and five Tanmātras. At his bidding the Tanmātras too, create the great Bhūtas entirely in their order; the great Bhūtas create the physical bodies of all beings from Brahmā to the grass. Intellect determines and resolves. Ego feels pride in and identifies with what is possessed. Consciousness observes and becomes conscious of things. Mind conceives and imagines. The organs of knowledge apprehend the objects separately.

21-22. The sense-organs grasp their objects and not others and this is due to the divine command of the lord. The organs of activity too do their own duties. Nothing else. It is due to Śiva's order that sound, etc. are grasped, speech, etc. are made. Śiva's weighty command is not to be transgressed by any.

23-26. It is only at the behest of the lord that ether pervades all, yields space to the elements. At the bidding of Śiva the wind sustains the entire universe, internal and external, under different names of Prāṇa, etc. At the bidding of the lord the firegod bears offerings to the gods and oblations to the Pitṛs. It facilitates cooking etc. At his behest the waters enliven all. At the bidding of the lord the earth holds up the universe for ever.

27-30. In respect of Śiva's inviolable command lord Indra protects the gods, kills the Asuras and guards the worlds. By Śiva's command lord Varuṇa rules over the waters and binds those who are to be punished, by means of his noose. At the behest of Śiva the lord of wealth, the lord of the Yakṣas, distributes wealth to the living beings in accordance with their merit. At the bidding of Śiva, Īśāna bestows knowledge on the intelligent ones and affords them riches, and curbs the evil-doers.

31-34. It is at the direction of Śiva that the earth is supported by Śeṣa. The Raudrī and Tāmasī form of Viṣṇu that brings about destruction is created by the four-faced lord. At his behest, through other forms of his own, he protects the universe and annihilates it in the end. He protects, creates and devours the universe through his own three bodies. At his bidding alone Rudra annihilates the universe in the end.

35-37. The Ātman of the universe thus assuming three different forms creates and protects too. Time creates, protects and destroys at his behest. At his bidding with the three parts of his splendour, the sun supports the universe, commands the shower and rains in the heaven. At the behest of the moon-crested lord, the moon nourishes the plants, delights the living beings and is imbibed by the gods.

38-43. Ādityas, Vasus, Rudras, Aśvins, Maruts, heaven-walkers, Sages, Siddhas, Serpents, human beings, beasts, animals, birds, worms, immobile beings, rivers, oceans, mountains, forests, lakes, Vedas with their ancillaries, the scriptures, the compendiums of mantras, sacrifices, etc., the worlds beginning with Kālāgni and ending with Śiva and their overlords, the innumerable Brahmāṇḍas, their coverings, the past, present and future, the quarters, interstices, the different units of time, Kalā etc.—all these, whatever is seen or heard in the world, are presided over by the order of Śiva.

44. It is through the power of his order that the earth, the mountains, clouds, oceans, luminary bodies, Indra and other gods, the mobile and immobile beings sentient or non-sentient are sustained.

45. O Kṛṣṇa, listen to the wonderful feat performed by the order of Śiva of unmeasured activity and heard by me from the Upaniṣads.

46. After conquering the Asuras in the war formerly, the gods including Indra began to argue with one another "I am the victor, I am the victor".

47. Then lord Śiva assumed the guise of a Yakṣa and stood in their midst devoid of his characteristic features in the limbs.

48. He set a blade of grass on the ground and told the gods, "He who can deform this grass is the conqueror of the Daityas."

49. On hearing the words of the Yakṣa, the thunderbolt-bearing consort of Śacī became infuriated. Smiling a little he attempted to take up the grass.

50. When he could not lift it up he hurled his thunderbolt at it in order to cut it.

51. The thunderbolt coming into contact with the grass appeared to clash with a steel and fell aside.

52. Then the guardians of the quarters and the worlds, of great strength exerted themselves and hurled thousands of their weapons at the grass-blade.

53. The great fire blazed, the fierce wind blew and the

lord of the waters swelled as if the hour of dissolution had arrived.

54. Thus everything initiated by the gods strenuously against the grass was a flop. O Kṛṣṇa, it was due to the power of that Yakṣa alone.

55. Then the infuriated lord of gods asked the Yakṣa, "Who are you, sir?" Then even as they were watching, the Yakṣa vanished.

56. In the meantime the goddess Haimavatī bedecked in divine ornaments, appeared in the sky smiling and shining brilliantly.

57. On seeing her the wonderstruck gods, Indra and others bowed to her humbly and asked, "Who is this uncommon Yakṣa?"

58. The goddess smiled and said—"He is invisible to you. He is the lord by whom this wheel of the world including the mobile and immobile beings, revolves.

59. In the beginning the universe is created by him, and it is annihilated again by him. There is none to control him. Everything is controlled by him".

60. After saying this the great goddess vanished there itself. The surprised gods bowed to her and went to heaven.

CHAPTER THREE

(*Upamanyu's advice to lord Kṛṣṇa*)

Upamanyu said :—

1. O Kṛṣṇa, listen; this universe of the mobile and immobile beings is pervaded by the Mūrtyātmans of lord Śiva, the great Ātman.

2. Śiva presides over all these by means of his own Mūrtis. His Ātman is incomprehensible. This is said by the sages.

3. These shall be known as his Mūrtis whereby this universe is pervaded viz:—Brahmā, Viṣṇu, Rudra, Maheśāna and Sadāśiva.

4. There are other bodies as well, called Pañcabrahmans. There is nothing which is not pervaded by those bodies.

5. The famous Pañcabrahmans,[241] the bodies of the lord are Īśāna, Puruṣa, Aghora, Vāmadeva and Sadyojāta.

6. His greatest first Mūrti, Īśāna, presides over the individual soul the enjoyer of Prakṛti.

7. The Mūrti of Śiva the lord having embodied forms, named Tatpuruṣa, presides over the unmanifest which is worthy of being enjoyed and which is in the form of the support of the Guṇas.

8. The highly venerable Mūrti Aghora, of the trident-bearing lord, presides over the principle of cosmic intellect consisting of eight parts of Dharma etc.

9. Persons who know the Āgamas call the Mūrti Vāmadeva as the presiding deity of Ego.

10. The intelligent men say that the Mūrti Sadyojāta of Śiva of unmeasured splendour is the presiding deity of the mind.

11. Scholars understand that the Mūrti Īśāna is the presiding deity of the ear speech, sound and the all-pervasive ether.

12. Experts of the Purāṇas understand that the Mūrti Tatpuruṣa is the presiding deity of the skin, hand, touch and Vāyu.

13. The wise understand that the Mūrti Aghora is the presiding deity of the eye, leg, colour and fire.

14. The devotees understand that the Mūrti Vāmadeva is the presiding deity of the tongue, anus, taste and the waters.

15. They say that the Mūrti Sadyojāta is the presiding deity of the nose, sexual organ, smell and the earth.

16. The five Mūrtis of the lord, the sole causes of prosperity shall be assiduously saluted by men seeking Śreyas.

241. Īśāna, Puruṣa (Tatpuruṣa), Aghora, Vāma and Sadya are the five forms of Śiva. In the light of this version, the expression 'Vāmasañjña' in ŚRS I. 39 shall be emended to 'Vamassadyaḥ' and translated accordingly.

17. The universe consists of eight Mūrtis, of the primordial lord of the gods, wherein lies stretched the universe as the gems and beads in the string.

18. These famous eight Mūrtis[242] are Śarva, Bhava, Rudra, Ugra, Bhīma, Paśupati, Īśāna, and Mahādeva.

19. The earth, waters, fire, wind, ether, kṣetrajña, the sun and the moon are presided over by the eight Mūrtis, Śarva, etc, of the lord.

20. This is the conclusion of the scripture that the Mūrti of Śarva, in the form of the earth upholds the universe consisting of the mobile and immobile beings.

21. The Mūrti of Bhava the great Ātman, in the form of water enlivens the universe.

22. The Mūrti of Rudra having terrible form, is stationed all over the universe internally and externally and it consists of fire.

23. The Mūrti of Ugra in the form of the wind throbs itself and sustains everything and makes everything throb.

24. The Mūrti of Bhīma is in the form of the ether It splits the elements. It is all-pervasive and gives space to everything.

25. The Mūrti of Paśupati is the presiding deity of the Ātmans, immanent in the souls and splitting the binding cords of the Paśus.

26. The Mūrti of Maheśa named Īśāna, otherwise called the sun, illuminates the universe and moves about in the firmament.

27. The Mūrti of Mahādeva is the cause of the moon who delights and nourishes the universe with his nectarine rays.

28. The eighth Mūrti of the supreme lord Śiva is the Ātman. It pervades all the Mūrtis. Hence the universe has Śiva as its Ātman.

29. Just as the branches are nourished by watering

242. The Aṣṭamūrti concept of Śiva finds its parallel in Śrs Ch. 2. According to this concept, thr eight forms– Śarva, Bhava, Rudra, Ugra, Bhīma, Paśupati, Īśāna and Mahādeva symbolise the five gross material elements, the individual soul (kṣetrajña), the principle of heat (sun) and cold moon) respectively. There are variations in regard to their presiding position in certain purāṇas.

the roots of the tree, so also by the worship of Śiva his body, the universe, is nourished.

30. The propitiation of Śiva bestows protection, blessing and renders help unto all.

31. As the father is delighted at the pleasure of his sons and grandsons so also Śiva is pleased at the pleasure of all.

32. There is no doubt if any embodied soul is curbed it is a displeasing injury committed on the eight-bodied lord.

33. With pious emotions worship Śiva who presides over the universe in the form of Aṣṭamūrti Rudra, the great cause.

CHAPTER FOUR

(*The exalted magnificence of Gaurī and Śiva*)[243]

Kṛṣṇa said :—

1. O holy lord, it has been heard how this universe is pervaded by the Mūrtis of lord Śiva, of unmeasured brilliance.

2. Now I wish to know the innate nature of the great lord and the goddess. How is this universe having male and female traits presided over by them?[244]

Upamanyu said:—

3. I shall explain succinctly the glorious magnificene and the innate nature of Śiva and Śivā. It cannot be adequately explained in detail even by Śiva.

4. Śakti is Mahādevī herself and Mahādeva is one possessing Śakti. The entire universe of mobile and immobile beings is a fragment of their exalted magnificence.

5. Some objects are in the form of Cit and some in the form of Acit. Each of them is again twofold Śuddha and Para; Aśuddha and Apara.

243. For the similarity of expression and contents of this chapter see ŚRS. 3

244 Śiva in the half-male and half-female (ardhanārīśvara) form is the cause of the universe. The concept has its basis in the Puruṣa-Prakṛti doctrine of Sāṅkhya philosophers. For details see Sāṅkhyakārikā of Īśvarakṛṣṇa.

6. The wheel of Cit that undergoes worldly existence along with the wheel of Acit is Aśuddha and Apara. The other one is Śuddha and Para.

7. Both the Cit and Acit whether Para or Apara and the lordship of Śiva and Śivā are natural.

8. The universe is subject to the control of Śiva and Śivā, but Śiva and Śivā are not subject to the control of the universe.[245] Since the universe is to be ruled over, Śiva and Śivā are the sovereigns of the universe.

9. Just as Śiva so also the goddess. Just as the goddess so also Śiva. No difference shall be thought of between the two as between the moon and the moonlight.

10. Just as the moon does not shine without the moonlight so also though existing Śiva does not shine without Śakti.

11-12. Just as the sun does not exist without its light nor does the light thereof exist without the sun, so also there is mutual dependence between Śakti and Śaktimān. There is no Śakti without Śiva and no Śiva without Śakti.

13-14. The Śakti is the primordial and solitary one, of the form of Cit and depending on Śiva, by means of which Śiva can bestow worldly pleasures and salvation and which is of the same characteristics as Śiva, the great Ātman through the diverse befitting attributes of the lord.

15. The solitary and great Śakti of the form of Cit, is of parturient trait. It creates the universe with its manifold ramifications at the will of Śiva.

16. It is also called Mūlaprakṛti, Māyā and Triguṇā. It is threefold. The universe is hurled back by her and pervaded.

17. As one unit, as twofold, in hundreds and thousands Śaktis ramify themselves in their function.

18. At the will of Śiva, the great Śakti united with Śivatattva manifests from it at the first creation, like the oil from the gingelly seed.

19. Then the Śakti being agitated by the Kriyā

245 We aave emended the reading स विश्वस्य वशे शिवौ to न विश्वस्य वशे शिवौ and translated accordingly.

Śakti originating from the Śaktimān, the primordial sound originates atthe outset of creation.

20. The Bindu comes out of the Nāda; from Bindu comes out Sadāśiva. From him is born Maheśvara and Suddhavidyā originates from Maheśvara.

21. That is the deity of speech, the Śakti of Śiva named Vāgīśā; the same in the form of letters becomes manifest as Mātṛkā.

22. Then by the infusion of the infinite, Māyā creates Kāla, Niyati, Kalā and Vidyā and through Kalā, Rāga and Puruṣa.

23. From Māyā again originates the manifest consisting of the three Guṇas. From this Avyakta the three Guṇas become separated.

24-25. The three Guṇas are Sattva, Rajas and Tamas whereby the entire universe is pervaded. From the Guṇas, on being agitated and stirred up, the three deities are born as well as Mahat and other Tattvas in due order. At the behest of Śiva innumerable seeds are born. They are presided over by the infinite and other Vidyeśas, the Emperors.

26. In accordance with the difference in bodies, Śaktis are said to be different. They shall be known as having diverse forms both gross and subtle.

27. The Śakti of Rudra is called Raudrī, that of Viṣṇu Vaiṣṇavī; that of Brahmā Brahmāṇī and that of Indra Aindrī.

28. Of what avail is much talk? What is glorified as universe is pervaded by Śakti just as the physical body is pervaded by the immanent soul.

29-30. The entire universe of the mobile and immobile beings is full of Śakti. Kalā, the greatest Śakti of the great Ātman, is called Parā Śakti, and it follows the wish of the lord and creates the mobile and immobile universe.

31. Lord Śiva is Śaktimān possessing the three Śaktis of knowledge, activity and wish. He pervades the universe for ever and stays.

32. "This shall be this way." "This shall not be

this way." It is in this form that the wish of the lord permanently restrains activities.

33. Śakti of knowledge is in the form of Buddhi and it determines its effect, instrument, cause and purpose factually.

34. Śakti of activity in the form of conception formulates and evolves the effect—universe, in the manner wished for and in the manner determined.

35. When the threefold Śaktis are risen, the Śakti of parturient traits urged by the Paramā Śakti gives birth to the universe.

36. Śiva is called Śaktimān since he is in association with it. This universe born of both Śakti and Śaktimān is termed Śākta and Śaiva.

37. Just as no boy is born without parents, so also the universe of mobile and immobile beings does not originate without Śiva and Śivā. The universe has both a male and a female source, hence it is in the nature of male and female.

38. It is the effect of the superhuman power of male and female. It is presided over by a male and a female. Śiva is the great Ātman and Śivā the great Śakti.

39. Sadāśiva is Śiva and Manonmanī is Śivā, Maheśvara is known as Śiva and Śivā as Māyā.

40. Puruṣa is the great god and Prakṛti the great goddess. Rudra is the great god himself and Rudrāṇī is his beloved.

41. Viṣṇu is lord Viśveśvara and Lakṣmī his beloved. When Brahmā the creator is Śiva, Brahmāṇī is the beloved of Brahman.

42. The sun is lord Śiva and his light is Śivā. Mahendra is Śiva and Śacī is Pārvatī.

43. Firegod is Mahādeva and Svāhā Śivā. Yama is Śiva and Yamī is Śivā, the daughter of the mountain.

44. Nirṛti is lord Īśa. Nairṛtī is Śivā. Varuṇa is lord Rudra. Vāruṇī is Śivā.

45. Vāyu is the moon-crested lord Śiva and his wife is Śivā, the captivator of Śiva's mind. Sacrifice is the destroyer of sacrifice (=Śiva) and Ṛddhi is Śivā.

46. The moon is Śiva. Rohiṇī is Rudra's beloved. Īśāna is Siva. His Āryā is the goddess Umā.

47. Ananta the Serpent king is Śiva. Ananta's beloved is the goddess Śivā. Kālāgnirudra is Śiva. Kālī is Siva's beloved.

48. Puruṣa Manu is Śiva and Śatarūpā is Śiva's beloved. Dakṣa is lord Śiva himself and Prasūti is Parameśvarī.

49. Ruci is Śiva and Ākūti is Śivā. Bhṛgu is the lord, the destroyer of the eyes of Bhaga. Khyāti is the beloved of the three-eyed lord Śiva.

50. Marīci is lord Rudra. Sambhūti is Śarva's beloved. Aṅgiras is Śiva. Smṛti is Umā herself.

51. Pulastya is the moon-crested lord. Prīti is the wife of the trident-bearing lord. Pulaha is the destroyer of the Tripuras. His wife is the beloved of Śiva.

52. Kratu is Śiva the destroyer of sacrifice. Sannati is the beloved of the lord. Atri is the three-eyed lord. Anasūyā is Umā herself.

53. Kaśyapa is Śiva. His beloved is Śivā herself. Vasiṣṭha is Śiva and Arundhatī is the goddess herself.

54. All men are identical with Śiva. All women are identical with Maheśvarī. Hence all men and women are their exalted superhuman power.

55. Lord is the subject and his beloved is the object. Everything heard is the form of Umā and the hearer is the trident-holder Śiva.

56. All that is worthy of being enquired about is sustained by Śiva's beloved. The enquirer is the universal soul Śiva himself with crescent moon for an ornament.

57. Śiva's beloved holds all objects to be perceived and the perceiver is lord Viśveśvara himself with the crescent moon as the crest-jewel.

58. All objects of taste are identical with the goddess and Śiva is the taster. All lovable objects are identical with Śivā and Śiva is the lover.

59. Goddess Maheśvarī holds all objects of reflection. The reflecter is the all-pervading Lord himself.

60. Lord's beloved holds all objects to be understood. The understander is the lord himself.

61. Lord Śiva is the vital breath of all living beings. Śivā in the form of water is the existence of Prāṇa in all beings.

62. The beloved of Śiva is the abode of individual souls. Lord Śiva is the individual soul himself.

63. The day is the trident-bearing lord and Night is the beloved of Śiva himself. The ether is lord Śiva and the earth is Śiva's beloved.

64. The ocean is lord Śiva. The shore is the daughter of the king of mountains. The tree is the bull-bannered lord. The creeper is Śiva's beloved.

65. The lord holds all masculine beings. The goddess holds all feminine beings.

66. The beloved of Siva holds all words. The moon-crested lord holds all their meanings.

67. Whatever power is held by whatever object is identical with the goddess Viśveśvarī and Maheśvara.

68. O fortunate ones, whatever is great, holy, pure and auspicious is the expansion of their brilliance.

69. As the flame of the brilliant lamp illuminates the house so also their brilliance pervades the universe and illuminates it.

70. The great Śruti says that the excellence of the universe from the blade of grass to Śiva's Mūrti is due to their contact.

71. The two who are in the form of all and confer welfare on all shall be worshipped, bowed to and meditated upon always.

72. O Kṛṣṇa, the innate nature of the lord and the goddess has been explained to you by me in accordance with my ability but I have not exhausted it.

73. The innate nature of the lord and the goddess is beyond the minds of even great men. How can it be explained?

74. Just as it is present in the intellect and the minds, of the devotees who have dedicated their minds to the lord

and who do not turn to any one else, so also it is not present in the intellect of others.

75. The excellence and superhuman power that has been explained now is based on Prakṛti and is great as well. Those who know esoteric secrets understand the secret of non-Prākṛtika excellence.

76. The superhuman excellence of the lord which is non-Prākṛtika is that from which words recede along with the mind and the sense-organs.

77. That superhuman power of Parameṣṭhin is the greatest splendour, the greatest goal and the acme of achievement.

78. Persons who have conquered their vital breath and the sense-organs endeavour to achieve it in order to seal up the door to the prison in the form of womb.

79. A person who has understood the superhuman excellence of Śiva and Śivā which is the divine medicine to resuscitate the dead on being bitten by the serpent of worldly existence, is not afraid of anything.

80. The individual soul who understands factually the Parā and the Aparā excellences goes beyond the Aparā Bhūti and enjoys the Parā Bhūti (the greatest excellence).

81. O Kṛṣṇa, thus I have explained to you the innate nature of the great souls, Śiva and Śivā, though it is a secret because you are a qualified devotee of Śiva.

82. It. is the injunction of the Vedas that the Vibhūti of the lord and the goddess shall not be imparted to those who are not disciples or who are not devotees or who are not the followers of Śiva.

83. O Kṛṣṇa of great welfare, so you do not tell others about this. Mention it to people, like you, who are deserving.

84. He who imparts this Vibhūti of Śiva and Śivā to qualified and competent men is liberated from the ocean of worldly existence and attains Sāyujya[246] of Śiva.

246 Sāyujya is the fourth grade of liberation, the other three being Sārūpya, Sālokya aud Sānnidhya. Herein the aspirant attains absorption in the divine essence. But ŚP. recounts another grade also, namely *Kaivalya* which means the devotee's total merge or extinction in his godhead. See KRS II. 3 et seq.

85. By reciting this, crores of sins perish. Repeated thrice or four times it quells even more.

86. All displeasing enemies perish. Friends increase. Learning flourishes. Auspicious intellect functions in Truth.

87. He acquires devotion to Śiva, Śivā, their followers and attendants. He acquires whatever is pleasing and all other things undoubtedly.

88. One should recite this with purity of mind, devotion to Śiva and full conviction. If due to powerful previous Karmans the fruition is prevented, he shall repeat it again. There is nothing inaccessible to him.

CHAPTER FIVE

(*Knowledge of paśupati principle*)

Upamanyu said :—

1. This universe of the mobile and immobile beings is the cosmic body of the lord of the gods. The Paśus do not know it at all due to the intricacy of the Pāśa.

2. O scion of the family of Yadu, not knowing his great, nature, never subject to alteration or doubts, some sages call him many though he is one.

3. About the great lord, without beginning or death, some say he is Aparabrahmarūpa, some say he is Parabrahmarūpa.

4. According to them Aparabrahmarūpa is that aspect when the godhead is identified with the elements, Antaḥkaraṇa the Indriyas, the Pradhāna and the sensual objects. The Parabrahman is the great Brahman in the form of Cit.

5. The godhead is called Brahman because it is immense and it expands. Some say that the Īśa is of the form of Vidyā and Avidyā. Thus there are two forms of lord Brahman, the lord of Brahmā.

6. They say that Vidyā is Cetanā (consciousness) and Avidyā is Acetanā (insentience). The universe too

is in the form of Vidyā and Avidyā as belonging to the lord, the preceptor of the universe.

7. There is no doubt in this that the universe is his form because it is subservient to him. Others know the form of Śiva as delusion and Parā Vidyā.

8. Delusion usually means Ayathābuddhi (not knowing as it is) in regard to the objects. Vidyā is opposite to it where the knowledge is in the true form.

9. The great principle is devoid of alteration or doubts. The opposite thing is connoted by the word Asat as explained by those who propound the Vedas.

10. Since he is the lord of the two, Śiva is called the lord of the Sat and Asat. Some say that he is in the form of Kṣara and Akṣara. Others say that he is beyond Kṣara and Akṣara.

11. The living beings are called Kṣara. The Kūtastha is called Aksara. Both these are the forms of the lord because they are under his control.

12-13. Beyond the two is Śiva the quiescent. Hence he is Kṣarākṣarapara. Some say that Śiva is the great cause, that he is in the form of the universal as well as the individual and the cause of both. The Samaṣṭi is unmanifest, they say and the Vyaṣṭi is manifest.

14. They are the forms of the lord because they function at his will. Since he is their cause, those who know the meaning of the 'cause' say that Śiva the great cause is the cause of both the universal and the individual.

15-17. The lord is explained by some as the one who inheres in the form of Jāti and Vyakti. That which inheres whole bodies is called Jāti. Vyakti is in the form of the separate unit and is the support of Jāti. Both are protected by his Ājñā. So the lord is called Jātivyaktivapus.

18-21. By some Śiva is called Pradhāna-Puruṣa-Vyakta-Kālātman. Pradhāna is Prakṛti. Puruṣa is the individual soul. The twentythree principles constitute the Vyakta (manifest) Prakrti. Kāla is the sole cause of the transformation of the effected creation. Śiva is the lord, creator, activisor, router, and the cause of evolution and dissolution of all these, He is one, the emperor, the unborn.

Hence he is called 'Pradhāna-Puruṣa-Vyakta-Kāla-Svarūpavān'. He is the cause, leader, overlord and the creator of all these.

22. By some he is mentioned as the Ātman of Virāṭ and Hiraṇyagarbha. Hiraṇyagarbha is the cause of the worlds, Brahmā etc., Virāṭ is the cosmic form or being.

23. Śiva is called as the immanent and the great soul. Others say he is the Ātman of Prājña, Taijasa and Viśva.

24. Others say he is the fourth being Saumya. Others say that he is the measurer, measure and the measured as well as the intellect.

25. Others declare that he is the maker, the action, the effect, the instrument and the cause. Others say that he is the Ātman of wakefulness, dream and slumber.

26. Some call him the fourth one or the being beyond the fourth one. Some call him devoid of Guṇas or possessing Guṇas.

27-33. Some call him having worldly existence; Others having no worldly existence. Still others call him free, not free, terrible, gentle, passionate, passionless, inactive, active, possessed or devoid of sense-organs, stable, not stable, with colour or no colour, visible, invisible, expressible, inexpressible, in the form of word and sound or beyond that, possessed or devoid of thought and knowledge, comprehensible or incomprehensible, great and not great.

34. Thus his innate nature, the true form, is being doubted. The sages are unable to determine the true nature of the lord due to the presence of different ideas and beliefs.

35. On the other hand, only those who have resorted to the lord in all piety know Śiva, the great cause, without any strain.[247]

36. As long as the individual does not achieve the realization of the primordial lord who has no lord above him and who is the ruler of the worlds, he remains in misery

247 According to ŚP. the concentrated devotion, not the philosophical argumentation or the talented discour ses can resolve the perfect knowledge of Śiva.

bound by the noose. He undergoes the sufferings of the worldly existence in succession like the rim of the wheel.

37. When the seer sees the maker, the lord, golden in colour, the Puruṣa the origin of Brahma, he shakes off both merits and sins and becomes unsullied. He attains the great equality or union with the lord.

CHAPTER SIX

(The Principle of Śiva)

Upamanyu said:—

1-2. Śiva has no bondage due to the atoms, effects, Māyā, Prakṛti, cosmic intellect, ego, mind, sens-eorgans, Taṇmātras or the elements.

3. To Śiva of unmeasured brilliance there is no Kāla or Kalā; no Vidyā or Niyati; neither lust nor hatred.

4. He has no keen desire. He has neither happiness nor unhappiness; neither Karmans nor their after-effects; neither pleasure nor misery as a result of those Karmans.

5. He has no connection with the seats of feelings nor with the impressions of actions. He has no contact with enjoyments of pleasures nor with their impressions of the three units of time—past, present, future

6. He has no cause or maker; he has no beginning no end nor the intervening space. He has no activity or instrument. He has neither Akārya nor Kārya.

7. He has neither kinsman nor non-kinsman; he has no one to check or to urge. He has no lord, preceptor or protector. He has no superior or equal.

8. He has neither birth nor death; neither expectation nor disinclination. He is not subject to injunctions or prohibitions; he has neither liberation nor bondage.

9. He never has anything not conducive to welfare or inauspicious. He has everything auspicious since Śiva is the great Ātman.

10. Presiding over everything by means of his Śaktis, he is stationed without dropping his intrinsic nature. Hence he is known as Śiva.

11. Since the universe consisting of the mobile and immobile beings is presided over by Śiva, he is known as omniformed. One who knows him as such, is never deluded.

12. Śiva is Rudra. Obeisance to him. He is the great Puruṣa beyond the Sat. He has golden arms, he is the lord of gold.

13. Īśāna is the consort of Śivā. He is the trident-bearing, and bull-vehicled lord. The sole Rudra is the great Brahman. He is the black and tawny Puruṣa.

14. He shall be meditated upon in the cavity within the heart as minute as the tip of a hair, with golden hair, and lotus eyes. He is pink and copper-coloured.

15-16. He moves about golden in colour, blue-necked, both gentle and terrible and a mixure of the both, imperishable, deathless and unchangeable. Such is the great lord, the slayer of the god of death. He is liberated from the sentient and non-sentient. He is greater than the great universe.

17. Since the knowledge and supremacy of Śiva excels those of others he excels all the lords of the worlds so say the intelligent persons.

18. In the beginning he was the instructor of the scriptural texts to the Brahmans born during the period of re-creation.

19. He is not conditioned by time. He is the lord of all. He is the preceptor of all the preceptors, subject to the influence of Time.

20. His Śakti is pure, natural and all-excelling. His knowledge is unparalleled. His physical body is eternal and built to defy death.

21. His lordship is unrivalled, so also his happiness, undying strength, power of brilliance, virility, forbearance and mercifulness.

22. Since he is full and perfect he has no selfish end to be served by creation etc. The fruit of his activities is only the blessing of others.

23. Praṇava is the word expressive of lord Śiva. Praṇava is the greatest symbol of Śiva, Rudra and other words.

24. Undoubtedly the great Siddhi can be acquired by meditation on Praṇava that is expressive of Śiva and by the performance of its Japa.

25. Hence intelligent men well-versed in the Āgamas considering identity between the word and its meaning call the lord as single-syllabled.

26. In the Upaniṣads its Mātrās are four A,U, M and nāda.

27. The letter "A" is the Ṛgveda; "U" is the Yajurveda; "M" is the Sāmaveda and the Nāda is the Atharvaveda.

28. The letter "A" is the great Bīja, Rajas and the creator, the four-faced lord. The letter "U" is Prakṛti, the womb, Sattva and the protector Viṣṇu.

29. The letter "M" is Puruṣa, the seed, the Tamas and the annihilator Rudra. Nāda is the great Puruṣa, Īśa, Śiva, devoid of Guṇas and activities.

30. Praṇava expresses everything through the three Mātrās in three ways and indicates Śivātman through half a Mātrā.

31. All this is filled by that Puruṣa than whom there is nothing else greater; than whom there is nothing smaller nor bigger and who like a tree stands steady and stiff in the heaven.[248]

248 TĀ 10.10.3 ; Mahān. U. 10.4.

CHAPTER SEVEN

(*The principle of Śiva*)

Upamanyu said:—

1. His Śakti shall be known as natural and dissimilar to the universe in its characteristics. It is single but appears in many forms like the light of the sun.

2. Endless are the Śaktis, viz, wish, knowledge, activity and Māyā etc. just like the flames of fire.

3. The Puruṣas—Sadāśiva, Īśvaraaud others, Vidyeśvara Avidyeśvara and others and Prakṛti—greater than the greatest were born of this Śakti.

4. There is no doubt that the principles from Mahat to Viśeṣa, the deities Brahmā and others and whatever there is as effect are produced by it.

5. That Śakti is all-pervasive and subtle. It has the form of enlightenment and bliss. The moon-bedecked lord is called Śaktimān.

6. Śiva is the one who shall be known. Sivā is intellect, the Vedas, the firmness, stability, fixity and the Śakti of knowledge, wish and activity.

7. Ājñā is the great Brahman. The two Vidyās are Parā and Aparā, Śuddhavidyā and Śuddhakalā since everything is created by Śakti.

8. Māyā is Prakṛti. Jīva is Vikṛti. Whatever there is Sat or Asat is pervaded by Śakti.

9. The goddess enchants and deludes the universe without any strain through Māyā. She releases the Jīvas sportively.

10. With her ramified into twentyseven forms, the lord stands pervading the universe.[249] Hence the process of liberation functions.

11-17. Formerly some sages desirous of salvation held a discourse on Brahman. Their minds were pestered by doubts. They began to reflect and ponder. "What is the ultimate

249. Śiva-Śakti shall be distinguished from the Prakṛti of the Sāṅkhya system The Sāṅkhya conceives Prakṛti as the twentyfourth principle Śakti in the present context is identical with Śiva—the 27th principle (Liṅga P. 1. 71) and pervades all the Tattvas including Jīva and Īśvara.

reason? Whence are we born? Whereby do we live? Where is our final establishment? By whom are we presided over? Whereby do we permanently abide by happiness or other things? By whom was the untransgressable arrangement of the universe made? It is not befitting to take time, nature, destiny, chance as the ultimate reason. Nor can it be the Puruṣa or any of the living beings or a Yogin greater than these. Time etc. are insentient and cannot function as the ultimate reason. Though the Ātman is sentient and experiences happiness and misery yet it is incapable of ruling. After these reflections those who meditate can realise the Śakti of the lord, the splitter of the Pāśa but hidden by the Gunas. Through this Śakti when their binding cords are cut they can see the Śaktimān, the cause of all causes, through their divine eyes.

18. He is incomprehensible and through this Śakti he presides over all causes, including the Time-soul.

19. Then through his grace, the great Yoga and the path of devotion they can attain the supreme divine goal.

20. The Vedas declare that only those have permanent peace who see Śiva in their hearts along with that Śakti and none of the others.

21. Never is Śaktimān apart from the blissful Śakti due to the identity between Śakti and Śaktimān

22. In regard to salvation the sequence of knowledge and activity is not intended because if there is divine grace salvation is accessible to everyone.

23. Whether one is a god or an asura, an animal or a bird, a worm or a germ, one is liberated due to his grace.

24-25. There is no doubt that a child in the womb, a nascent child, a boy, a young, old or a dying man, a soul in heaven or hell, a fallen or a pious, or a wise man or a fool is immediately released if there is divine grace.

26. The merciful lord quells different dirts of his devotees though they may be unqualified. He is pleased with their devotion.

27. Their devotion is due to their grace and the grace is a result of devotion in view of the difference in states. A learned man is not deluded therein.

28. This devotion with grace as its antecedent and causing worldly pleasures and salvation cannot be acquired in a single birth.

29. Maheśvara is delighted with enlightened people not attached to worldly pleasures who follow the rules prescribed in Śrutis and Smṛtis and who achieve Siddhis in the course of several births.

30-31. When the lord of gods is delighted a modicum of devotion is generated in the individual with the consciousness, "My lord exists". Then he begins to be associated with penance and various Śaivite holy rites. After their performance and their frequent practice the devotion becomes greater.

32. As a result of that a greater grace is acquired. As a result of the grace liberation is attained. A liberated soul enjoys bliss.

33. There is no doubt that even a man of limited piety is spared the excruciating pain of being crushed in the machine of the vaginal passage after three births.

34. Service with or without the ancillaries is called devotion. It is threefold due to the three means of mind speech and body.

35. The meditation on Śiva's form is mental service. Repetition of mantras is verbal service. The rites of worship constitute the physical service.

36. This threefold service is called the holy rite of Śiva. It is of five kinds as explained by Śiva the great Ātman.

37-38. In brief they are penance, holy rites, repetition of mantras, meditation and knowledge. Penance is the rite of Cāndrāyaṇa, etc. What is termed holy rite is the worship of Śiva's phallic image. Japa is the repetition of the names of Śiva in three ways. Meditation is pondering over Śiva. What is mentioned in the Śaivite Āgamas as perfect knowledge is meant by the word knowledge here.

39. The Śaivite Āgama was narrated to Śivā by Śiva out of mercy for those who have resorted to him. That is the sole means of ultimate welfare.

40. An intelligent man seeking welfare shall avoid too

much adherence to sensual objects and increase devotion towards Śiva, the great cause.

CHAPTER EIGHT

(*The incarnations of Vyāsa*)

Lord Kṛṣṇa said :—

1-2. O lord, I wish to hear about Śiva's knowledge expounded by Śiva in the Vedasāra for the salvation of his devotees. It is incomprehensible to non-devotees, the unintelligent and those who do not practise Yoga. It consists of five topics. It is censured by the unwise stupid persons.

3. At places it is opposed to the rites prescribed for the different castes and men in different stages of life. At places it is the same. It has been adopted from the Vedas, their ancillary texts and from the systems of Sāṁkhya and Yoga.

4-5. It extends to a hundred crores of verses as narrated by lord Śiva. How shall the worship be performed, O lord? Who is authorised in the worship? What are the practices of Jñānayoga etc.? O sage of good rites, it behoves you to narrate all these things in detail.

Upamanyu said :—

6-7. I shall succinctly narrate the lore of Śiva condensed from the Vedas as narrated by Siva. I shall avoid its praises or condemnations. It is convincing and divine. It can be acquired only by the grace of the preceptor. It is conducive to salvation without any strain. A detailed explanation of the same is impossible.

8. Formerly, with th desire to create, lord Śiva, equipped with the causes of the effects already present, manifested himself from the unmanifest.[250]

250. The principle of evolution that the effect before its manifestation existed in the invisible form in its cause is the main doctrine of the Sāṅkhya system. In the present context ŚP. is influenced by this thought.

9. Then the lord, the sage, superior to all procreated the first of the gods Brahmā, the Brahmaṇaspati.

10. While being born, Brahmā saw the lord his father. The lord saw and commanded him.

11. Brahmā viewed by Rudra created the universe. He prescribed the rules for different castes and stages of life separately.

12. For the sake of sacrifice he created Soma. From Soma was born the heaven, earth, fire, sun, sacrifice, Viṣṇu and Indra.

13. They and the gods eulogised Rudra with the hymns dedicated to him. The lord stood before the gods with his face beaming with delight.

14. The lord took away their knowledge, sportively. The deluded gods asked him, 'Who are you, Sir?'

15-18. Lord Rudra said :—"I had been the only primeval being, O gods, I am and I shall be There is none except me or separate from me. I alone satisfy the universe through my splendour. There is none superior to or equal to me. He who knows me is liberated." After saying this the lord vanished there itself. Unable to see him the gods began to eulogise him with Sāmans. They performed the holy rites of Pāśupata as prescribed in the Atharvaśiras Upaniṣads. They smeared Bhasma all over their bodies.

19-25. In order to please them the lord came there with the Gaṇas and Umā. The leading gods saw the lord whom the awakened sinless Yogins of restrained breath see within their hearts. To the left of lord Śiva they saw the beautiful goddess, the greatest Śakti who followed the wish of the lord. The chiefs of the gaṇas who had forsaken worldiness and acquired the region of Śiva and the Siddhas were also seen. Then the gods eulogised the lord and the goddess with the divine hymns from the Vedas and the Purāṇas. The delighted bull-bannered lord saw the gods with mercy and spoke sweetly, 'I am delighted.' Then, bowing to him the gods asked him about this important topic

The gods said :—

26. O lord, how shall they worship you on the earth? What is the path? Who is authorised in the worship?

27. Glancing smilingly at the goddess, Śiva the chief of the gods revealed his terrible form brilliant as the sun.

28. It was equipped with the attributes of lordship. It comprised all splendours. It was surrounded by the Śaktis, images, planets and the gods.

29-31. The lord had eight arms and four faces. Half of that form was female. On seeing this wondrous form, Viṣṇu and other gods understood the lord as the sun and the goddess as the moon and the remaining parts as elements. They realised the universe of the mobile and immobile beings identical with him. Then they worshipped the lord and made obeisance to him.

32-33. O lord, be pleased to accept our worship. You have the colour of the saffron, the excellent disc and the colourful ornaments of gold. Your eyes resemble the lotus; you hold a lotus and you are the cause of Brahmā, Indra and Nārāyaṇa. The golden vessel is filled with excellent gems and water of brilliant hue. Vermilion and other things, Kuśa grass and flowers too are offered.

34. Obeisance to Śiva the quiescent, the primordial cause, to Rudra accompanied by the Gaṇas; obeisance to him in the form of the sun, to Viṣṇu, to Brahmā.

35-36. He who worships Śiva thus in the solar disc with pure mind, in the morning, midday and at dusk and offers the excellent Arghya, or bows and reads the verses pleasing to the ears does not find anything inaccessible. If he is a devotee he is certainly liberated.

37. Hence for the sake of virtue, wealth, love and salvation, one shall mentally verbally and physically worship Śiva in the form of the sun.

38. Then the lord stationed in the disc glanced at the gods, revealed the sacred scripture, the sequel to all the Āgamas and vanished.

39. Understanding that the Brahmins, Kṣatriyas and the Vaiśyas are authorised in the worship, the gods bowed to the lord and went the way they had come.

40. After a pretty long interval the sacred scripture was forgotten. The goddess seated in the lap of her husband asked him about it.

41. Urged by her, the moon-crested lord narrated to her the sacred scripture—the sequel to all Āgamas.

42. At the behest of Brahmā, it was propagated in the world by me, by my preceptor Agastya and the sage Dadhīca.

43. In the revolution of Yugas the trident-bearing lord incarnates himself on the earth and propagates the knowledge for the salvation of his devotees.

44-48. Now listen to the incarnations of Vyāsa who were masters of Yoga in the different Kalpas:—Ṛbhu, Satya, Bhārgava, Aṅgiras, the brahmin Savitṛ, Śatatejas, Dharma as Nārāyaṇa, Svaraksa, the intelligent Āruṇi, Kṛtañjaya, Kṛtañjaya (the second), Bharadvāja, the wise Gautama, sage Vācaḥśravas, the pious Sūkṣmāyaṇi, sage Tṛṇabindu, Kṛṣṇa, Śakti Śākteya, Uttara, Jātūkarṇya, Hari and sage Kṛṣṇadvaipāyana.

49-51. These incarnations of Vyāsa are up to the end of Dyāpara. There are the incarnations as Yogācāryaṣ of Śiva and their disciples. In different yugas the lord's disciples are four. Their disciples and future disciples are in hnndreds and thousands. By their endeavour, these are purified by their devotion and are liberated by their carrying out the behests of Śiva in the world.

CHAPTER NINE

(Śiva's incarnations as Yogācāryas)

Śrī Kṛṣṇa said:—

1. O lord, please enumerate the incarnations of Śiva as Yogācārya and his disciples in the different circles of Yugas.

Upamanyu said:—

2-6. The following twentyeight are the Yogācāryas in the seventh Manvantara, in the Vāraha Kalpa:—Śveta, Sutāra, Madana, Suhotra, Kaṅka, Laugākṣi, Mahāmāya, Jaigīṣavya, Dadhivāha, Ṛṣabha, sage Ugra, Atri, Supālaka, Gautama, sage Vedaśiras, Gokarṇa, Guhāvāsin, Śikhaṇḍin, Lāngulin, Mahākāla, Śūlin, Muṇḍīṣa, Viṣṇu, Somaśarman, and Lakulīśvara. These are in the order of the Yugas.

7. Each of these had four disciples of quiet minds. They are from Śveta to Ruṣya. I shall enumerate them in the proper order.

8-20. Śveta, Śvetaśikha, Śvetāśva, Śvetalohita, Dundubhi, Śatarūpa, Ṛcīka, Ketumān, Vikośa, Vikeśa, Vipāśa, Pāśanāśana, Sumukha, Durmukha, Durgama, Duratikrama, Sanat, Sanaka, Sananda, Sanātana, Sudhāman, Virajas, Śaṅkha, Aṇḍaja, Sārasvata, Megha, Meghavāha, Survāhaka, Kapila, Āsuri, Pañcaśikha[251], Bāṣkala, Parāśara, Garga, Bhārgava, Angiras, Balabandhu, Nirāmitra, Ketuśṛṅga, Tapodhana, Lambodara, Lamba, Lambatman, Lambakeśaka, Sarvajña, Samabuddhi Sādhyasiddhi, Sudhāman, Kaśyapa, Vasiṣṭha, Virajas, Atri, Ugra, Guruśreṣṭha, Śravaṇa, Śraviṣṭhaka, Kuṇi, Kuṇibāhu, Kuśarīra, Kunetraka, Kāśyapa, Uśanas, Cyavana, Bṛhaspati, Utathya, Vāmadeva, Mahākāla, Mahānila, Vācaḥśravas, Suvīra, Śyāvaka, Yatīśvara, Hiraṇyanābha, Kauśalya, Lokākṣi, Kuthumi, Sumantu, Jaimini, Kubandha, Kuśakandhara, Plakṣa, Dārbhāyaṇi, Ketumān, Gautama, Bhallavī, Madhupiṅga, Śvetaketu, Uśija, Bṛhadaśva, Devala, Kavi, Śālihotra, Suveṣa, Yuvanāśva, Śaradvasu, Akṣapāda, Kaṇāda, Ulūka, Vatsa, Kulika, Garga, Mitraka and Ruṣya.

21. These are the disciples of the lord, the Yogācārya. Their number is hundred and twelve.

22. These had become Śiddhas by Pāśupata rites. They used to dust their bodies with Bhasma. They knew the principles and meanings of the sacred texts. They were masters of the Vedas and Vedāṅgas.

23. They were engaged in Śiva's hermitage. They were devoted to Śiva's lore. They were free from attachments. Their minds were attached to Śiva alone.

24. They could bear the mutually clashing pairs—extreme cold, heat etc. They were self-possessed and engaged in the benefit of living beings. They were straightforward,

251. Kapila, Āsuri and Pañcaśikha are the originators of the Sāṅkhya system. (See Īśvarakṛṣṇa, Sāṅkhyakārikā) Here they are mentioned as the disciples of Yogācārya incarnation of Śiva.

soft and healthy. They had covered anger and their sense-organs.

25. They had strings of Rudrākṣa beads for their ornaments. Their foreheads were marked by Tripuṇḍras. Some had tufts of matted hair. Some had matted tresses. Some had shaven heads.

26. Mostly their diet was confined to fruits and roots. They regularly practised Prāṇāyāma. They were rich in their pride in Śiva. They were devoted to meditations upon Śiva alone.

27. They had destroyed even the seeds of the poisonous tree of worldly existence. They were ready to proceed to the city of Śiva.[252]

28. He who worships Śiva everyday after thinking about these and their preceptors attains Sāyujya with Śiva. No doubt need be entertained in this respect.

CHAPTER TEN

(*Devotion to Śiva*)

Śrī Kṛṣṇa said:—

1-2. O lord, foremost of all Yogins, O leader of the Gaṇas, O excellent sage, O preceptor having the lustre equal to that of the six-faced deity, O storehouse of knowledge, you have assumed the form of a sage but are really the supreme lord. You have incarnated on the earth for breaking the binding cords of men.

3. There is none else but you, among the gods and Dānavas in this universe who knows the true nature of Śiva.

4. Hence my mind is not satiated by drinking in the nectarine lore of the lord coming out of your mouth as if from that of the trident-bearing lord himself.

252. A mythical city 'Śivapura' on the Himālayas particularly on the Kailāsa peak is conceived as the abode of Śiva.

5. O holy lord, what was it that the goddess seated in the lap of her husband, the creator of the universe, had asked him?

Upamanyu said:—

6. You have very pertinently put the question O Kṛṣṇa. I shall explain it precisely to you of auspicious mind. You as the devotee of Śiva are the person fit to hear it.

7. Accompanied by the goddess, the lord went to his beautiful garden on the beautiful mountain Mandara abounding in beautiful caves.

8. Then Śubhāvatī, the beloved friend of the goddess with a smiling face, brought many full-blown flowers of great beauty.

9. Thereupon Śiva, the chief of the gods, seated the goddess on his lap and bedecked her with the flowers. He was much pleased with himself.

10-11. The gentle ladies bedecked in glittering ornaments working in the harem and the confidential attendants, the chiefs of Gaṇas served the goddess and the lord, with chowries in their hands.

12. Then pleasing discourses ensued for the diversion of the lord and the goddess and for the succour of the devotees who sought refuge in him.

13. Then seeing an opportune moment the goddess asked Śiva, the lord of the worlds.

The goddess said:—

14. How can the lord be brought under control by slow-witted men who are not interested in spiritual principles and who do not have self-control?

Lord Śiva said :—

15. I cannot be enticed either by holy rites or penance or Japas or postures or knowledge or by any other means except faith.[253]

16. If men have faith in me I can be brought under

253. The statement is reminiscent of the 'Śraddhā' doctrine of the Bhakti cult.

control, be touched, seen, worshipped and spoken to by some means or other.

17-18. Hence faith shall be sought and acquired by him who desires to subject me to his control. Faith supports the duties of the different castes and is generated in him alone who abides by all duties of the castes and stages of life. No one else has faith in me.

19. At my bidding, the duties as derived from the Vedas of the various stages in life were mentioned formerly by Brahmā.

20-21. That compendium of duties is called Brahmā's Dharma. It consists of expensive rites, and is attended with great stress and strain. The fruits are not comparatively plentiful. By resorting to this great Dharma it is possible for those persons of different castes who resort to me without seeking the support of others, and who have attained the rare faith, to attain virtue, love, wealth and salvation.

22-24. The duties of various castes and stages of life have been re-organised by me. This is my permanent injunction that only those who have devotion to me are authorised in those duties and not others. Hence those who resort to me along the path directed, become liberated from the binding cords of dirt, Māyā, etc. due to my grace. They attain my city[254] whence there is no return. Then they become identical with me and secure bliss.

25-26. Hence, after securing or not securing the duties mentioned by me if my devotee lifts himself up by his efforts, it is an acquisition of what is not acquired superior in qualities crores and crores of times. Hence, one shall practise the duties mentioned by me.

27. O noble lady, these are my incarnations as Yogācārya[255] in all the Manvantaras and thousands of generations.

28. O goddess, the knowledge of generations is inaccessible to those who are not my devotees, who are devoid of

254. The word 'pura' is synonymous with 'city' as well as 'body' gross or subtle.

255. The Yogācārya incarnations of Śiva are recounted in the previous chapter.

intellect and who do not practise Yoga. Hence one shall assiduously resort to these.

29. That is a great loss, a great blemish, a delusion, blindness and muteness, if excluded from the path of salvation one shall exert oneself elsewhere.

30. O goddess, my eternal Dharma is fourfold : Jñāna, Kriyā, Caryā and Yoga.

31. Jñāna is the knowledge of Paśu, Pāśa and Pati. Kriyā is the purificatory rite in regard to the six paths under the instructions of the preceptor.

32. Caryā is the practical application of the holy rites such as my worship and the duties of the different castes and stages in life as prescribed by me.

33. Yoga is the fixation of the mind in me, along the path indicated by me, restraining other activities.

34. O goddess, disciplining of the mind is far more excellent than many a horse-sacrifice. It is conducive to salvation. It is inaccessible to those who adhere to sensual objects.

35. The Yoga that removes previous sins, belongs only to the unattached who has conquered the group of sense-organs by restraints and observances.

36. Detachment gives birth to knowledge. Knowledge facilitates the functioning of Yoga.

37-41. One conversant with Yoga, though fallen, is surely liberated. The following shall be carefully maintained. Mercy shall be practised along with non-violence. Knowledge shall be acquired. Truth, non-stealing, faith in scriptures and God, self-restraint, teaching, studying, performing sacrifice, presiding over sacrifice, meditation, piety towards God and practice of knowledge. A brahmin who follows all these for the acquisition of the path of knowledge, attains perfect knowledge ere long and secures Yoga too. O beloved, the wise devotee burns the physical body in a trice with the fire of knowledge. Due to my grace, the devotee conversant with Yoga eschews the bondage of the Karmans. Karman is in the nature of both merit and demerit. Both these are hindrances to liberation. The Yogin shall eschew both the merit and demerit.

42. One is not subjected to bondage merely by the performance of rites. If the rites are performed with desire for the fruits thereof it results in bondage. Hence one shall abandon the fruits of actions.

43. O beloved, at the outset the devotee shall worship me externally by means of Karmayajña. Then he shall resort to the path of knowledge. Afterwards he shall practise Yoga.

44. The Yogins who have understood my innate nature by karma-yajña and who view a clod of earth, a pebble and a gold ingot all alike do not worship me further.

45. A Yogin engaged in the path of knowledge, an excellent sage permanently engaged in Yoga, my devotee enriched by purity of mind, shall attain my Sāyujya.

46. Those who have not had sufficient detachment in their minds but have resorted to me are authorised only in Jñāna, Caryā and Kriyā according to their deserts.

47. My worship shall be known to be two-fold: external and internal. My adorative service is three-fold, differing in view of speech, mind and body.

48. The same adorative service is further explained as fivefold, viz, penance, holy rites, Japa, meditation and knowledge.

49. My external worship is performed in the view of other persons. The same thing known and knowable to oneself alone is the internal worship.

50. The mind that is devoted to me is the true mind and not any mind as it is. The speech that pertains to my name is true speech and not anything else.

51. The body that is marked by the characteristic symbols as prescribed by me such as Tripuṇḍras, and that is engaged in rendering service unto me is the true body—nothing else.

52. By Karman my worship shall be understood and not such extraneous rites as sacrifice, etc. Tapas or penance is the withering of physical body for my sake and not the rites Kṛcchra, etc.

53. Japa is the repetition of either the five-syllabled mantra or the Praṇava or the Rudrādhyāya hymn and not the study of the Vedas.

54. Meditation is the pondering over my form and not the trances of the soul. Jñāna is the knowledge of my Āgamas and not the understanding of other topics.

55. O gentle lady, stability in the Tattvas shall be practised beginning with an external or internal object where the mind feels interested urged by previous impressions.

56. The internal worship is hundred times more excellent than the external one in view of the absence of flaws seen and their intermixture avoided.

57. Purity too is the internal one. External purity is not enough. A man though physically pure is not pure if he is devoid of inner purity.

58. O gentle lady, the adorative service whether external or internal shall be attended with devotion. If devoid of devotion, it is the cause of deceit.

59. I am content and pure. What shall be done unto me by men? Externally or internally only devotion is taken into consideration by me.

60. That activity the soul of which is devotion, O gentle lady, is my eternal Dharma. It shall be performed without yearning for the fruit thereof mentally, verbally and physically.

61. O goddess, resorting to me with the fruit in view is easily feasible since the seeker of the fruit can abandon me in case there is no desired fruit.

62. O pious lady, I am the bestower of fruits in accordance with the extent of devotion even to him who, though seeking fruits, keeps his mind well established in me.

63. Those devotees are dearer to me whose minds are attached to me without reference to fruits but who may later on solicit for favours.

64. Dearer unto me are those who resort to me with abject helplessness, unmindful of fruition or otherwise due to the impressions of previous actions.

65. Verily, they do not acquire any further gain than acquiring me. O goddess, my gain too is nothing else but acquiring them into my fold.

66. Their piety dedicated unto me due to my blessing is compelled to bestow the fruit on them, the fruit being the great beatitude.

67-69. They mention about eight traits for those authorised in Dharma, the noble souls who have dedicated their minds unto me without having recourse to anyone else, those who have favourable disposition to my devotees, who encourage my worship, or offer worship to me themselves or perform all activities of the body for my sake or have interest in listening to my stories, flutter in tones, eyes and limbs, remember me perpetually or surrender to me completely.

70-72. If these eight traits are present even in an out-caste he is equal to a leading brahmin, a sage, a glorious ascetic and a learned scholar. A master of four Vedas is not dearer to me than a Cāṇḍāla[256] devoted to me. Things can be given to and taken from him. He shall be worshipped like me. I am not lost to him nor is he lost to me who offers unto me with devotion, even a leaf, a flower, a fruit or mere water.

CHAPTER ELEVEN

(*The Śaivite knowledge*)

Lord Śiva said:—

1. O goddess, I shall now succinctly mention the duties stipulated on the basis of caste for my authorised devotees, the learned brahmins.

2-7. Daily bath thrice, rites in the holy fire, worship of the Liṅga, charitable gifts, pious feelings for the lord, mercifulness everywhere at all times, truthfulness, contentedness, belief in scriptures and God, non-violence to all living beings, bashful modesty, faith, study of scriptures, Yoga, imparting of knowledge to others, commenting on scriptures, celibacy, listening to spiritual topics, austerities, forbearance, purity, wearing of the sacred thread, upper garment and turban,

256. Here the use of the word 'Mleccha' is important. It signifies the proselytizing attempts of the Śaivite Ācaryas to induce the laity to their fold.

growing the tuft, not resorting to forbidden things, smearing and dusting with Bhasma, wearing Rudrākṣa, O goddess, the worship on festival occasions especially on the fourteenth day, the rite of drinking Brahmakūrca every month in accordance with injunctions, O beloved, worship after performing my ablution with the same, avoidance of the Śrāddha food offered for the propitiation of the manes and of the rice in all sacred rites, stale rice and rice gruel.

8. The avoidance of wine and even its smell or of Naivedya is applicable to all castes, especially the Brahmins.

9-11. The traits of Yogins are ten viz:—forbearance, quietude, contentment, truthfulness, non-stealing, celibacy, my knowledge, non-attachment to worldly objects, using Bhasma and refraining from too much adherence to all. The Vānaprasthas have all these traits as also the partaking of alms during the day. The Brahmacārins shall not take food during the nights.

12. Teaching, presiding over sacrifices and acceptance of monetary gifts are not prescribed by me for the Kṣatriya and the Vaisya class.

13-16. The following are the duties and traits of kings —protection of the people of all castes, slaying of the enemies in battle, chastisement of the wicked and hunting of harmful birds and animals, distrusting everyone everywhere but belief in my Yogins, intercourse with women on proper occasions, maintenance of armies, keeping themselves well informed about the activities of the people through spies spread everywhere always, wearing weapons, armour dusted with Bhasma. These are in brief the duties of kings following my instructions. The characteristics of a Vaiśya are cattle-breeding, trading and agriculture.

17. The duty of a Śūdra is service unto the persons of the other castes, making of parks and resorting to my holy centres.

18. Sexual approach only to one's own wife duly wed is prescribed for a householder and celibacy for all the other three, viz. Brahmacārins, Vānaprasthas and Sannyāsins.

19. The duty prescribed for women is service to their own husbands. Nothing else is an eternal Dharma for them.

O good woman, if the husband directs her she can worship me.

20. If a woman engages herself in holy rites thereby prejudicing her service to her husband she goes to hell undoubtedly.

21-25. Now I shall mention the eternal Dharma of widows. Holy rites, charitable gifts, penance, purity, lying on the bare ground, taking food only at night, celibacy, ash-bath, water-bath, quietness, silence, forbearance, self-composure in accordance with injunctions, observance of fasts on the eighth, eleventh and fourteenth days and on the full moon days and worship to me. Thus I have succinctly mentioned the eternal virtues of persons of differen stages and castes, of brahmins, Kṣatriyas, Vaiśyas, ascetics, Brahmacārins, vānaprasthas, householders, Śūdras and women, O gentle lady.

26. O goddess, I shall be meditated upon along with you for ever. The Japa of six syllables[257] shall be performed always. This is the brief compendium of duties as mentioned in the Vedas.[258]

27-30. Those who possess excellent devotion as a result of good impressions in their souls of previous actions, who possess the physical bodies assumed by themselves, who are purified by the essence of my perfect knowledge and who have become holy due to my grace are not effected by sins as the lotus-leaves are not effected by water whether they be attached to it or not. It may not be possible for them to maintain the duties of the different stages in life. They have neither duties to be performed nor evils to be avoided. They have no trance to be practised, no great goal to be attained. They are not subject to do's and dont's like me.

31. Just as I have nothing to be achieved since I am perfect, so also they have nothing to be attained because they are contented. It is undoubtedly so.

32. There is no doubt in this that they are fallen from the Rudraloka. They are Rudras who have assumed human forms for the benefit of my devotees.

257. The six-syllabled mantra of Śiva : Oṁ Namaḥ Śivāya.
258. Though prescribing rituals, yoga and other activities of the Śiva-cult, the Purāṇa does not reject the authority of the Vedas.

33. Just as my injunctions make Brahmā and others act so also their injunctions make other men act.

34. Their sins are quelled by their very vision in view of their excellence of good piety and in view of their carrying out my behests.

35. Proofs indicating excellent fruits are visible in men who have pious feelings for me. They comprehend things not seen before.

36. Suddenly their bodies may throb and tremble; they may perspire, shed tears; their voice may grow hoarse or cracked; they may have a sensation of great bliss. This may recur again and again.

37. The excellent men can be understood by these never-failing indications severally or collectively or by means of the pious feelings of the low, excellent and the middling types.

38. Just as iron piece in conjunction with the fire is no mere iron piece so also they are not mere human beings. Thanks to my grace.

39. A learned man shall not treat these Rudras with contempt by considering them ordinary men because they have assumed human forms with hands, feet and the like.

40. Insult offered to them by men of confused intellect quells glory, longevity, family and conduct and may cause their fall into hell.

41-43. All those regions except mine, i.e. those of Brahmā, Viṣṇu, Indra, and others who have been uprooted though they may be great souls, are easily to be destroyed like cotton. The prosperity of Buddhi, Prakṛti, and Puruṣa is impure. Hence it shall be eschewed by those who are desirous of the region beyond Guṇas. Of what avail is this talk? By whatever means it may be, fixing of the mind in me is the only way to achieve welfare.

Upamanyu said:—

44. Thus the brief resume of essential knowledge has been expounded by lord Śiva, the great Ātman, for the welfare of the worlds.

45. The Vedas, Śāstras, Itihāsas, Purāṇas and other

lores are but extensive glosses and commentaries of this succinct account of perfect knowledge.

46. This succinct account contains the six topics, viz., Jñāna, Jñeya, Anuṣṭheya, Adhikāra, Sādhana and Sādhya.

47-48. Jñāna is the knowledge acquired from the preceptor. Jñeya is the Pāśa, Paśu and Pati. The Anuṣṭheya is the worship of the Liṅga. It is the devotee who is authorised. Sādhana is Śiva's mantra and Sādhya is the equality with Śiva. If one has the knowledge of the epitome of the six topics one has attained omniscience.

49. After worshipping Śiva externally at the outset by means of Karmayajña with devotion and in accordance with one's affluence, the devotee shall afterwards be engaged in inner sacrifice.

50. If for more virtue one is interested in the inner and not in the external working, the noble soul need not perform the external worship.

51. O Kṛṣṇa, neither within nor without has he ever any duty, he who is contented with the nectar of knowledge and who has identified his Ātman with Śiva by means of his devotion.

52. The devotee shall eschew in order the external and internal worships. Through Jñāna he shall see the Jñeya and then eschew the Jñāna also.

53. If the mind is not concentrated on Śiva, of what avail is the rite even when performed? If the mind is concentrated, of what avail is the rite duly performed ?

54. Hence one shall fix the mind in Śiva by some means or other without performing the rites or performing them internally or externally in order.

55. Persons who have fixed their minds in Śiva, good men who have stabilised their intellect will have the greatest bliss everywhere both here and hereafter.

56. The Siddhis are achieved by the mantra, 'Oṁ Namaḥ Śivāya'. Hence the mantra shall be acquired for the acquisition of the great magnificence which has nothing parallel to it.

CHAPTER TWELVE

(*The glory of the five-syllabled mantra of Śiva*)

Lord Kṛṣṇa said:—

1. O omniscient excellent sage, ocean of all knowledge, I wish to hear precisely about the glory of the five-syllabled mantra.

Upamanyu said:—

2. It is impossible to explain in detail the glory of the five-syllabled mantra even in hundreds of crores of years. Hence hear it in brief.

3-5. The six-syllabled mantra is found in the Veda and Śivāgama. It facilitates the understanding of all topics by the devotees of Śiva. It consists of very few syllables but is pregnant with meaning. It is the essence of the Vedas. It is conducive to salvation. This expression of auspicious nature is devoid of doubts. It is achieved by the order of Śiva. It is attended by many Siddhis. It is divine and delightful to the mind. That expression 'lord Śiva' is majestic and decisive in meaning.

6. The omniscient lord Śiva mentioned the mantra, "Oṁ Namaḥ Śivāya" for the acquisition of all topics and meanings by the embodied beings since it can be easily uttered through the mouth.

7. The first mantra consisting of six syllables is the seed of all lores. It is very subtle but serves a great purpose. It shall be known like the seed of the banyan tree.

8. The omniscient lord, the creator of everything, the all-pervasive Śiva who is beyond the three attributes, is stationed in the single-syllabled mantra Om.

9-10. The five subtle Brahmans are stationed in the mantra "Namaḥ Śivāya" occupying one syllable each. Thus in the six-syllabled subtle mantra, Śiva in the form of Pañca Brahmans[259] is stationed in the way of Expressed and Expressive. Innately Śiva is 'Expressed' and the mantra is 'Expressive' due to its comprehensibility.

259. See Vāyu II. 3. 5.: ŚRS 1. 36.

11. This state of being the expressive and the expressed is beginningless inasmuch as this terrible ocean of worldly existence functions without a beginning.

12-16. Śiva too is beginningless and he is the releaser of persons from the worldly existence. Just as the medicine is naturally antagonistic to ailments so also Śiva is antagonistic to the ills of worldly existence. If the lord of the universe had not been in existence, the whole universe would have been gloomy, since the Prakṛti is insentient and the Puruṣa is ignorant. Pradhāna, the atom etc. are insentient. They never function as the makers themselves without an intelligent cause. The instruction in virtue and evil, the bondage and salvation, the activity of reflection—in view of all these things the first creation of men would not have been possible without the omniscient lord. Just as the patients will be devoid of joy and be distressed without the physician so also the people would be in distress without the lord.

17. Hence, surely there is the lord, the primordial omniscient, perfect, Sadāśiva, the protector of persons from the ocean of worldly existence.

18. Śiva is devoid of beginning, middle and end. He is the lord innately pure, omniscient and perfect as mentioned in Śaivite Āgamas.

19. This mantra expresses him. He is the person expressed by the great Mantra.

20. The Śivajñāna, is as extensive as the expression of Śiva, the six-syllabled mantra, 'Oṁ Namaḥ Śivāya'.

21-23. This mantra is a positive statement and not a parable. How can Śiva, who is all-perfect, all-pervasive, innately pure and who blesses the worlds, mention a false theory ? As things stand by nature along with their virtues and flaws, and the fruits they are capable of producing, how can the omniscient being mention untruth ? Only one influenced by passion, ignorance and other flaws will speak untruth.

24. Those two faults are not present in the lord. How can he then make a wrong statement ? Surely therefore the expression that is uttered by Śiva, the omniscient without any flaw, is authoritative.

25. Hence, the statements of lord Śiva shall be faithfully considered by a learned man. In regard to merits and sins as they are, a person having no faith in him falls.

26. The good statements uttered by the sages quiet and calm for the achievement of heaven and salvation shall be considered 'sacred utterances.'

27. The utterances that are actuated by passion, hatred, falsehood, anger, lust and greediness are bad. They cause one's fall into hell.

28. Of what avail is that statement of ignorance and lust which is the cause of worldly pain even if it be polished, soft and charming?

29. Even that ugly statement which on being heard brings in welfare and the destruction of lust etc., should be considered auspicious.

30. Although there are many mantras, there is nothing like the holy mantra uttered by Śiva.

31. The Vedas and Śāstras along with their ancillaries are present in the six syllables. Hence there is no other mantra equal to this.

32. Just as an aphorism is ramified and expanded by its gloss, the six-syllabled mantra is expanded by seven crores of great and subsidiary mantras.

33. Whatever texts there are, the texts expounding Śiva's knowledge, the repositories of lore, they are the commentaries of the succinct aphorism, the six-syllabled mantra.

34. Of what avail are many mantras and Śāstras full of details to one whose heart is firmly established in the mantra "Oṁ Namaḥ Śivāya?"

35. If anyone has stabilised the Mantra "Oṁ Namaḥ Śivāya" by frequent practice, he has learnt all, heard all and performed all.

36. Life is fruitful indeed, of the person, at the tip of whose tongue is present the set of three syllables 'Śivāya' prefixed with the word denoting obeisance.

37. A person steady in the Japa of the five-syllabled mantra is released from the cage of sins whether he be a Śūdra, base-born, fool or a learned man.

38. This was mentioned by the lord when asked by the goddess, for the benefit of all men, particularly of brahmins.

CHAPTER THIRTEEN

(The greatness of the five-syllabled Mantra)

The goddess said :—

1-3. O great lord, how are your devotees liberated in the defiled period of Kali, invincible and untransgressable, when the world is enveloped by the darkness of sin, when people are averse to the practice of holy rites, when the legitimate activities of different castes and stages in life have declined, when great danger is imminent, when the question of the rights of the people is involved in doubts, when deviation from duty is certain, when the continuity of spiritual instructions is broken and when the order of preceptors and disciples has disappeared?

Lord Śiva said:—

4. Men of the Kali age are liberated when their souls are purified by devotion after resorting to my pleasing Mantra of five syllables.

5-6. My five-syllabled Mantra affords protection from the fear of worldly existence to those whose minds are inclined towards me although they may be of distorted outlook, greedy, deceitful, ruthless, ungrateful and defiled by unimaginable and inexpressible faults, mental, verbal and physical.

7. O goddess, often I have promised that in this world even a fallen man may become liberated through this Mantra if he happens to be my devotee.

The goddess said :—

8. If a fallen man does not deserve holy rites in any respect, the rites performed by him are conducive to hell.

Then how can the fallen man be liberated through this Mantra ?

Lord Śiva said:—

9. O good woman, what you have said is true. Now listen to what has been a great guarded secret hitherto.

10. Yes, surely, if the fallen man, under delusion, were to worship me with other mantras, excluding the five-syllabled one, he is sure to fall into hell.

11. Persons who live on water or air and those whose bodies are emaciated due to holy rites do not attain my region through those holy rites.

12. But he who worships me even once with devotion repeating the five-syllabled mantra, attains my region through the weightiness of this Mantra alone.

13. Hence, penances, sacrifices, observances and holy rites are not equal to even a croreth part of the worship with the five-syllabled mantra.

14. Indeed he who worships me with the five-syllabled mantra becomes liberated if he is in bondage.

15. He who worships me even once with the five-syllabled mantra with or without the Rudra mantra is liberated even if he is a fallen or a foolish man.

16. O goddess, he who worships me with the six-syllabled or with the five-syllabled mantra, with the Vedic mantra as its ancillary, with devotion to me, is liberated.

17-18. A fallen man or one not fallen can worship with this mantra. My devotee who has conquered anger may or may not be one who has attained me. One who has attained me is a billion times superior to one who has not attained. Hence one should try to attain me by worshipping me with this mantra.

19. He who worships me with this Mantra, being equipped with friendship and other attributes with devotion and celibacy attains similarity to me.

20. Of what avail is much talk ? The devotees are authorised in my five-syllabled mantra which is the most excellent one.

21. It is the efficacy of the five-syllabled mantra where-

by the worlds, the Vedas, the sages, the eternal virtues, the entire universe, and the gods stand steady.

22. At the advent of dissolution when the mobile and immobile beings perish, everything becomes merged in its cause.

23. O goddess, I am the only one staying then. There is no second one anywhere. Then all the Vedas, scriptures etc. are stationed in the five-syllabled mantra.

24. Protected by my Śakti they do not perish. The creation is evolved out of me differently through the Prakṛti and the Ātman.

25-27. Then comes a subsidiary dissolution of the forms and attributes. Then lord Nārāyaṇa assumes the physical body of Māyā and lies on the serpent couch in the midst of the water. The five-faced lord Brahmā born of his umbilical lotus becomes desirous of creating the three worlds. But having none to assist him he becomes incapable. Hence he creates at the outset the ten sages of unmeasured splendour, his mental sons.

28. In order to enhance their achievement Brahmā said to me 'O great lord, please bestow the power on my sons.'

29. Thus requested by him, I who had assumed five faces, mentioned the five syllables, to the lotus-born one.

30. Accepting them with his five faces, the grandfather of the worlds understood me as the great lord, the expressive of great meaning.

31. After understanding the process of its application in accordance with the rules, the patriarch who achieved the Mantra imparted it along with its meaning to his sons in the exact manner.

32-34. After securing the excellent Mantra from him, they desired to propitiate me along the way indicated by him. There is a mountain Mūjavat on the beautiful peak of Meru. It is my favourite resort, ever glorious and always guarded by my devotees. Eager to create the world they performed penance there for a thousand years according to the calculation of the gods, taking in only air.

260. It is a peak of mount Meru, well known for Soma production; it is also mentioned in the RV.

35-36. On seeing their devotion I appeared before them immediately and explained to them all the details, viz., the sage, metre, Kīlaka, Bījaśakti, deity, Nyāsa, the six ancillaries, the limits of the quarters and their application. The aim was to multiply creation through the sages.

37. Thenceforth as a result of the efficacy of the mantra, the sages reinforced by austerities are performing the creation of the gods, asuras and human beings in a splendid way.

38. Now I mention the form of this great mantra. The word 'Namaḥ' shall be uttered at first. It shall be followed by the word 'Śivāya'.

39. This five-syllabled lore is present in all Upaniṣads. It is eternal as well as the seed of all living beings.

40-42. It is the goddess, my own expression coming out of my mouth at first. The goddess having the splendour of molten gold, plump, lifted-up breasts, four arms, three arees, and the crescent moon as the crest-jewel. Her hands are as tender as lotuses. She is gentle with the gestures of boon and protection; she is possessed of all characteristics. She is bedecked in ornaments. She is seated on a white lotus. Her tresses are blue and curly.

43. She has five colours with beaming discs, viz., yellow, black, smoky, golden and red.

44-45. If they are separately worshipped, they shall be adorned with Bindu and Nāda. Bindu is in the form of the semicircular moon. Nāda is in the form of the flame of the lamp. O excellent-faced lady, the Bīja of this Mantra is ranked as the second among the well-known Bījas. The Bīja of the fourth begins with a long vowel. The fifth one is mentioned as Śakti.

46. O good-faced lady, the sage of this mantra is Vāmadeva; the metre is Paṅkti; the deity, I am myself.

47. The several individual sages of the letters are, O good lady, Gautama, Atri, Viśvāmitra, Aṅgiras and Bharadvāja.

48. The metres severally are Gāyatrī, Anuṣṭup, Triṣṭup, Bṛhatī and Virāṭ. The deities severally are Indra, Rudra, Viṣṇu, Brahmā and Skanda.

49. As their places, my faces beginning with the one in the east and ending with the one above are taken. They are identified with the letters "Na" etc. in order.

50. The first, second and the fourth letters are Udātta. The fifth is Svarita and the third is Anudātta.

51. This mantra is otherwise called Mūlavidyā, Śivaṃ, Śaivasūtra, and five-syllabled. This Śaiva mantra is my great heart.

52-53. The letter "Na" is the head; "Maḥ" the tuft; "Śi" the armour; "Vā" the eye; "Ya" the missile. At the end of each letter shall be uttered—Namaḥ, Svāhā, Vaṣaṭ, Huṁ, Vauṣaṭ, Phaṭ.

54. There too, the same is the Mūlamantra with a slight difference. The fifth Varṇa is bedecked by the twelfth vowel ('ḥ')

55. The devotee shall worship me with Japa, Homa, etc., mentally, verbally and physically through this Mantra.

56. Let it be in accordance with their intellect, injunction in the scripture, time, inclination, capacity, wealth and their taste.

57. O Goddess, my worship will lead to salvation whenever, wherever and by whomsover it may be done if it is with devotion.

58. O good woman, whatever is done unto me by one whose mind is attached to me, whether in the proper order or in the reverse order, is dear and is auspicious to me.

59. I have made certain rules governing my devotees who are not unduly helpless in regard to all sacred scriptures.

60. There at the outset, I shall explain the procedure of practising the mantra without which the Japa is futile and with which it is fruitful.

CHAPTER FOURTEEN

(*The glory of the five-syllabled Mantra*)

Lord Śiva said :—

1. O good-faced lady, a Japa without the behest of the preceptor, holy rites, faith and the prescribed fees is fruitless though the behest might have been secured.

2. If a mantra is well practised with the acquisition of behest, attended with holy rites, equipped with faith in me and accompanied by fee it is greatly efficacious.

3-4. The devotee shall approach the brahmin preceptor who knows the principles, performs Japa, is devoted to meditation and endowed with virtues. He shall strenuously propitiate him mentally, verbally, physically and monetarily. He shall possess the purity of piety.

5-6. A brahmin devotee shall worship the preceptor always strenuously. If he is affluent he shall present devoutly to his preceptor excellent horses, elephants chariots, ornaments, garments, grain and riches.

7-8. He shall not be stringent about money if he desires to achieve Siddhi for himself. Dedicating himself thereafter along with his possessions to the preceptor and after undeceitfully worshipping him to his capacity, he shall learn the mantra and derive knowledge in due order.

9-13. When the preceptor is satisfied he shall let him stay for a year serving him without arrogance. On an auspicious day thereafter he shall make him take his bath after observing fast. For the sake of purity he shall again be subjected to ablution with vessels full of ghee and sacred water wherein holy materials shall be put. He shall dress him well and bedeck him with fragrant garlands, ornaments and garments. The Puṇyāha mantras shall be recited and brahmins worshipped. Then in a holy spot, near the seashore, river bank, cowpen temple or in the house itself, at an auspicious hour when the day is conducive to achievement, when the conjunctions of stars are devoid of defects, he shall bless him and impart to him my knowledge duly.

14-15. In a secluded spot the preceptor delighted in

mind shall repeat the mantra with due accents. He shall then make the disciple repeat it. Then the preceptor shall say 'Let there be welfare. Let there be auspiciousness around. Let everything be pleasing and auspicious'. Thus the preceptor shall impart the mantra and allow him to practise it.

16. Getting thus the mantra and the permission from the preceptor the disciple shall perform the Saṁkalpa with pure mind and repeat the mantra with the rite of initiation.

17. As long as he lives he shall repeat the mantra one thousand and eight times everyday without thinking of anything else and devotedly attached to it alone. He attains the greatest goal.

18. He who completes the Japa four hundred thousand times with great devotion, taking food only in the nights with full self-control, is said to be a Pauraścaraṇika.

19. There is none equal to him in the world who, after the Puraścaraṇa is over, continues to perform the Japa everyday. He is Siddha himself and confers Siddhi on others too.

20-23. He shall take bath, sit in a pleasing posture in a sacred spot. He shall meditate on me in his heart along with you and shall remember his preceptor. He shall sit facing the north or the east, observe silence and concentration of the mind, purify the five principles by means of Dahana and Plāvana rituals. He shall perform the Mantranyāsa, make his body worthy and pure, meditate on us restraining Prāṇa and Apāna. He shall remember the respective place, form, sage, metre, the presiding deity, Bīja, Śakti and the statement. Then he shall perform the Japa of the five-syllabled mantra.

24. Experts in the meanings of Āgama texts say that the mental Japa is excellent, the Upāṁśu Japa (in a low voice) is the middling. The verbal Japa is of the lowest quality.

25. The Japa with Rudra as the presiding deity is the most excellent, that with Viṣṇu as the presiding deity is the middling and that with Brahmā as the presiding deity is of the lowest quality.

26. The muttering of the mantra with high, low or middle accentuation, the words and the letters being clear or otherwise, is called the verbal japa.

27. Upāṁśu Japa is the one where the tongue throbs and there is slight utterance. It may not be heard by others or may be slightly heard.

28. Mental Japa is that where the series of letters are thought well and the words and their meanings are pondered over.

29. If the efficacy of the Vācikajapa is one, that of the Upāṁśu Japa is hundred ; that of the Mānasajapa is a thousand; that of the Sagarbha Japa is hundred times more.

30. The Japa performed with the prāṇāyāma is Sagarbha Japa. In the first and the last even Agarbha Prāṇāyāma is commended.

31. After performing the Prāṇāyāma forty times, the intelligent devotee, knowing the meaning of the mantra, shall remember the mantra. If he is unable to repeat so many times he shall repeat as many times as his physical strength permits him.

32. He shall perform five, three or one Prāṇāyāma whether Agarbha or Sagarbha. The Sagarbha Prāṇāyāma is better of the two.

33. The Sadhyāna Japa is a thousand times better than the Sagarbha Japa. One of the five types of Japas shall be performed upto the extent of one's ability.

34-36. There are various ways of counting the number of times the mantra has been repeated. Counting with the fingers is one mode. Eight times that number can be calculated by lines, ten times by dolls, hundred times by shells or gems, thousand times by corals, ten thousand times by crystal pieces, hundred thousand times by pearls, million times by seeds of lotuses, a crore of times by gold pieces, infinite time by a bundle of Kuśa grass or Rudrākṣa beads.

37-38. A rosary containing thirty beads of Rudrākṣa for Japa bestows wealth, containing twentyseven beads yields nourishment, containing twentyfive beads bestows salvation, containing fifteen beads bestows the fruits of black magic.

39. The thumb used in counting the number bestows salvation. The index finger destroys enemies. The middle finger bestows wealth. The ring finger brings about calmness and peace.

40-41. If there are hundred and eight beads that rosary is the most excellent. If it has hundred beads it is excellent. If it has fifty beads it is the middling. With fifty-four beads it is good. The Japa shall be performed with these different rosaries. They must not be exhibited to anyone.

42. The use of little finger in the Japa shall be avoided. In the act of Japa it is held to be auspicious. The Japa shall be performed by means of the thumb in contact with other fingers.

43. If Japa is performed without the thumb it is futile. If performed in the house it is ordinarily efficacious. If performed in the cowpen it is hundred times more.

44. In a holy forest or park it is thousand times more. On a holy mountain it is ten thousand times more. On the banks of a river it is hundred thousand times more.

45-46. They say that the Japa performed in a temple is a crore of times more efficacious. That performed in my presence is infinite number of times more efficacious. Japa in the presence of the sun, fire, preceptor, moon, lamp. water, brahmins and cows is commended. Sitting east of these is conducive to favourable control; south of these is of the same nature as black magic.

47-50. West of these is conducive to riches and north of these is peace-bestowing. If Japa is performed in the presence of sun, fire, brahmins, gods, preceptors and others one should not turn the face away from them. One should never perform Japa with the turban on, or wearing an armour or a bodice, in the nude, or with the hair dishevelled, or the neck covered, or without the Pavitra in the hand or while impure or while lamenting. While performing Japa the following must be avoided—anger, intoxication sneezing, spitting, yawning and seeing a dog or a lowborn person. If they happen, Ācamana shall be performed or I shall be remembered along with you.

51-53. Or he shall see the luminary bodies or he shall

perform a Prāṇāyāma. One should not perform Japa without a seat to sit on nor shall it be performed lying down, or standing up and walking. One shall not perform Japa in the open street or in an inauspicious place or in darkness. Legs shall not be stretched while performing the Japa nor shall one be in the cocklike posture, or seated in a vehicle or in a couch. Japa shall not be performed when one is worried. If one is competent one shall perform many Japas. Weak persons shall perform Japa according to capacity.

54. Of what avail is much talk? Hear these words in brief. A person of good conduct, performing Japa and meditating purely attains welfare.

55. Good conduct is the greatest virtue. It is the greatest wealth, the greatest knowledge and the greatest goal.[261]

56. A person devoid of good conduct is censured in the world. He will not be happy in the other world Hence one must possess good conduct.

57. Doing the duties prescribed by the Vedas, Śāstras and the followers of the Vedas is meant by the word good conduct, nothing else.

58. Good conduct is also the conduct of the good. Theism is the source of goodness.

59. If he is a believer he will not err from the path of good conduct or commit errors or get defiled. Hence one shall be a believer in God and the Vedas.

60. Faith is the conviction that happiness and misery are attained by means of good and evil deeds hereafter too just as in this world.

61. O beloved, I shall tell you another secret which shall be guarded well. It shall not be mentioned to any one and every one or to an atheist brute.

62. In the age of Kali there is no greater protective factor than the five-syllabled Mantra to a fallen or a low-born person devoid of good conduct.

63. This mantra is not ineffective when repeated by a person whether walking or standing or doing any other work or whether he is pure or impure.

261. Manu I. 108-110.

64. This mantra is not ineffective even if it is not properly imparted by the preceptor. It is not ineffective even in the case of persons not caring for good conduct and who have not purified the six paths.

65. This mantra is not ineffective in the case of a base-born, a fool, a deluded person, a fallen man and a lowly one transgressing the bounds of decency.

66. There is no doubt in this that this mantra becomes efficacious in the case of a man endowed with devotion to me whatever be his condition. It is not so in the case of other mantras.

67. O beloved, in the case of this mantra, the auspicious hour, date, star, day of the week etc. need not be taken into consideration too much. It is ever wakeful, not slumbering.

68. This great mantra is never harmful to anyone. It may be either Susiddha, or Siddha or Sādhya.

69. It is Susiddha if it is imparted by a preceptor who is a Siddha. If it is imparted by a preceptor who is not a Siddha it is Siddha. The mere mantra is Sādhya.

70. If one has faith in me, the mantra and the preceptor, the mantra will undoubtedly be achieved whether it is Asādhita or Sādhita.

71. Hence a scholarly devotee shall resort to the five-syllabled mantra eschewing other mantras attended with risks in the matter of authorisation.

72. There is no guarantee that if the other mantras are achieved this mantra too will be achieved. But if this mantra is achieved all the other mantras will be achieved.

73. Just as, O goddess, I am not achieved even if the other gods are attained but if I am attained the other gods too are attained so also is the case with the Mantras.

74. Since this mantra functions without reference to castes, the defects found in the other mantras are not found in this mantra.

75. Still this mantra shall not be used for the trivial benefits or against insignificant opponents. Then alone this is very efficacious.

Upamanyu said:—

76. Thus the mode of repeating this mantra of five syllables was explained to the goddess by lord Śiva himself for the benefit of the worlds.

77. He who glorifies this with devotion or listens to it with a pious mind is liberated from all sins and attains the greatest goal.

CHAPTER FIFTEEN

(*The greatness of the Preceptor*)

Śrī Kṛṣṇa said :—

1-2. O holy lord, the greatness of the mantra has been mentioned by you as well as the rules governing its practice as found in the Śruti itself. Now I wish to hear the details of Śivasaṁskāra. While explaining the mode of accepting the mantra it has been slightly indicated.

Upamanyu said :—

3. Well, I shall mention to you the holy and sin-destroying details of consecration as explained by Śiva.

4. The consecration is so called because thereby the devotee is authorised in a splendid manner. It is the mode of purifying the six paths.

5. The same Saṁskāra is called initiation because thereby the perfect knowledge is imparted and the bondage of Pāśa is quelled.

6. The initiation as ordained by Śiva the great Ātman in the Śivāgama is threefold—pertaining to Śiva, Śakti and mantra.

7-8. The initiation of Śiva is that whereby at the mere sight, touch and talk of the preceptor the individual soul gains immediately the consciousness quelling the bondage. It is twofold in view of the difference in the destruction of bondage, viz. acute and more acute.

9. That is Tīvratara whereby the bliss is immediately attained. The acute one purifies the sin of the living man effectively.

10. The Śaktī form of initiation coupled with knowledge is performed by the preceptor with knowledge for his vision, after entering the body of the disciple along the path of Yoga.

11. The Mantra form of initiation is coupled with the rites performed in the sacrificial altar. This has to be performed by the preceptor externally with respect to the dull-witted disciple.

12. The disciple receives blessing in respect of his Śakti,[262] because the pursuit of Śaivite virtue has that as the condition in brief.

13. Where the Śakti is not grasped neither purity nor Vidyā nor right conduct nor salvation nor any achievement is secured.

14. Hence, observing the symbols for securing Śakti, the preceptor shall purify and consecrate the disciple either by knowledge or by means of rites.

15. He who performs otherwise is the wicked person who perishes. Hence the preceptor shall test the disciple in every respect.

16. Since Śakti is enlightenment and bliss, the two are the signs of its manifestation.

17. The symbol of bliss and enlightenment is constituted by the changes and alterations in the mind in the manner of shivering, horripilation and alterations in the voice, eyes and other parts of the body.

18. The disciple too shall carry out the test of the preceptor through these characteristic symbols and contacts with him during the worship of Śiva or through those associated with him or resorting to him.

19. The test for the disciple has in view his worthiness of being taught and for the preceptor the gravity of his pursuit. Hence the disciple shall endeavour in every respect to honour the preceptor.

262. The Śaktipāta doctrine of the Śaivas is concerned with the receptivity of the disciple or the communicability of the preceptor in receiving or imparting instructions in the principles of Śaiva cult.

20. He who is the preceptor is Śiva and he who is Śiva is the preceptor. Whether the preceptor or Śiva the same person is stationed in the form of knowledge.

21. As is Siva so the knowledge. As is the knowledge so is the preceptor. The benefit is similar in the worship of Śiva, knowledge or the preceptor.

22. The preceptor is in the form of gods and the mantras. Hence every endeavour shall be made to accept his behest with bent head.

23. The seeker of welfare shall never even think of transgressing the commands of the preceptor, because only he who carries out the behests of the preceptor attains the wealth of knowledge.

24. He shall not do any thing without the permission of the preceptor, nor even walk, stand, sleep or eat. Especially if the work is performed in the presence of the preceptor it must necessarily be with his permission.

25. Since the preceptor is the lord himself and his house is the temple of the lord, the disciple shall not sit as he pleases in the house of the preceptor or in his presence.

26-28. He becomes a fallen man due to his sins as due to the contact with the sinners. As the price of gold sheds off its impurities when put in fire so also the disciple sheds off his sins due to the contact with the preceptor. As the ghee melts when kept near the fire, so also the sin melts in the presence of the preceptor. As the blazing fire burns the twig whether dry or damp, so also the delighted preceptor burns off his sins.

29-31. The disciple shall never incite the anger of the preceptor mentally, verbally or physically. Due to his anger the longevity, prosperity, knowledge and sacred rites all these are burnt. The sacrifices of those who incite his anger are futile as also their restraints and observances. No doubt need be entertained in this respect. No man shall ever make any statement against the preceptor. If out of delusion he were to make such statements he will fall into the Raurava hell.

32-37. If the man is intelligent and seeks welfare he shall not act falsely to the preceptor mentally, verbally or physically. Whether expressly bidden or not, the disciple shall perform what is beneficent and pleasing to the preceptor. He shall carry out his task in his presence or otherwise. He who conducts himself like this, who is ever devoted, alert in mind and performs what is pleasing to the preceptor is entitled to the Śaivite rites. If the preceptor is intelligent, endowed with virtues, is capable of illumining the great bliss, knows reality and is attached to Śiva he is competent to bestow salvation. None else. The principle of producing knowledge is born of great bliss. Only he by whom that principle is known can point out bliss and not the one who is that only in name but is devoid of true knowledge.

38. Two boats can carry each other across the river. A piece of rock cannot take another piece of rock across the river. If the preceptor is nominal, the liberation too is nominal.

39. Those by whom this principle is known are liberated and can liberate others. There can be no enlightenment, no realisation of the self in one who is devoid of principles.

40. He who is devoid of realisation is an animal. One urged by an animal cannot eschew his animal nature.

41. Hence, only a knower of principles is sought as the liberated and liberator. He is endowed with all characteristics and he is the knower of all Śāstras.

42-43. One devoid of principles is inefficient though he may know all means and rules of procedure. The greatest bliss is generated by the sight of the preceptor whose intellect extending upto personal realisation functions in the principle. Hence an intelligent person shall choose one as his preceptor who can impart enlightenment and bliss.

44-46. The right preceptor shall be served by the disciples who desire salvation and who are expert in humble conduct to that end. When realisation dawns upon him he shall abide in him with stable devotion. He shall never eschew the principles nor neglect them. If neither enlightenment nor bliss is obtained by the disciple even after a year, even slightly, the disciple shall resort to another preceptor.

47. Even though he may resort to another preceptor

he shall never dishononr his previous preceptor, his brothers, or sons or illum'ners or urgers.

48-49. Having at the outset approached the brahmin preceptor who has mastered the Vedas, who is intelligent, handsome, of pleasant sight, the bestower of protection and merciful, he shall propitiate him and endeavour to delight him mentally, verbally and physically.

50. He shall continue to propitiate him till he is pleased. If the preceptor is pleased the sins of the disciple are immediately quelled.

51-52. Hence he shall give the preceptor coins, gems fields, houses, ornaments, garments, vehicles, beds, seats etc. in accordance with his wealth and resources. If he wishes for the great goal he shall not be stringent with regard to wealth.

53. Since he is his father, mother, master, kinsman, wealth, happiness, friend, comrade etc. he shall offer everything to him.

54. After offering these, he shall dedicate to him, himself, his family and all his possessions along with water and remain subservient to him for ever.

55. Since he has offered himself to Śiva as his devotee he shall ever remain so. He will have no rebirth thereafter.

56. The teacher shall test the brahmin disciple for a year, the ksatriya for two years and the vaiśya for three years.

57. He shall test the disciples, with commands to give up life and wealth or by engaging the superior devotees in mean tasks and the inferior ones in noble tasks.

58. Even when rebuked or beaten if they do not feel distressed they shall be considered self-controlled and pure and hence deserving consecration in Śaiva rituals.

59-61. The decision of the sacred texts is this that brahmin devotees with the following qualifications shall be consecrated properly and enlightened. They shall be non-violent, merciful, ever active and alert in mind, free from arrogance, intelligent, devoid of rivalry sweet-tongued, straightforward, soft-hearted, pure, humble, steady, endowed with purity of conduct, and well-behaved in every respect.

62. Women by themselves are not authorised in Śaivite consecration. If they are devoted to the lord they can be consecrated at the instance of their husbands.

63-64. A widow can be consecrated with the permission of her sons; a virgin with the permission of her father. The purificatory rite for the pathways is not prescribed for Śudra men, particularly the fallen ones and the intercastes. If they have pious feelings for Śiva, the purification of sins shall be performed by administering holy washings of his feet.

65-67. The consecratory rite for people born of Anuloma marriage shall be performed in the manner customary to the family of the mother. The girl who is authorised in Śaivite rites by her father shall be given in marriage only to a devotee of Śiva and not to a non-devotee. If inadvertently she is given in marriage to a non-devotee she shall try to convince her husband about the Śaivite faith. If she is unable to do so she shall leave him off and perform holy rites mentally.

68-70. The chaste lady Anasūyā abandoned her husband Atri the excellent sage and propitiated Śiva by penance; Draupadī who was not engaged in holy rites of the elders propitiated Nārāyaṇa by penance and attained the Pāṇḍavas as her husbands. In view of the weightiness of Śiva's behest, the woman engaged in Śaivite virtue does not incur sin as she has no choice of freedom.

71-72. Of what avail is much talk? Whoever solely resorts to Śiva shall be purified if he is subservient to the preceptor. The rite of consecration does not differ. He who develops consciousness by the mere sight, touch or talk of the preceptor is not faced with failure.

73-74. The mental consecratory rite which is performed along the path of Yoga is not mentioned here. It is a great secret and shall be known straight from the mouth of the preceptor. The consecratory rite with holy rites shall now be mentioned briefly. Its detailed explanation is not possible.

263. Cp. Vāyavīya S II. 19-20.

CHAPTER SIXTEEN

(*The consecration of the disciple*)

Upamanyu said:—

1. On an auspicious day, in a pure spot devoid of major defects, the preceptor shall at the outset perform the consecration 'Samaya.'

2. After testing the ground duly by way of smell, colour, taste etc., he shall cause a platform to be constructed along the path mentioned in the science of architecture.

3-4. After making the altar, he shall make eight pits in the eight quarters making the chief one in the north-east. It may also be in the west when only the important pit need be dug. It shall be beautified by smearing it with powder.

5. It shall be decorated with garlands, festoons, banners and canopy. In the middle of the altar a mystic diagram shall be drawn. It shall have auspicious characteristics.

6. The powder used for the mystic diagram shall be gold dust mixed with saffron so as to befit for the invocation of the lord. If the devotee is poor he can use the powdered Nīvāra grain mixed with saffron.

7. The width of the mystic lotus diagram may be one hand or two hands. It may be white or red in colour. The pericarp of the lotus of a hand's width shall be eight angulas.

8. The filaments shall be half that length. The remaining portion is occupied by the eight petals. If the width of the lotus is two hands, the measurements will be doubled.

9. Another diagram shall be made on the altar one hand in width or half of it, to the north-east of the previous one and decorated well.

10. Paddy or rice grains mixed with gingelly seeds and flowers shall be strewn on it and covered with Darbha grass. The water-jar with the necessary characteristics shall be placed thereon.

11-12. The water-jar shall be made of gold, silver or copper or it may be earthen. It shall contain scents, flowers,

Akṣatas, Kuśa and Dūrvā grass. It shall be tied round with two cloths and a white thread round the neck. It shall be filled with pure water with bundle of Kuśa grass inserted in it. It shall contain the materials of worship and a covering lid.

13-14. The vessels Bhṛṅgāra and Vardhanī as well as Śaṅkha and Cakra shall also be put. Except the thread the other thing may consist of lotus petals and leaves. On the northern petal of the lotus conceived as seat shall be placed the Vardhanī of the Astrarāja (?) with sandal paste and water.

15. To the east of the diagram the great worship of the lord shall start on the consecrated jar.

16-19. What has been mentioned before can be performed on the seashore, or river-bank, or in the cowpen or on a mountain, or in a temple or in the house or in any other charming place, except the platform. After making the diagram as before and the raised ground for fire the preceptor shall enter the worship chamber with a delighted face. He shall invoke all auspicious things about him. He shall have completed all the daily rites. He shall perform the great worship in the middle of the mystical diagram. He shall invoke Śiva again in the water-jar and worship.

20-21. He shall meditate upon the lord the protector of sacrifice facing the west. In the vessel Astravardhanī he shall worship the weapon of the lord on the south. He shall place the Mantra in the Mantra vessel. Expert in the mantras he shall exhibit the mystic gestures and begin the sacrifice with the mantra.

22. The excellent preceptor shall perform the sacrifice in the sacred fire in the main pit. The other brahmins shall perform the sacrifice all round in the other pits.

23. The excellent preceptor shall perform the sacrifice only in the main pit. The number of sacrifices made by the others is half or one fourth of those of the chief priest.

24. Some shall recite the Vedic mantras or auspicious hymns. Some shall perform the Japa duly.

25-26. Dance, music. instrumental as well as vocal, and other auspicious conventional rites shall be performed.

After propitiating the assembled brahmins he shall make them recite the Punyāha mantras. He shall then worship. He shall pray to the lord with a desire to bless the disciple.

27. 'O lord of the chief of gods be pleased. O lord, ocean of mercy, please enter my body mercifully and release me from the bondage'.

28-30. The preceptor shall perform the Saṁkalpa 'I shall do thus' and with the formal permission, he shall bring the disciple who had been observing fast taking only Haviṣya once and who had taken bath and performed daily rites. The disciple shall continue the Japa of Pranava and meditate on the lord. Auspicious rites shall then be performed for him. In the Maṇḍala in front of the western or the southern door he shall be made to sit on the Darbha grass. The disciple shall sit facing the north.

31-32. The preceptor shall stand facing the east and sprinkle the water from the vessel Prokṣaṇī, on his haed as the disciple sits straight with palms joined in reverence. He shall lightly touch with flowers the eyes of the disciple and bind them with a strip of new silk cloth repeating the mantras.

33. Then he shall make the disciple enter the Maṇḍapa through the door and circumambulate thrice.

34. Then after offering a handful of flowers with a piece of gold to the lord he shall prostrate on the ground facing the east or the north.

35. Then as before, the preceptor shall sprinkle the water on his head and strew flowers. The bandage around his eyes shall be removed.

36-37. After seeing the Maṇḍala, he shall bow to the lord again with palms joined in reverence. The preceptor shall make the disciple sit to the south of the Maṇḍala and to his left on a Darbha grass seat. After propitiating the lord, the preceptor shall place his auspicious hand over his head.

38. Uttering the mantra of Śiva, the preceptor, identical with Śiva, shall place his hand refulgent with Śaivite splendour, on the head of the disciple.

39. With the same hand the preceptor shall touch

all the parts of his body. The disciple shall prostrate on the ground before the lord in the form of the preceptor.

40-41. He shall worship the lord duly and perform three Āhutis. He shall sit as before. The preceptor shall touch the disciple with the tips of the Darbha grass. By means of his Vidyā he shall enter the Ātman. After bowing to the lord he shall perform the rite of Nāḍīsandhāna.

42-44. He shall perform the rite of Prāṇanirgama as mentioned in Śiva Śāstras. Remembering the mystical entry into the body of the disciple he shall perform the Tarpaṇa rite with the mantras. For the Tarpaṇa he shall offer thrice the ten Āhutis with the ancillary mantras. After offering the Pūrṇāhuti, the expert preceptor shall offer again ten Āhutis repeating the Mūlamantra, by way of expiation.

45-46. Worshipping the lord of the gods again and performing the Ācamana the preceptor shall perform Homa duly and uplift the disciple from his caste. If he is a vaiśya he is first lifted into a kṣatriya. Then performing these rites the preceptor shall lift him into a brahmin.

47. If the disciple is a kṣatriya he is first raised into a brahmin and then to the form of Rudra. If the disciple is a brahmin he is raised into the form of Rudra.

48-49. After sprinkling and striking lightly the disciple and remembering the Ātman of the disciple in his own, the preceptor shall drain out the wind that throbs like a flame, through the veins as mentioned. He shall then enter the vein and the heart of the disciple.

50. After entering his consciousness that appears to him like a blue spot he shall meditate on it as blazing with its brilliance free from dirt.

51-52. After breathing in the vein repeating the mantra and showing the Saṁhāra mudrā (the gesture of annihilation) he shall refill it with Pūraka for uniting the Ātmans. Now taking it again with Kumbhaka as with Recaka before, he shall place it in the heart of the disciple.

53. After touching him and giving him the sacred thread secured from Śiva he shall offer three Āhutis and the Pūrṇāhuti thereafter.

54-56. To the south of the lord, the disciple is made to

sit on a splendid seat over which Kuśa, and flowers are strewn. He shall join his palms with reverence and face the north. He shall sit in the posture of Svastika. He shall face the east and sitting in a splendid seat shall repeat the mantras with the auspicious songs and music and take the water-jar. Meditating on the joyous Śiva he shall pour water over the disciple.

57. Wiping off the water over his body and wearing a white cloth, he shall perform the Ācamana. Fully bedecked he shall go to the Maṇḍapa with palms joined in reverence.

58. He shall make him sit as before on the Kuśa seat and worship the lord in the Maṇḍala. He shall perform the Karanyāsa rite.

59. Meditating on the lord he shall take Bhasma in both the hands and smear it over the body of the disciple repeating Śiva's names.

60-61. He shall then perform the rites of Dahana and Plāvana and conclude with the rite of Mātṛkānyāsa. Meditating on Śiva's seat and invoking him on the head of the disciple he shall mentally worship him in the prescribed manner.

62. With palms joined in reverence he shall pray to the lord. 'Stay here permanently'. After submitting this he shall remember him shining with refulgent splendour.

63. After worshipping Siva and securing his behest in the form of Śiva he shall slowly mutter Śiva's Mantra into the ear of the disciple.

64. At the behest of the preceptor he shall repeat the mantra with palms joined in reverence and mind concentrating on it.

65. Then after instructing him in the Śakti mantra, the expert preceptor shall make him repeat it easily and bless him with auspiciousness.

66. After briefly explaining to him the syllabic meaning of the mantra, the preceptor shall advise him about the form of the lord and instruct him in different postures.

67. Then at the behest of the preceptor, in the presence of Śaivite fire and the preceptor, the disciple shall think with devotion and repeat the statement of initiation.

68. 'Better to abandon life, better to cut off the head than to take food without worshipping the three-eyed lord.'

69. The lord alone will invariably give till the delusion is removed. The disciple shall propitiate the lord with concentrated devotion till delusion is quelled.

70. Thereafter the disciple will be known as Samaya in the preceptor's hermitage. He shall carry out the behests of the preceptor and remain subservient to him.

71. Then after performing the rite of Karanyāsa the preceptor shall take the Bhasma with his own hand and hand it over to the disciple along with the Mūlamantra and the Rudrākṣa over which the mantra has been repeated.

72. If it is possible he shall give him the phallic[264] or the embodied idol of the lord, the requisites of worship, sacrifice, Japa and meditation.

73. The disciple shall take these things from the Śaiva preceptor with great respect only at the behest of his family preceptor. Not otherwise.

74. He shall keep on his head everything obtained from the preceptor, with great devotion and preserve it carefully. He shall worship Śiva in the hermitage or in his own house.

75. The preceptor shall impart to him the Śaivite conduct of life in proportion to his devotion and faith as well as his grasping capacity.

76. Whatever is mentioned, or commanded, or even glorified by the preceptor to the Samaya, he shall retain in his intellect.

77. Understanding of Śaivite Āgama, reading it and listening to it shall be done at the behest of the preceptor. Not by himself at his will nor from anyone else.

78. Thus the consecration 'Samaya' has been briefly explained to you. It is the greatest means in attaining the city of Śiva himself.

264. Before re-creation after dissolution, the universe remains unmanifest in the phallic form of Śiva. Hence Śiva is Gūḍhadeha.

CHAPTER SEVENTEEN

(The rules governing Śaivite initiation)

Upamanyu said :—

1. Hereafter the preceptor shall perform the purification of the six pathways after understanding the disciple's capacity, for the sake of liberation from bondage.

2. The six paths[265] are Kalā, Tattva, Bhuvana, Varṇa, Pada and Mantra in brief.

3. The five Kalās, Nivṛtti etc. are the pathway of Kalā. The five Kalās pervade the five paths.

4. The principles from Śivatattva to the earth constitute the paths of principles. They are twentysix, both pure and impure.

5. Those beginning with Ādhāra and ending with Unmana constitute the paths of worlds. They are sixty in number without difference and subsidiary divisions.

6. The fifty letters in the form of Rudras constitute the path of letters. The path of words has many varieties.

7-8. The path of mantras consisting of subsidiary Mantras is pervaded by the excellent mantra. Just as Śiva, the leader of Tattvas, is not included among Tattvas so also the leader of Mantras is not included in the path of Mantra. The Kalādhvā pervades and the other Adhvās are pervaded.

9-10. He who does not know that factually should not perform the rite of the six Adhvās. He who has not understood the form of the six paths cannot understand the order of pervasiveness and is incompetent to perform the rite.

11-14. After making the pits and the Maṇḍapa as before, to the east he shall make the mystic diagram measuring two hastas for keeping the water-jar on. The preceptor shall perform his routine rites and enter the Maṇḍapa with his disciples to begin the worship of Śiva as before. Milk pudding shall be made with rice measuring not less than one Āḍhaka. Half of that shall be offered to the lord as Naivedya and the remaining shall be kept reserved for Homa. In the

265. The purificatory rites of the six pathways are the pre-requisites for the initiation of the disciple in Śiva's cult.

Maṇḍala drawn in front with various colours, the preceptor shall place five water-pots, one in each of the four quarters and one in the middle.

15-17. The preceptor, most expert in the procedural code, shall invoke the five Brahmans[266] on them, repeating the Mūlāvaraṇas along with Bindu and Nāda, and the letters beginning with Namaḥ and ending with Ya. Īśāna is invoked in the middle jar, Puruṣa in the eastern, Aghora in the southern, Vāma in the northern and Sadyojāta in the western jar. After performing the rites of protection, mystic gestures and invocation of the jar he shall sacrifice in the Śiva fire as before.

18-20. The milk pudding reserved for sacrifice shall be offered and what still remains shall be kept for the disciple to eat. The rites upto the Tarpaṇa shall be conducted in the manner mentioned before. After the Pūrnāhuti the rite of illumination with the ancillaries shall be performed.

21-22. In this rite three Āhutis shall be given.[267] With the specific mantras the refulgent deities shall be meditated upon. He shall then take the thrice-spun white threads made by brahmin girls, strung into three and with these bind the tip of the tuft of the disciple.

23-26. The thread shall be let loose till the tip of the toe of the disciple standing straight. The Suṣumṇā (the nerve of the backbone) shall be joined with it. The consciousness shall be invoked with the basic mantra and he shall offer three Āhutis to create its presence. With the flowers he shall strike the chest of the disciple as before and invoke consciousness. It shall then be conceived as placed in the twelve-petalled lotus. The thread shall be joined with the other thread (?) with the Astra and Varma mantras. After veiling the body of the disciple the thread shall be meditated upon (?)

27-30. It shall then be imagined that the three strings

266. The five forms of Śiva 'Pañcabrahmans, viz. Īśāna, Puruṣa, Aghora, Vāma and Sadya are invoked in the water-jars placed in different directions with the basic mantra of Śiva.

267. The mantra is 'ओं हु शिवाय फट् स्वाहा'.

represent a bond with the objects and the state of enjoyment. The Kalās Śāntyatīta etc. in the forms of the elements ether etc. shall be joined to the thread (?) with their respective names and worshipped. With these as the base the foregoing rites shall be performed. Then he shall survey the pervasion of the dirt etc. in Tattvas. After offering as Āhuti, the pervasion of Kalā in the dirt etc. the Kalās shall be illuminated.

31. After striking the disciple on the head and the thread worne on the body he shall bedeck the sūtra in the Śāntyatīta Pada, repeating the mantra.

32. In this manner after offering the Āhutis of Śāntyatīta upto the end of Nivṛtti he shall perform three Āhutis and worship Śiva in the Maṇḍala.

33. The preceptor shall make the disciple sit to the south of the lord facing the north, on the Maṇḍala strewn with Darbha grass. He shall give him the rice soaked in ghee left after the Homa.

34. The disciple shall take the Caru offered by the preceptor, and eat it repeating the name Śiva. After performing the Ācamana twice he shall repeat the mantra of Śiva.

35. The preceptor shall give him the Pañcagavya on the other Maṇḍala. The disciple shall drink it upto his capacity, perform the Ācamana twice and remember Śiva.

36. He shall make the disciple sit on a third Maṇḍala as before, and hand over a tooth brush twig having the characteristics mentioned in the scriptures.

37. The disciple shall sit silently facing the east or the north and clean his teeth with its soft tip.

38. He shall cast off the tooth brush, wash his hands and mouth, perform Ācamana and remember Śiva. Then at the behest of the preceptor he shall enter Śiva Maṇḍapa with palms joined in reverence.

39-40. If the cast-off tooth brush is seen by the preceptor in the north-east or west or in front it is auspicious, otherwise it is inauspicious. If it is seen in an inauspicious quarter the preceptor shall perform a hundred, or a fifty or twentyfive Homas with the basic Mantra for the removal of the defect.

41. Then he shall strike the disciple and whisper the name of Śiva into his ears. He shall make him settle to the south of the lord.

42. During the night the disciple shall lie on a Darbha mattress covered with an unwashed bed-sheet and consecrated with mantra. While lying he shall meditate on Śiva and keep his head to the east.

43-44. To his tuft the thread has already been tied. Along with that tuft the preceptor shall tie the unwashed bed-sheet. With Varma mantra he shall cover him up. All round him he shall make three lines with gingelly seeds and mustard fully consecrated by Astra mantra. Outside the lines he shall offer oblations to the guardians of the quarters.

45. The disciple shall not take anything in after settling down like this. After getting up the next day he shall intimate to the preceptor if he had any dream.

CHAPTER EIGHTEEN

(*The purification of the six paths*)

Upamanyu said :—

1. After completing ablution and other rites the disciple shall, at the bidding of the preceptor, go near the Maṇḍala of Śiva meditating on Śiva, with palms joined in reverence.

2. All rites upto the binding of the eyes shall be performed as on the previous day, except the worship. Then the preceptor shall show him the Maṇḍala.

3. When flowers are strewn by the disciple whose eyes are tied, the preceptor shall tell him the places where the flowers fell.

4. The preceptor shall take him to the Maṇḍala where worship had already been performed. As before he shall worship lord Īśāna and perform homa in the fire.

5. If any bad dream had been seen by the disciple,

the preceptor shall perform hundred, or fifty, or twentyfive homas with the basic mantra for the removal of that defect.

6-8. The thread tied to the tuft shall be loosened to hang down as before, He shall perform the worship of Ādhāra based on Nivṛttikalā and conclude with the worship of Vāgiśvarī with due homas. He shall bow to Vāgīśa and Satī who pervade Nivṛtti. He shall worship the lord in the.. Maṇḍala and make three Āhutis Then the mystical rite of making the simultaneous entry into all types of living beings, shall be performed.

9-10. The rites of striking and sprinkling shall be performed in the gross body of the disciple and then the Ātman shall be taken and placed in the twelve-petalled lotus. It shall be taken again from there through the repetition of the basic mantra and the gestures as prescribed in the scripture. The preceptor shall unite it mentally with all types of living beings simultaneously.

11. The living beings are fourteen in number: the eight types of the gods, five types of the lower animals and birds, and human beings forming one type.

12. In order to facilitate the simultaneous entry into all of them, he shall deposit the Ātman of the disciple along with his mind into Vāgīsānī duly.

13. For the accomplishment of the spiritual knowledge he shall worship and bow to the lord. After performing the homa he shall remember it as developed.

14. He shall duly perform the mystical rites of nativity, the pursuit of previous actions, straightforwardness and the great pleasure of enjoyment.

15. For the sake of redemption and the achievement of birth, longevity, enjoyment and purificatory impressions, the preceptor shall perform three Āhutis and pray to the lord.

16. Thus he shall purify his body that contains the dirt of enjoyment of pleasures and contact with sensual objects. He shall cut off the three bondages of the disciple.

17. By the complete splitting of the bondage he shall make the disciple clean.

18. After making the Pūrṇāhuti in the fire he shall worship Brahmā. After performing three Āhutis for him he shall submit to him the behest of Śiva.

19. 'O Pitāmaha, no hindrance shall be placed for this disciple who is going to the great region of Śiva. This is the behest of Śiva'.

20. Thus imploring him, he shall worship and ritualistically dismiss him. He shall worship Mahādeva and perform three Āhutis.

21. Uplifting the Ātman of the disciple, as before, when it has been purified by Nivṛttikalā he shall deposit it in his own Ātman. He shall then worship Vāgīśa.

22. He shall perform three Āhutis now and ritualistically dismiss him. Returning he shall make it united with Pratiṣṭhākalā.

23. Performing the worship and the three Āhutis simultaneously he shall imagine the entry of the Ātman of the disciple into the Pratiṣṭhā Kalā.

24. Then after invoking Pratiṣṭhā and performing everything as previously mentioned he shall conceive its pervasion and the pervading Vāgīśānī.

25. He shall imagine Vāgīśānī as lustrous as the disc of the full moon. After doing everything as before he shall submit to Viṣṇu the behest of Śiva the great Ātman.

26-28. Performing everything like the ritualistic dismissal of Viṣṇu by means of Vidyā he shall think of Pratiṣṭhā and its pervasion and Vāgīśā too in order. He shall then perform everything concluding with the Pūrṇāhuti in the blazing fire as before. Nīlarudra shall be invoked and its worship performed. As mentioned before, the behest of the lord shall be carried out.

29. Then the lord shall be ritualistically dismissed. For the purpose of quietening him, Vidyākalā shall be conceived and its pervasion surveyed.

30. He shall then as before invoke Vāgīśī that pervades his Ātman, that has the form and features of the early morning sun and that illuminates the ten quarters.

31. He shall perform the remaining rites as before. He shall invoke lord Śiva and propitiate him. After

performing homa he shall mentally submit to the behest of Śiva.

32. After ritualistically dismissing the lord he shall lead another Kalā to Śāntyatītakalā and survey its pervasion.

33. As before he shall meditate on Vāgīśā that pervades the Ātman as resembling the permanent. Upto the final offering (Pūrṇāhuti) everything is as before.

34. After doing everything in accordance with injunctions and worshipping Sadāśiva he shall submit to him the behest of Śiva of unmeasured activity.

35. There too, after worshipping Śiva as before on the head and bowing to Vāgīśa he shall ritualistically dismiss him.

36. Sprinkling then the disciple on the head as before with Śiva mantra he shall think of the merging of Śāntyatītakalā in the Śakti Tattva.

37. On the other side beyond the six pathways he shall think of the greatest Śakti of Śiva that pervades the pathways and that equals a crore of suns.

38-39. He shall bring the disciple as pure as the crystal in front of it. After washing the scissors, the preceptor shall cut off the tuft of the disciple as well as his thread in the manner mentioned in the Śaivite Scriptures. He shall place it in cowdung and consign it to Śiva fire.

40. Then with the basic mantra ending with Vauṣaṭ he shall wash the scissors and hands. He shall restore the consciousness of the disciple to his body.

41-42. The disciple shall take bath and perform Ācamana. Good wishes and blessings shall be conferred on him. He shall be brought to the Maṇḍala and made to prostrate. In order to expiate for the shortcomings in the rites due worship shall be performed. The preceptor shall pour three Āhutis by reciting the mantra.

43. In order to expiate for the shortcomings in the Mantra he shall worship the lord of the gods and pour three Āhutis by muttering the mantra.

44. He shall pour three Āhutis by repeating the mantra mentally. After propitiating Śiva there, in the

Maṇḍala and Pārvatī, he shall pour three Āhutis. With palms joined in reverence the preceptor shall pray thereafter.

45. 'O lord, due to your grace the purity of the six pathways of the disciple has been completed. Now, O lord, lead him unto your imperishable abode.'

46. After submitting thus to the lord he shall perform every thing as before, from Nāḍisandhāna to the Pūrṇāhuti. Then he shall purify the elements

47. Then, for conducting purity he shall meditate on the regions stable or unstable, hot or cold in the purificatory rite of the Bhūtas in the form of unity that is pervaded.

48. After cutting off the knot of the Bhūtas he shall join the Bhūtas on to the great lord Śiva by the path of steady concentration.

49. He shall purify his body, burn it, and drench it with drops of nectar. Steadying the Ātman he shall make his body in consonance with the pure pathways.

50-51. There at the outset he shall place on the head of the disciple the Śāntyatīta kalā that pervades the pathways; the Śāntikalā on the face; Vidyā kalā in the spot beginning with the throat and ending with the navel; Pratiṣṭhā kalā upto the knees; Nivṛtti kalā beneath it. Thereafter he shall meditate on it.

52. With the basic mantra, its Bījas and ancillaries he shall meditate on him in the form of Śiva. He shall invoke the lord in the lotus of the heart and worship him.

53. The teacher shall pray for the perpetual presence of Śiva in the disciple. He shall impose good qualities on the disciple possessed of Śaivite splendour.

54-55. He shall perform three Āhutis praying—'O lord, be pleased to bestow on him the attributes Aṇimā, etc.'[268] Likewise he shall invoke the lord for the presence of these qualities in him, viz:—omniscience, contentment, eternal enlightenment, unviolated Śakti, freedom and infinite power.

268. While offering three Āhutis he shall thrice utter the mantra ओं नमः शिवाय प्रसीद.

56. Then securing permission from the lord and meditating on him in the heart he shall pour water over the disciple from the vessels[269] of Sadyojāta etc. in order.

57. Then after making the disciple sit and worship Śiva as before he shall secure permission from the lord and impart Śiva's knowledge to him.

58. He shall impart also the plicated Mantra[270] beginning with Om and ending with Namaḥ and the Śaktividyā of a similar nature, accompanied by Śiva and Śakti.

59. He shall instruct him in the name of the sage, metre, deity and the efficacy of Śiva and Śivā, the worship of Śiva, his Āvaraṇa and the postures.

60. Worshipping the lord of the gods again he shall submit to Śiva—'Please make whatever has been performed by me a well accomplished thing'.

61. Followed by his disciple the preceptor shall prostrate before the lord on the ground. Thereafter he shall ritualistically dismiss him from the Maṇḍala and the fire.

62. Then those assembled there and worthy of worship shall be duly worshipped.

63. The members of the assembly including the Ṛtviks shall be honoured with the gifts. He who desires his welfare shall not be niggardly.

CHAPTER NINETEEN

(*The consecration of the aspirant and the greatness of the Mantra*)

Upamanyu said :—

1. Hereafter I shall explain the consecratory rite 'Sādhaka' indicated by me while explaining the greatness of the mantra.

269. It refers to the water-jars wherein the five forms of Śiva are invoked. See Vāyavīya II. 17. 16-17.

270. The mantra is ओं ह्रीं शिवाय नमः ह्रीं ओं ।

2. As before the lord shall be worshipped in the Maṇḍala and the vessels and the homa performed. The disciple shall be brought to the Maṇḍala without his head-dress.

3-4. After performing hundred Āhutis and the rites upto the Pūrṇāhuti, and the rite of Tarpaṇa with the water from the jars repeating the Mūlamantra, the preceptor shall make offering and perform every rite as mentioned before. He shall pour water on the disciple and impart the excellent Mantra.

5. There, after imparting the Śaivite lore in detail, he shall place this in the disciple's hand with water from the flowers.

6. 'By the grace of the supreme lord this great Mantra shall certainly confer on you the Siddhis both of this world and the next one.'

7. After saying this, the preceptor shall worship lord Śiva and secure his formal permission. He shall then impart to the aspirant the Yoga of Śiva, the means of liberation.

8-9. On hearing the instructions of the preceptor, the aspirant disciple shall practise the Mantra before utilising it. This practice of the Mūlamantra is called Puraścaraṇa since it has to be practised before the rite Viniyoga.

10. A devotee who desires salvation need not practise the mantra too often. If practised moderately it is auspicious here and hereafter.

11-16. On an auspicious day, in a holy spot, in the favourable season, the devotee shall take bath and perform the rites of the forenoon scrupulously keeping the teeth and the nails sparkling white in colour. He shall bedeck himself in scented flowers, garlands and ornaments readily available. He shall wear a white head-dress and a white upper cloth. His dress shall be white and pure. He shall sit comfortably in the manner to which he is accustomed either in the temple or in his own house or in any charming place. He shall make his body worthy of Śaivite rites along the path mentioned in the Śaivite scriptures. He shall worship the lord Nakul-Īśvara. He shall offer milk pudding as Naivedya and conclude the rite of propitiation. After bowing to him he shall formally take his permission. He shall repeat the mantra ten million or five million, or two and a half million or two million or a million times.

17. Thereafter his diet shall be limited in quantity and confined to milk pudding and such other as is devoid of salt and acidity. He shall not be violent. He shall be forbearing, quiet and self-possessed for ever.

18. If milk pudding is not available he shall take fruits and roots. They are ordained by Śiva himself and in the series of order gradually they are better.

19-20. Whatever he eats daily whether, Caru, ground flour of fried grains, gruel, vegetables, milk, curd, ghee, roots, fruits and water he shall take in only after consecrating it with the mantras while the practice of the mantra is being kept up. He shall remain silent too.

21. He shall take bath in the water from east-flowing or west-flowing rivers and purify himself by repeating hundred and eight mantras or sprinkle himself as strength permits him.

22. He shall perform the rites of Tarpaṇa and homa in the Śaivite fire with seven, five or three materials of worship or with ghee alone.

23. Nothing is inaccessible in this world or the next to him who is a devotee of Śiva and who is an aspirant practising the mantra of Śiva thus with devotion.

24. Or he shall perform the Japa of the mantra a thousand times everyday, with full concentration of the mind. He shall not take food before the thousand Japas are completed.

25. Nothing is difficult of access to him. Nothing is inauspicious to him. He attains learning, prosperity, happiness, and salvation.

26. Whether in the course of practice or application, whether done as a Nitya rite or a Naimittika rite he shall perform the Japa after taking bath with water or with Bhasma.

27. He shall perform the Japa of the five-syllabled mantra, pure in person and mind, with the tuft tied up,

wearing the sacred thread on the body and having the Pavitra round the finger. He shall have the Tripuṇḍra marks and shall wear Rudrākṣa beads.

CHAPTER TWENTY

(*Special consecration*)

Upamanyu said:—

1. The preceptor shall crown consecrated disciple as a preceptor after he has performed the Pāśupata rite if he has the requisite qualities and not otherwise.

2. The Maṇḍala shall be made as before and after worshipping the lord he shall, as before, place five water-jars one in each of the four quarters and one in the middle.

3. Nivṛtti Kalā shall be installed in the vessel in the east, Pratiṣṭhā Kalā in the vessel in the west; Vidyā Kalā in the south. Śānti Kalā in the north and the Parā Kalā in the middle.

4. The following rites shall be performed as before, viz. those of Rakṣā, the Mudrābandha or the gesture of the cow, repetition of mantra over the vessels and the homa till the Pūrṇāhuti.

5. The preceptor shall make the disciple enter the Maṇḍala. He shall not wear the head-dress. The Tarpaṇa and other rites too shall be performed as before.

6. Then the lord shall be worshipped and his permission obtained ritualistically. He shall make the disciple sit on the seat for the pouring of water.

7. The disciple imagined as the five-fold offering of fruits shall be united with the Kalās and conceived as Śiva inasmuch as the mantra has been installed on his body; he shall be worshipped then.

8. Then the water from the vessels beginning with Nivṛtti Kumbha and ending with the middle shall be poured over the disciple repeating the names of Śiva.

9. Then the preceptor shall place his hand, repeating the Śiva mantra on the head of the disciple. The preceptor equipped with the piety towards Śiva shall call him Śivācārya.

10. He shall be adorned. Then the preceptor shall propitiate him in Śivamaṇḍala. After performing hundred and eight Āhutis he shall offer the Pūrṇāhuti.

11. The preceptor shall worship the lord and prostrate on the ground with palms joined in reverence over the head. He shall submit to the lord Śiva.

12. "O lord, by your grace this disciple has been made a preceptor by me. O lord, after blessing him, may the divine behest be bestowed on him.

13. After submitting thus, the preceptor shall bow to Siva again along with the disciple. He shall worship the divine Śiva-Āgama in the same manner as Śiva himself.

14. Then he shall take the ritualistic permission from Śiva. The preceptor shall take the book "Śivajñāna" with both the hands and hand it over to the disciple.

15. The disciple shall accept it with his bent head and place the Vidyā over the seat. He shall then respectfully adore it.

16. The preceptor shall give him royal paraphernalia since one who has attained the status of Ācārya deserves even a kingdom.

17. Then he shall impart to him the modes of discipline followed by elders as mentioned in Śaivite sacred literature and as honoured amongst the people.

18. The preceptor shall test the disciples assiduously through the characteristics mentioned in Śaivite scriptures. He shall consecrate them and impart to them the Śaivite knowledge.

19. He shall infuse in him all these qualities without difficulty, viz. purity, forbearance, mercifulness, non-covetousness and absence of jealousy even strenuously.

20. After thus urging the disciple he shall ritualistically dismiss Śiva from the Maṇḍala. He shall worship the Sivakumbha, fire and others who had been invited there.

21-23. Or the preceptor accompanied by his attendants shall simultaneously perform all the consecratory rites; the rites shall be repeated twice. The water-vessels shall be installed in the beginning itself as in the rite of the purification of the paths. After performing the Samaya consecration, wholly without ablution Śiva shall be worshipped again after the purification of the path. When that is concluded he shall worship the lord again.

24. After homa the Tarpaṇa rite of the mantra shall be performed. After the blessing of the lord the mantra shall be placed in the hand of the disciple and the remaining rites concluded.

25. Or beginning with the consecration of the Mantra and concluding with the rite of Abhiṣeka the rites of the purification of the path shall be performed by the preceptor.

26. In the purificatory rite of the three Tattvas the rites mentioned for the Kalās Śāntyatīta and others shall be performed.

27. Śiva, Vidyā and Ātmatattva—these are the three Tattvas. Śiva came out of Śakti and from Śiva the Vidyā and from Vidyā the Ātman.

28. The Śāntyatīta path is pervaded by Śiva. The next path is pervaded by Vidyā and the remaining paths are pervaded by Ātman.

29. Intelligent persons who have mastered Śaivite Scriptures laud the consecration through Śakti after considering that the consecration through Śiva is very difficult of access.

30. O Kṛṣṇa, thus the four types of consecratory rites have been narrated to you. What else do you wish to hear?

CHAPTER TWENTYONE

(*Nitya and Naimittika rites*)

Sri Kṛṣṇa said:—

1. O holy lord, I wish to hear the compulsory and optional rites of those who follow Śaivite conduct of life, as mentioned in Śaivite scriptures.

Upamanyu said:—

2. He shall rise early in the morning and meditate on the lord and the goddess For performing necessaries he shall go out of the house when the sun has risen.

3. In a secluded spot where there is no hindrance he shall evacuate his bowels. After washing in accordance with the rules he shall clean the teeth.

4. On the eighth and other days whenever tooth-brush twig is not available he shall gargle twelve times and clean the teeth.

5. After performing Ācamana he shall take bath either in a river or in a pond or in an eddy or in the house itself.

6. The toilet articles shall be kept on the bank. The dirt of the body shall be washed off. The clay shall be applied over the body. After taking bath he shall apply cow-dung over the body.

7. He shall take bath again and abandon the old cloth. Like a king he shall put on new dress.

8. Neither a Brahmacārin nor an ascetic nor a widow shall take bath with the scented soaps. They shall not use tooth-brush twig for cleaning the teeth.

9. He shall tie his tuft and have the sacred thread in the normal way. He shall enter water and plunge therein. After performing the Ācamana he shall take plunge thrice in the water.

10-11. After plunging in, he shall repeat the mantra and think on Śiva and Śakti. He shall get up and perform Ācamana. Then he shall pour water over the body with the cow-horn along with Darbha, or with the leaf of a Palāśa tree, or the lotus leaf or with both the hands, five or three times.

12. If he is taking bath in a garden or in the house he shall pour water with Vardhanī or a water-jar. When taking bath he shall pour water with the mantras.

13. If one is unable to take water-bath, one shall take a wet cloth and wipe the body from foot to head.

14. Or he shall take the self-bath. That is, one shal' repeat the name Śiva. That bath wherein Śiva is remembered is called the self-bath of a Yogin.

15. In accordance with the rules prescribed in one's code he shall perform the rites of Tarpaṇa for the gods beginning with Ācamana and ending with Brahmayajña.

16. Meditating on lord Śiva stationed in the Maṇḍala and worshipping him duly he shall offer Arghya to Śiva in the form of the sun.

17-19. Or after performing what is prescribed in one's own Sūtra he shall wash his hands and perform the rite of Karanyāsa. He shall make his body united with the Kalās through water taken in the left palm and containing scents and white mustard. He shall then sprinkle water over him through the bunch of Kuśa grass repeating the mantras 'Āpo hi ṣṭhā'[271] etc. accompanied by the basic mantra. Sniffing at the water remaining in the left nostril he shall think on lord Śiva again.

20. Taking off the dark-complexioned sin of the body through the left nostril and that outside, he shall conceive it as gone to the rock.

2 . He shall perform the Tarpaṇa rite to the gods, to the sages in particular, to the Bhūtas and to the Pitṛs. He shall offer Arghya duly.

22. With a handful of red sandal water he shall make a circular Maṇḍala on the ground and embellish it with red powder.

23. There he shall worship the sun with the covers along with his ancillaries repeating the mantra "Khakholkāya" for securing happiness.[272]

271. VS. 11. 50
272. Khakholkāya svāhā. Mahān. U. 20. 23.

24-25. He shall make another Maṇḍala and worship it with its ancillaries. He shall place there a gold-vessel of the size of the Prastha[273] current in the Magadha land. He shall fill it with scented water and red sandal along with red flowers, gingelly seeds, Akṣatas and Kuśa grass.

26-29. Or it can contain Dūrvā, Apāmārga and other articles or mere water. He shall keep that pot over his head. Kneeling down he shall bow to the lord in the Maṇḍala and offer it as Arghya to Śiva. Or he shall take water in the palms joined together and throw it up as an offering to Śiva stationed in the sky in the form of the sun. The water shall contain Darbha grass and the basic Mantra shall be repeated. Again he shall wash his hands and perform the Karanyāsa realising Śiva in the form of the five Brahmans[274] from Īśāna to Sadyojāta. He shall take Bhasma, in the hand and repeating mantra yā dināntaiḥ[275] he shall touch limbs in order, viz—the face, chest, private parts, feet.

30-31. Then repeating the basic mantra he shall touch all parts of the body and wear another cloth. After performing Ācamana twice he shall sprinkle water over himself eleven times repeating the mantra. He shall wear another cloth, perform Ācamana twice and remember Śiva.

32. He shall perform Karanyāsa again and repeating the mantra he shall apply the Tripuṇḍra marks. On the forehead the marks shall be clear, broad and straight. Scented water shall be used to paste the Bhasma.

33-34. It may also be circular or square in shape. It may be a single dot or a semicircular figure. But he shall apply the marks in the same way on the arms, head and chest as on the forehead. Dusting with the Bhasma is not on a par with Tripuṇḍra.

273. According to the present context, the golden jar shall weigh a measure of prastha in vogue in the Magadha country. But it is not clear why Māgadha-prastha is preferred.

Magadha is an eastern country identical with Bihar. But in the Purāṇas it is sometimes located in Madhya deśa and sometimes in Prācya. Cp GAMI p 12 note 4; p 29 note I.

274. Cp. Śrs. 1. 39. Here the word 'Sañjñaḥ' shall be emended to Sadyaḥ and translated accordingly.

275. TB. 2. 7. 16. 4. The printed text reads 'yā' dinā°' which is emended to yā divyā°.

35. Hence it is better to have Tripuṇḍras above without dusting. He shall wear Rudrākṣa beads on the head, round the neck, in the ears and hands.

36. The Rudrākṣa bead with the lustre of gold is excellent. It shall not be cut. What is not worn by others is the most auspicious. To the three castes the colours yellow, red and black are respectively excellent.

37. If the excellent bead is not available whatever is available shall be used for wearing. But it shall not be defective. The lower caste men shall not wear the bead intended for the higher caste. The higher caste men can wear the other types too.

38-39. Impure men shall not wear the Rudrākṣa bead. Everyone shall take bath twice, twice or once a day according to his strength, and worship the lord seated in a charming pose in the pedestal.

40. He shall face the east or the north while meditating on the lord and the goddess. He shall worship the preceptor and the disciples from Śveta to Nakuliśa.[276]

41-42. Again he shall bow to the lord and repeat his eight[277] names, viz. Śiva, Maheśvara, Rudra, Viṣṇu, Pitāmaha Saṁsāravaidya, Sarvajña and Paramātman. Or he shall repeat the name Śiva eleven times or more.

43. For the removal of sickness he shall meditate on the mass of splendour at the tip of his tongue. He shall wash his feet and apply sandal paste on his hands. He shall perform Karanyāsa after wiping off his hands.

276. Vāyavīya S. II. 9. 2-6.
277. Ibid., I 32. 23-24.

CHAPTER TWENTYTWO

(The compulsory and optional rites of Śaivite Scriptures)

Upamanyu said:—

1-2. Nyāsa[278] is of three types: Sthiti, Utpatti and Laya. The first is for householders, the second for Brahmacārins, the third for ascetics, forest-dwellers and widows. For housewives the Sthitinyāsa is recommended.

3-4. For a virgin Utpatti Nyāsa is praiseworthy. I shall now mention the characteristics of the Nyāsas. The procedure from the thumb to the little finger is the Sthitinyāsa. The procedure from the right thumb to the left little finger is the Utpattinyāsa. The reverse is Saṁhṛti (Laya).

5. The letters "Na" etc. along with the Bindus shall be fixed in order in the fingers. Śiva shall be fixed on the palms and on the little fingers.

6-7. The Astranyāsa shall be made in the ten quarters by means of the Astramantra. The five Kalās—Nivṛtti etc. in the form of the five elements along with the lords of the elements and accompanied by their respective symbols shall be fixed in the chest, neck, palate, middle of the eye-brows and the Brahmarandhṛa. One shall conceive them in the different Bījas.

8-10. In order to purify them one shall perform the Japa of the five-syllabled mantra. Restraining the vital breath thrice he shall cut off the knot of the elements repeating the Astra mantra and showing the mystic gesture of Astra. The Ātman urged by the vital breath through the Suṣumṇā vein and going out through the Brahmarandhra shall be united with the Śaivite splendour.

11-13. Afterwards the body is withered up by the wind burnt by the deadly fire. Then upwardly the Kalās are dissolved through the wind. Dissolving the burnt body and touching the Kalās with the ocean he shall drench and flood the body through Amṛtas and keep it in its normal

278. Nyāsa is an assignment of the various parts of the body to the deity. It is usually accompanied with prayer and corresponding gesticulation. This forms an essential part of Karma-Yajña.

place. Killed and burnt without the creation of Kalā he shall flood with Amṛta that which is reduced to ashes.

14. In the body consisting of Vidyā, he shall join the Ātman that has come out of Śiva in the form of the flame of a lamp. He shall join it through the Brahmarandhra.

15. After meditating on the Ātman that has entered the body, in the lotus of the heart, he shall sprinkle with the shower of nectar the body consisting of Vidyā.

16. Then he shall perform the rite of Karanyāsa after duly purifying it. Thereafter he shall perform the Dehanyāsa by means of the great Mudrā.

17. After performing the rite of Aṅganyāsa in the manner mentioned by Śiva, he shall perform the Varṇanyāsa in the joints of hands, feet and other parts of the body.

18. After the Nyāsa of the six limbs accompanied by six types, he shall bind the quarters from the south-east onwards.

19. Or he need perform only the Nyāsa of the five limbs beginning with the head. Similarly the Nyāsa of six limbs without the rites of purification etc. of the Bhūtas shall be performed.

20. Thus he shall succinctly perform the purification of the body and Ātman. Attaining the status of Śiva he shall worship Parameśvara.

21. He who has sufficient leisure and is not confused in mind shall perform the rite of Nyāsa in a detailed manner.

22-23. The first is Mātṛkānyāsa; the next is Brahmanyāsa; Praṇavanyāsa is the third; the next is Haṁsa Nyāsa and the fifth Nyāsa is mentioned as Pañcākṣarātmaka (consisting of the five-syllabled mantra).

24-29. The Nyāsa of the various letters is as follows:—the letter A in the head; Ā in the forehead; 'I' and Ī in the eyes; "U" and "Ū" in the ears; "Ṛ" and "Ṝ" in the cheek; 'lṛ' and 'lṝ' in the nostrils; 'e' and "ai" in the lips; o and "au" in the rows of teeth; "aṁ" in the tougue and "aḥ" in the palate; the gutturals are in the five joints of the right hand; the palatals in the joints of the left hand; The linguals and the Dentals in the legs; Pa and Pha in the sides; "Ba" in the back and "Bha" in the navel; "Ma" in the heart; "Ya" to "Sa" in the seven constituent elements, skin etc; "ha" in the cavity of the heart and "kṣa" in the middle of the eyebrows.

3o. After performing the Nyāsa of the letters in the manner of fifty Rudras the five Brahmans shall be fixed in the limbs, face etc. and Kalā.

31. The Karanyāsa may or may not be performed through them. The Brahmans shall be fixed in the head, face, chest, private parts and legs.

32. The Kalās of Īśāna are five; these are fixed in the five faces beginning with the one above and ending with the one in the west.

33. Then the four Kalās of Puruṣa shall be fixed in the four faces beginning with the one in the east.

34-36. The eight Kalās of Aghora shall be fixed in the heart, neck, shoulders, navel, belly, back and the chest; then the thirteen Kalās of Vāmadeva are fixed in the anus, penis, thighs, knees, calves, hips, buttocks, sides, nose, head and the arms. Thus the experts perform the Nyāsa of the thirtyeight Kalās in due order.

37-41. Afterwards the experts of Praṇava shall perform the Praṇavanyāsa in the arms, elbows wrists, sides, belly, thighs, calves and the back. After performing the Praṇavanyāsa thus, the expert devotee shall perform the Haṁsanyāsa as mentioned in Śaivite scriptures, in the eyes, nostrils, arms, eyes, face, forehead, armpits sides, breasts, hips, hands and heels. Or in the manner of five limbs the Nyāsa shall be performed. Then he shall perform the Nyāsa of the five-syllabled mantra.

42-44. Hereby Śivahood is generated along the path as mentioned before. A non-Śiva shall neither practise the mantra of Śiva nor worship Śiva nor meditate upon Śiva nor attain Śiva. Hence one shall dedicate himself to Śiva and eschew his identity. Thinking "I am Śiva" one shall perform Śaivite rites, viz. Karmayajña, Tapoyajña, Japayajña, Dhyānayajña and Jñānayajña.

45-46. Some are engaged in Karmayajña; others in Tapoyajña; still others in Japayajña; others in Dhyānayajña; and others in Jñānayajña. The latter ones are better than the earlier ones. Karmayajña is of two kinds : one with a specific desire and the other without that.

47-51. A person with a desire, even when he enjoys those pleasures becomes more and more attached to lust. If he is without desire he enjoys pleasures in Rudra's abode and after a descent therefrom is reborn as a person engaged in Tapoyajña. There is no doubt in this. An ascetic enjoys pleasures in Rudra's abode and after a fall therefrom is reborn in the world as a man devoted to Japa and Dhyāna. Such a man devoted to Japa and Dhyāna, thanks to heir excellence, attains knowledge ere long, and thereby attains Śiva's Sāyujya. Hence he becomes a liberated soul even when he is devoted to Karmayajña at the behest of Śiva, if he is without desire. But a person with lust will always be in bondage. Hence one shall be devoted to Dhyāna and Jñāna among the five Yajñas.

52-55. He who has meditation and knowledge crosses the ocean of worldly existence. Dhyānayajña which is freedom from the defects of violence etc. is a pure mental process for salvation and is therefore the greatest means. Just as the persons working outside the palace are seen not enjoying much of the benefits within the royal palace so also the Karmins. To those who meditate, the subtle body of Īśvara becomes visible. But to the Karmins, only the clay, wood etc. are visible. Hence those who are devoted to Dhyānayajña do not accept deities in the form of stone and clay, since they know the reality of Śiva.

56-57. The man who eschews Śiva stationed in the Ātman and worships him externally, resigns the fruit in his hand and licks his elbow. From knowledge, meditation is generated and from meditation knowledge functions better. Through these two, one attains liberation. Hence one shall be devoted to meditation.

58-61. One shall worship the lord and the goddess by means of external service, or with the mind full of faith meditate on them in the twelve-petalled lotus, head, forehead, the middle of the eyebrows, the tip of the nose, face, neck, heart, navel or in any permanent spot. Or he shall worship in a phallic image or an embodied idol or in an artificial fire or on the ground with devotion in accordance with one's affluence. Or he shall worship the lord both internally and externally. A person engaged in mental worship may or may not perform the external worship.

CHAPTER TWENTYTHREE

(A gloss on the rules governing worship)

Upamanyu said:—

1. I shall briefly give a commentary to the rules governing worships mentioned by Śiva to Śivā in the Śaivite scriptures.

2. With or without performing the internal worship which is its ancillary and which concludes with the rites in fire, one shall perform the external worship.

3-4. The materials are mentally conceived and purified. After meditating on Vināyaka and worshipping the lord in accordance with the injunctions, the learned devotee shall propitiate Nandīśa and Suyaśā in the south and the north and offer mentally well-conceived seat.

5. It may be a throne or a yogic seat or lotus-seat equipped with the three principles.[279]

6. Śiva shall be meditated on it. He is accompanied by Ambā. He is charming, endowed with all characteristics, auspicious in every limb.

7. He possesses all excellences. He is bedecked in all ornaments. His face, hands and feet, are red. His face beams with smiles resembling the Kunda flower and the moon.

8. He is as pure as the pure crystal. He has three eyes resembling full blown lotus. He has four arms and splendid body. He wears the charming digit of the moon.

279. Āsana is a particular posture or mode of sitting in religious meditation or worship.

9. His hands show the gestures of granting the boon and protection. He holds the deer and an axe. He has serpents for necklaces and bangles. His neck is charmingly blue.

10. He has none to compare with. He is accompanied by his followers and attendants. Then the devotee shall think of him to his left.

11. She is as tender as the petals of full blown-lotus. Her eyes are large and broad. Her face has the lustre of the full moon. Her tresses are dark-blue and curly.

12. Her complexion has the lustre of the petals of a blue lotus. She has the half moon for her coronet. Her breasts are round, weighty, lifted up, smooth and plump.

13. Her middle is slender. Her buttocks are large. She wears an exquisitely fine yellow garment. She is richly bedecked in all ornaments. The Tilaka mark on her forehead is dazzlingly brilliant.

14. She shines with flowers of various colours embellishing her braid of hair. In every respect her features are in consonance with her qualities. Due to bashfulness her face is slightly lowered.

15. In her right hand she bears a shining golden lotus. She is seated on a splendid seat with the other hand placed on it like a supporting staff.

16-19. She splits the Pāśa. She is in the form of existence, knowledge and bliss. After conceiving the lord and the goddess thus and meditating on them in an excellent auspicious seat, the devotee shall worship with piety as flowers along with all types of service. Or he can conceive the form of the lord in any of the following ways:—as Śiva, Sadāśiva, Maheśvara, or as one having the name of twenty-six principles or as Śrīkaṇṭha. Just as Mantra Nyāsa is performed in the body so also in this form the devotee can meditate on embodied Śiva who is beyond Sat and Asat as in the manner of external worship. He shall complete the worship mentally.

20-23. He shall then mentally imagine the Homa in the navel with sacrificial twig, ghee etc. He shall meditate on Śiva in the middle of the eye-brows in the form of the flame of the pure lamp. Thus in this mentally conceived auspicious worship whether in the body or independently, the rules until the concluding rites in fire are the same. Or after concluding the imaginary procedure of propitiation the devotee shall worship the lord in the phallic image or on the ground or in the fire.

CHAPTER TWENTYFOUR

(*The ritual of lord Śiva*)

Upamanyu said:—

1. The devotee shall sprinkle the place of worship with scented sandal water for the sake of purity, with the basic mantra. He shall put flowers there.

2. The obstacles shall be warded off. The place shall be veiled with Varma mantra. After performing the rite of Astranyāsa in the quarters, the place of worship shall be arranged.

3. Darbha grass shall be strewn over and washed by means of sprinkling. After cleaning the vessels he shall sanctify the materials.

4-5. He shall wash and sprinkle the vessels[280] of Prokṣaṇī Arghya, Pādya and Ācamanīya. After examining them he shall pour auspicious water therein. He shall place holy materials of worship there to the extent of their availability.

6. The holy materials of worship are many such as gems, silver, gold, scents, flowers, Akṣatas, fruits, sprouts and Darbha grass.

7. In the water for ablution and particularly in that

280. Prokṣaṇī, Arghya, Pādya and Ācamanīya are the vessels containing holy water to be used in the religious ceremonies. Prokṣaṇī contains water used for sprinkling or consecrating, Arghya for respectful offering, Pādya for washing the feet and Ācamanīya for sipping.

intended for drinking, sweet scents as well as cool and charming flowers shall be put.

8-9. Sandal and Uśīra shall be put in the Pādya water. In the Ācamanīya, nutmeg, berry, camphor, Bahumūla, and Tamālaka shall be put, preferably powdered. Cardamom seeds, camphor and sandal can be put in the vessels.

10. In the Arghya vessel all these materials shall be put—shoots of Kuśa grass, Akṣatas, barley, gingelly seeds, other grains, ghee, white mustard, flowers and Bhasma.

11. The following materials shall be put in the Prokṣaṇī vessel :—Kuśa, flowers, Yava grains, Bahumūla and Tamālaka along with Bhasma.

12. Every vessel shall be blessed by chanting the mantras; externally covered by the Varma mantra and protected by Astra mantra. He shall show the Mudrā of cow.

13. He shall purify the materials of worship by means of the water from the vessel Prokṣaṇī sprinkled on them repeating the basic mantra.

14. If all the vessels are not available the excellent aspirant shall arrange the vessel Prokṣaṇī in every holy rite. Arghya etc. shall be performed by the water therefrom.

15-17. Lord Vināyaka shall be worshipped with various foodstuffs. After that, near the southern doorway he shall duly worship the chief of harem Nandin himself. He resembles the golden mountain in lustre. He is bedecked in all ornaments. The crescent moon is his coronet. He is gentle. He has three eyes and four arms. He is the lord bearing shining trident, deer, axe and sharp-pointed baton. His face resembles the disc of the moon or he is conceived with the face of a monkey.

18-20. In the north the wife of the doorkeeper, the daughter of the Maruts, Suyaśā who bedecks the feet of Ambā shall be worshipped. He shall enter the sanctum sanctorum of Brahmā and worship the Liṅga. The remnants of the previous worship shall be removed. It shall be washed. The flower shall be worn on the head for the sake of purity.

21. With the flower in the hand he shall perform the Japa of the mantra upto the extent of his ability for the purity; through the Mantra Caṇḍa shall be worshipped in the north-east and the Nirmālya given over to him

22-24. Thereafter the seats Ādhāra etc. shall be conceived. The Ādhāra Śakti shall be meditated upon as dark-complexioned and auspicious resting on the ground. In front of Ādhāra Śakti the serpent of curly form with uplifted neck shall be conceived. He is white in colour with five hoods seeming to lick the sky. Above that is the seat in the form of a lion of four feet. The feet are virtue, knowledge, absence of attachment, glory and prosperity.

25-26. They are respectively in the south-east, south-west, north-west and north-east and are coloured white, red yellow and black. Adharma etc. are in the directions east etc. ending with the north. His bodies shall be conceived resembling the jewel Rājāvarta.* Covering for him is the pure white lotus seat.

27. Its petals are eight in number representing the eight attributes, Aṇimā etc. The filaments are the Rudras Vāma etc. in the company of Vāmā and other Śaktis.

28. The seeds too are those Śaktis alone Manonmanī etc. within. The pericarp is the greatest detachment and the stalk is the Śaivite knowledge.

29. The bulbous root at the extremity of the pericarp with the three zones shall be used in the Śaivite rites. Over the three zones the three Tattvas, Ātman etc. are the seats.

30. Above the seats shall be conceived the divine seat refulgent with the pure learning or knowledge, very comfortable and covered over by a covering sheet of colours.

31. He shall perform the rites of invocation, installation prevention, surveying and obeisance showing separate Mudrās for each.

32. After offering Pādya, Acamana, Arghya, scents, flowers, incense, light and Tāmbūla, the devotee shall perform the ablution of Śiva and Śivā.

33-38. Or after conceiving the seat and the deity thus and uniting it into a complete unit with the five Brahmans and others, repeating the basic mantra, the devotee shall invoke Śiva the great cause along with the goddess. The lord is as pure as the crystal, steady and imperishable. He is the

***Rājāvarta is one of the five gems famous for brilliance.**

cause of all worlds. He is the great Being who pervades everything from within and without. He is the minutest of all minute things, the greatest of all great things. He is easily visible to the devotees. He is the unchanging lord. He is invisible to Brahmā, Viṣṇu, Rudra and other gods. He is the essence of the Vedas. He is heard by the learned men as the incomprehensible being. He is without beginning, middle or end. He is the medicine for the ailing patients of worldly existence. He is famous as Śivatattva. He is steady and insistent for the welfare of the universe. The devotee shall worship this excellent lord with five types of devotional service.

39. The phallus is the image of Śiva the great Ātman. At the rite of ablution auspicious shouts of victory shall be raised.

40-41. The phallic idol shall be bathed with the liquid Pañcagavya, curds, milk, ghee, honey etc., powdered roots, essence of fruits, powdered gingelly seeds, mustard and fried grains, yava seeds etc. and the meritorious powder of black gram. After bathing the idol it shall be smeared with paste of flour and bathed in hot water.

42-44. The devotee shall rub the idol with the leaves of Bilva etc. for the removal of the smell. Again he shall bathe it with water. Royal service shall be rendered, such as the appliances of scents myrobalan or turmeric paste. Again the phallic and the embodied image shall be washed with scented water, sprinkled with Kuśa grass and flowers or with the water from gold and gemset vessels purified by the chanting of mantras.

45. If the materials are not available whatever is available shall be used. Mere water with chantings of mantra can also be used for the ablution of Śiva. The devotee shall faithfully perform the rite.

46. The water shall be poured with a pot, or couch, or Vardhanī or with the hand holding Kuśa grass and flowers all the time repeating the mantras.

47-48. The hymns of Pavamāna, Rudra, Nīla and Tvarita or the hymns of Liṅga Sūkta or the hymns from Atharvaśiras Upaniṣad or the hymns from the Ṛgveda or Sāmaveda relating to Śiva or the five Brahmans be used for the ablution of the lord of the chiefs of the gods. The name Śiva and the Praṇava too shall be used.

49. There is no difference in the manner in which the rite of ablution is performed in regard to the lord or the goddess since they are equal.

50. After performing the rites of ablution to the lord those to the goddess shall be performed. This is what the lord of the gods has ordained.

51. When the half-female form of the lord is to be worshipped, no serial order in the performance of rites shall be observed. Similarly in regard to the services rendered to the phallic or the embodied image.

52. After performing the ablution of the phallic idol it shall be wiped with a pure fragrant cloth. The devotee shall then offer garment and the sacred thread.

53-56. These are offered in order—Pādya, Ācamana, Arghya, scents, flowers, ornaments, incense, light, Naivedya, water for drinking, water for rinsing, Ācamanīya once again, substance for the fragrance of the mouth, good and auspicious coronet studded with all gems, ornaments, sacred garlands of different types, fans, chowries, palmyra leaf fan, mirror, and Nīrājana. At the time of Nīrājana there shall be all sorts of auspicious sounds like songs, instrumental music, dance and shouts of 'Victory'.

57-59. In a big flat vessel made of gold, silver, copper or clay he shall worship the lord with lotuses, seeds, flowers, curd, Akṣatas, Nandyāvarta flowers etc. in the forms of Śrīvatsa, Svastika, mirror, Vajra, fire etc. Eight lamps shall be lighted all round and one lamp shall be kept in the middle. In these the nine Śaktis Vāmā etc. shall be meditated upon and worshipped.

60. After covering with Kavaca mantra and protecting with the Astra mantra he shall show the Mudrā of cow and lift the vessel with both the hands.

61. Or only five lamps shall be kept, four in the four quarters and one in the middle, or only one lamp need be lit.

62. Lifting the vessel, the devotee shall whirl it thrice

above the phallic image in the manner of circumambulation, with the basic Mantra.

63. He shall offer Arghya and apply the scented Bhasma on the head. After offering a handful of flowers the rite of Naivedya shall be performed.

64. After offering water for drinking he shall offer Ācamana once again. Tāmbūla with five-scented[281] spices shall be offered.

65. All materials of worship shall be sprinkled with water. Music and dances shall go on. Conceiving the presence of Śiva and Śivā in the phallic image he shall perform the Japa of Śiva according to his ability.

66. Circumambulation, obeisance, eulogy, dedication of the self and submission of one's wish shall be humbly made.

67. Arghya and handful of flowers shall be offered and Mudrā shall be shown in accordance with injunctions. Forgiveness shall be prayed and the lord shall be ritualistically dismissed. The devotee shall meditate on the lord only in his Ātman.

68. In distress the offerings are restricted to those beginning with Pādya and ending with Tāmbūla, or to those beginning with Arghya, or to mere offering of flowers, but with pious feelings.

69. Even that much is enough for earning virtue. As long as he lives the devotee shall not take meals without worshipping Śiva.

70-72. If a sinner takes meals freely there is no atonement for him. If he takes in anything inadvertently he shall vomit it off, take bath and worship the lord and the goddess twice. He shall observe fast thereafter and repeat the names of Śiva ten thousand times. He shall observe celibacy also. The next day he shall make a charitable gift of gold to a devotee of Śiva. Then he shall perform great worship and sanctify himself.

281. The preparation of five kinds of aromatic substances contains कर्पूर, कक्कोल, लवङ्गपुष्प, गुवाक and जातीफल. Cp. कर्पूरकक्कोललवङ्गपुष्पगुवाकजातीफलपञ्चकेन । समांशभागेन च योजितेन मनोहर पञ्चसुगन्धकं स्यात् ।

CHAPTER TWENTYFIVE

(*The Worship of Śiva*)

Upamanyu said :—

1. What has not been mentioned because I was afraid of losing the sequence of worship, I shall now mention briefly.

2. After offering the light but before offering the Havis, the devotee shall perform the worship of the Āvaraṇa; or just when the time of Nīrājana has arrived.

3-5. In the first Āvaraṇa of Śiva and Śivā, the mantra of Rudra etc. upto the Astra shall be used for Japa. The five Brahmans from Īśāna to Śadyojāta shall be meditated upon in the north-east, east, south and north or in the west, south-east, north-east and south-west or in the north-west north-east and in the four quarters. Beyond that he shall perform the Garbhāvaraṇa and repeat the mantras.

6-8. Or he shall worship everything from the heart to the Astra. Outside he shall worship Indra in the east, Yama in the south, Varuṇa in the west, Kubera in the north, Īśa in the north-east, fire in the south-east, Nirṛti in the south-west, Vāyu in the north-west, Viṣṇu in the south-west, Brahmā in the north-east and the weapons from thunderbolt to the lotus outside the lotus.

9-11. He shall worship the famous forms of the lord in the quarters in order. The deities of the Āvaraṇa shall be meditated upon as looking at the lord and the goddess with palms joined and seated comfortably. He shall worship the Āvaraṇa deities with their names with the word 'Namaḥ' with flowers and bow to them in order. He shall worship the Garbhāvaraṇa with its Āvaraṇa.

12-13. In the Yoga, meditation, Japa and homa whether external or internal, the Haviṣ of six types shall be given as pure rice or rice mixed with green gram. The milk-pudding mixed with curd or honey-soaked jaggery shall be offered with side-dishes.

14. Churned curd shall be given with jaggery and

sugar-candy. Tasteful foodstuffs especially sweet pie and fruits shall be given.

15-16. Cold water with red sandal and flowers thrown in shall be given. A piece of Areca nut soaked in Cardamom juice shall be given. Betel leaves with Khadira etc. shall be given. White and yellow are auspicious. The white lime powder shall be rocky but neither very hard nor defective.

17-18. The camphor, Kankola and Jāti, if fresh, are auspicious. As an unguent the sandal shall be in powdered form. The lower stem is better. The musk and saffron shall be pasted. Only fragrant flowers are holy and auspicious.

19. Flowers devoid of smell, of obnoxious smell, defiled, stale and broken at fall shall not be used for the worship of lord Śiva.

20-21. Soft fine cloths and golden ornaments shall be given along with camphor, gum-resin and sandal, well fumigated and rendered fragrant with flowers.

22. Incense mixed with sandal, gum-resin, camphor, ghee and honey is excellent.

23. Lamps lighted with fragrant ghee from the milk of tawny cows, accompanied by camphor are excellent.

24. Pañcagavya consisting of sweet milk, curd and ghee all taken from tawny cows is favourite of Śiva for bath and drink.

25. Seats of ivory framed in gold and set with gems and the covering cloths of various colours shall be used.

26. Beds shall be comfortable, charming, high and low with soft pillows. They shall be filled with fine cotton.

27. Water taken from an east-flowing or west-flowing river is excellent for bath and drink. It shall be cool and filtered with a cloth.

28. The umbrella shall resemble the moon. It shall be embellished with pearls and nine[282] varieties of gems. It shall be divine and charming with a golden handle.

282. The nine precious gems are : Muktā, Māṇikya, Vaidūrya, Gomeda, Vajra, Vidruma, Padmarāga, Marakata and Nīla.

29. The chowries shall be white and fine. They shall be embellished with gold. The handle shall be studded with gems. They shall shine like two royal swans.

30. The mirror shall be smooth and polished. Divine sweet smelling unguents shall be smeared over it. It shall be studded with gems all round. It shall be decorated with excellent garlands.

31. The conch shall be white like the swan, Kunda flower or the moon. It shall have a majestic resonant sound. At the mouth, back and other places it shall be studded with gems and framed in gold.

32. The bugles shall be charmingly made of gold and decorated with pearls. They shall be capable of producing different notes.

33. Different kinds of drums like Bheri, mṛdaṅga, Muraja, Timiccha, Paṭaha shall be used, capable of sounding like the roaring sea.

34. All pots and vessels shall be beautiful. Their supporting stands shall be made of gold.

35. The temple of Śiva shall be made like a royal palace with all the characteristics mentioned in the science of architecture.

36. It shall be encircled by high walls with the ornamental gateway as lofty as a mountain. It shall be studded with gems. The doors shall be made of gold.

37. It must have a hundred columns of molten gold studded with gems. The canopy shall be embellished with pearls and the festoons at the gateway shall be brightened with corals.

38. Its top shall be decorated with golden domes resembling divine crowns and marked with the lordly missile.

39-40. It shall be richly decorated in the border all round by palatial buildings with tall minarets, great mansions for the residence of kings, royal highways and excellent halls of assembly situated in the different quarters appearing like an inner rampart.

41. It shall contain thousands of courtezans in dance and music and those adepts in playing on flutes and lutes.

42-44. It shall be guarded by heroic guards and watchmen equipped with elephants, horses and chariots. It shall contain many flower gardens, lakes, and tanks in the different quarters. It shall be inhabited by the brahmin devotees of Śiva, who must know the truth of the Vedas and Vedānta, who are devoted to Śaivite scriptures who are engaged in Śaivite way of life, who must have the characteristics prescribed in Śaivite scriptures, who must be quiet, prosperous and devoted to good conduct, who have smiling faces and who follow lord Śiva.

45-48. All people whether rich or poor shall worship the lord with devotion through the wealth legitimately earned by them. They shall worship in a place built by the people according to their capacity. The temple shall be built in stone, or ivory, or wood or brick or even clay. It may be in a holy forest or on a mountain or on the banks of a river. The worship may be performed in any other holy spot or in the house. Even if the wealth is illegitimately acquired he does not incur sin or hindrance if he worships Śiva with devotion since the lord is subservient to piety.

49. If one worships without devotion even with legitimately earned wealth he does not derive the benefit thereof. Devotion alone is the main concern.

50. The benefit of even a little or a great service rendered by a poor or a rich man, according to the affluence, to Śiva with devotion is the same.

51. Even a poor man urged by devotion, may do what a rich man devoid of devotion will not do.

52. If a man devoid of devotion were to dedicate his entire possession to Śiva he will not derive the benefit thereof. Devotion is the sole criterion.

53. Without this none can go to the divine city of Śiva[283] through any sort of penances.

54. O Kṛṣṇa, this is the secret of secrets in regard to the lord. There is no doubt that a devotee becomes liberated through devotion.

55. The Japa of Śiva's Mantra meditation, Homa, Yajña, penance, learning, charitable gift, study of Vedas—all

283. See p. 1945 note

these are conducive to piety. There is no doubt about this.

56. A person devoid of piety and devotion is not liberated even after doing everything but one with devotion is liberated even without doing anything.

57. To a devotee of Śiva, of what avail are thousands of Cāndrāyaṇas,[284] hundreds of Prājāpatyas,[285] and other monthly fasts.

58. In this world, even non-devotees perform penances in mountain caves for the enjoyment of insignificant pleasures. But only a devotee is liberated through pious feelings.

59. The Sāttvic activity yields salvation. Yogins abide by the Sattvaguṇa. The ritualists perform Rājasic rites bestowing Siddhis because they are enveloped by Rajas Guṇa.

60. Asuras and Rākṣasas possessing Tamas Guṇa and men like that worship the lord for securing worldly pleasures.

61. Whether the attitude is Sāttvic, Rājasic or Tāmasic one performing worship etc. with devotion attains welfare.

62. Since devotion is a boat that saves one from the ocean of sins, of what avail are Rajas and Tamas to one who is endowed with devotion?

63. O Kṛṣṇa, a low born, a base or a fool, or a fallen man, if he resorts to Śiva is worthy of being worshipped by the gods and Asuras.[286]

64. Hence, by all means, one shall worship Śiva with devotion alone, since non-devotees secure no benefit from anywhere.

284. Yājñavalkya 3. 324 et seq; Manu 11. 217. It is a religious observance or expiatory penance regulated by the period of the moon's waxing and waning. Herein the daily quantity of food consisting of fifteen mouthfuls at the full moon is diminished by one mouthful every day during the dark fortnight till it is increased in like manner during the bright fortnight.

285. It is a religious fast or penance. Herein he shall take food for 3 days in the morning, for 3 days in the evening, for 3 days both in the morning and evening and thereafter shall abstain from food for 3 days.

286. The verse is indicative of the proselytizing attempts of the Śaivite Ācāryas to allure the laity to their fold. See Vāyavīya S. II. 10. 70-72 and the footnote thereon.

65. O Kṛṣṇa, I shall tell you a great secret. Listen to my words. This is what has been decided conclusively by the Vedas, scriptures and those who know them, after careful consideration.

CHAPTER TWENTYSIX

(*The worship of Śiva with the ancillary rites*)

Upamanyu said:—

1-2. Even a slayer of brahmin, a wine-addict, a thief, a defiler of the preceptor's bed, one guilty of matricide or patricide, a murderer of a hero and one guilty of destroying a child in the womb becomes absolved of those sins within twelve years by worshipping Śiva with devotion even without mantras.

3. Hence by all means let even a fallen man worship Śiva sustaining himself on alms and conquering the sense-organs. This he shall do if he is a devotee and none else.

4. Even if one commits a great sin he is liberated from that if he worships the lord of the gods with devotion, repeating the five-syllabled mantra.

5. There are many persons who live solely on water or air and who emaciate their bodies by means of holy rites. They cannot attain Śivaloka through these rites.

6. He who worships Śiva even once with devotion repeating the five-syllabled mantra goes to the abode of Śiva due to the efficacy of the mantra of Śiva.

7. Hence the penances and the sacrifices wherein the entire possession may be given as Dakṣiṇā, are not equal to even a croreth part of the worship of Śiva.

8. Whether bound or free, if the devotee worships with the five-syllabled mantra he is liberated. No doubt need be entertained in this respect.

9. Whether a man is a follower of Rudra or not, whether

he is fallen or deluded if he worships but once with Rudra Sūkta he is liberated.

10. A devotee of Śiva who has conquered anger, whether he has or has not secured grace shall worship the lord with the Sūktamantra or the six-syllabled mantra.

11. Surely the former is better than the latter. He becomes liberated and absorbed into Brahman.

12. Hence one shall always worship Śiva with devotion repeating the mantras, once, twice or thrice or always.

13-15. Those who worship the lord shall be known as Maheśvaras themselves. If one does not worship him through knowledge assisted by the prompting of the soul he suffers for long in the world which is an ocean of misery. Even after attaining the rare human body, if a deluded individual does not worship Śiva, his life becomes futile since it does not lead to salvation. After attaining the rare human birth those who worship the lord are excellent and blessed. Their life alone is fruitful.

16-19. Those who are devoted to the lord, whose minds are inclined to him and who endeavour to remember the lord are never subjected to misery. The fruit of the worship of Śiva is the sufficient wealth, charming houses and women folk seductively bedecked in ornaments. Those who desire great pleasures and kingdom in heaven shall love his lotus feet for ever. Good fortune, handsome and brilliant features, good strength, compassionate and renouncing temperament, heroism, fame in the world—all these are secured by one who worships the lord.

20-22. So desiring welfare, one shall invariably worship Śiva, forsaking everything else and dedicating the mind solely to him. The life passes off quickly. Youth goes off rapidly. Sickness approaches all too suddenly. Hence the lord shall be worshipped. Worship Śiva before death overtakes you, before old age attacks you, before the sense-organs become atrophied and inefficient.

23-28. Realising that there is no holy rite in the three worlds, on a par with the worship of Śiva, Sadāśiva shall be worshipped assiduously. If the worship is conducted in a palace the following rites too shall be performed—sacrifice at the gateway, worship within the screen, offering oblation to Śiva's attendants and perpetual festivities. After offering libation the devotee or his servant shall offer oblation to the attendants in the palace. The devotee shall come out to the accompaniment of instrumental music and facing the northern direction he shall offer flowers, incense, lamp and cooked rice with water. Then he shall stand on the Mahāpīṭha facing the north and offer oblations. Thereafter, whatever had been offered to the lord before, as Naivedya, cooked rice shall be offered to Caṇḍa as Naivedya. The remnants also shall be offered thus.

29-30. Performing Homa, the latter part of worship shall be concluded. After conducting the regular rites he shall perform the perpetual festivities, Japa etc. in accordance with the injunction in Śaivite scriptures. In a large metallic vessel shining splendidly with a red lotus the divine Pāśupata missile shall be invoked and worshipped.

31-35. The vessel shall be carried on the head by a Śaivite brahmin well-bedecked. He shall hold a lighted torch. With dances and songs to the accompaniment of auspicious instrumental music the party shall make three circumambulations round the palace of the lord. The movement shall be neither quick nor slow. Thereafter the devotee shall stand a the door with palms joined in reverence shall take it in and ritualistically dismiss the Astra. After one more circumambulation he shall offer eight flowers and conclude the worship.

CHAPTER TWENTYSEVEN

(*The rite of sacrifice*)

Upamanyu said:—

1-2. I shall mention the sacrificial rites in the fire to be performed in sacred pits, or raised ground or in altar. Fire shall be taken in an iron vessel or a fresh mud pot in accordance with the injunctions and transferred to the actual place of sacrifice. After due consecration he shall propitiate the lord and commence sacrifice.

3. The pit may be one or two Hastas wide. The altar shall be made in the form of a circle or a square.

4. In the altar he shall make the eight-petalled lotus. It shall be two or four Aṅgulas high above the altar.

5-6. The navel within the altar shall be two Vitastis high One Aṅgula is the distance between the middle and the first knot in the middle finger. Twentyfour such Aṅgulas constitute a Hasta. Three, two or only one Mekhalā (circular girdle) shall also be made.

7-8. The altar shall be made with smooth clay. In the middle of the Mekhalā to the west or south the passage shall be made like the leaf of the Aśvattha tree or like the lower lip of an elephant. It shall be beautifully made slightly lower than the fire. It shall close in gradually.

9-10. The Mekhalā shall be left out a little where it faces the pit. There is no stipulated height for the altar. It shall be made of clay or sand. The circular ground shall be smeared with cowdung and water. The measurement of the basin is not stipulated. The Kuṇḍa shall be made of clay. The altar shall be smeared with cowdung and water.

11. The vessel shall be washed and warmed in fire The sacrificial material shall be sprinkled with water. The devotee shall draw lines on the pit etc. in the manner prescribed in his own branch of learning.

12. The seat of fire shall be made after due sprinkling, with Darbhas or flowers. He shall gather the material for the purpose of worship and sacrifice.

13-15. Things to be washed shall be washed and to be sprinkled shall be sprinkled and purified. Then he shall fetch fire in a supporting vessel. The fire may be one produced from crystals, lens etc. or from wood. It shall be brought from the house of a Vedic scholar. It shall be whirled round the sacrificial pit thrice repeating the Bīja mantra of the fire. The fire shall be placed in its seat through the passage or straight in front.

16-18. Seated near the passage the devotee shall survey

the fire and think that the internal fire stationed in his umbilicus has risen in the form of flames and has merged in the external fire in the form of a disc. The expert devotee shall repeat the basic mantra in the manner prescribed in his Sūtra and shall perform the rites of Anvādhāna[287] and Ājya-saṁskāra. To its south he shall worship the idol of Śiva, perform the rite of Mantranyāsa with the butter and show the Mudrā of cow.

19-20. The sacrificial spoons shall be metallic but not of bell metal, iron or lead. These shall be made of sacrificial wood as mentioned in Smṛtis and approved by artisans. The leaves of the Brahma tree shall be holeless. They shall be raised in the middle.

21-22. The leaves shall be scrubbed with Darbhas, warmed in the fire, then sprinkled with water in the manner prescribed in his Sūtra, repeating the name of Śiva. He shall then make offering to the fire with the eight Bīja mantras. The seven Bījas for the seven flames are respectively Bhrum, Stum, Brum, Śrum, Pum, Ḍrum and Drum.

23-24. The middle tongue has three flames. The flame in the east is yellow. The flame in the south-east is red; that in the south-west is black and the other one is refulgent. As its name implies it is brilliant. It is the flame in the north-west.

25-26. After repeating their Bīja mantras the tongues shall be mentioned and the rite concluding with Svāhā performed in due order. The Ājya shall be used for Āhuti with the mantras of the tongues one by one. In the middle he shall perform three Āhutis repeating 'Ram Vahnyeti Svāhā' either with ghee or with sacrificial twigs. Then the rite of Pariṣecana shall be performed.

27. When this is performed it becomes fire of Śiva. The devotee shall conceive it as the seat of Śiva. The lord shall be invoked there and worshipped, in the half-male and half-female form. After sprinkling everything ending with the light he shall perform the sacrifice with the sacrificial twigs.

287. It is the rite of depositing fuel on the sacred fire

28-29. The sacrificial twigs shall consist of Palāśa or other trees worthy of sacrifice. They shall be twelve Aṅgulas in length. They shall not be crooked. They shall not be dry by themselves. The bark shall be intact, even and without cuts. Or they shall be ten Aṅgulas in length, as thick as the small finger or they may be of the length of Prādeśa.[288] If they are not available any kind of twig shall be offered in the fire.

30. The Ājya Āhuti shall be made with the leaf four Aṅgulas wide, shaped in the form of a Dūrvāpatra. Afterwards, cooked rice of the size of an Akṣa shall be offered.

31. Fried grains, mustard seeds, barleys, gingelly seeds, foodstuffs soaked in ghee etc. shall be offered if possible.

32. The number of Āhutis shall be ten, five or three according to capacity. It is enough even if one Āhuti is made.

33. The butter shall be offered with the wooden spoon and the articles with the wooden ladle or with hand. The Homa shall be performed at the divine or saintly spot.

34. If full articles are not available only one material shall be offered with devotion. As an expiation he shall perform three Āhutis repeating the mantra.

35-36. He shall fill the Sruk with the ghee that has been left after Homa and put a flower on it. The Sruva shall be placed above it upside down along with the Darbha. Through the root of the Darbha the ghee shall fall in drops of the size of a barley grain repeating the mantra ending with Vauṣaṭ.

37. Performing the Pūrṇāhuti he shall perform the rite of sprinkling water. He shall ritualistically dismiss the lord and preserve the fire.

38-42. Or it can also be discharged and placed in the umbilicus of the altar and worshipped everyday. Or, bringing the fire along the path prescribed in Śaivite scriptures it shall be conceived as born of the womb of the goddess of speech, consecrated duly and worshipped. Sacri-

288. i.e. from the tip of the thumb to the tip of the little finger with both of them stretched.

ficial fuels shall be put on the fire again and the sacred sticks laid round the fire covered with a cloth. The vessels shall be placed in pairs. Śiva shall be worshipped then. After purifying the Prokṣaṇī vessel the vessels shall be sprinkled with the water. The Praṇītā vessel shall be filled with the water and placed in the north-east. Then come the rites concluding with the consecration of ghee. After the Sruk and Sruva are purified, the rites of Garbhādhāna Puṁsavana and Sīmantonnayana[289] shall be performed with the rites of Homa in each case. Then he shall think of the fire as born.

43-45. Agni shall be conceived in the form of having three feet, seven hands, four horns, two heads and three eyes, as tawny as honey, having the matted hair, with the moon for his crest, of red colour, red garments and red unguents, bedecked in garlands and ornaments, richly equipped with all characteristics, having the sacred thread and three girdles, holding the Sruk and Sruva in the right hand, iron club, fan and the vessel of ghee in the other.

46-50. After meditating on the fire thus with these features he shall perform post-natal rites. The umbilical cord shall be removed and the purificatory rite for the post-natal pollution shall be performed. The rite of naming shall be performed by giving him the title of Śivāgni with due Āhuti. The rite of ritualistic dismissal of the parents as well as of tonsure, sacred thread shall be performed till the end of Āptoryāma. As a consecratory rite the Homa of ghee-pouring shall be performed. Agni shall be conceived as Sviṣṭakṛt. With the Bīja mantra "Raṁ" the water shall be sprinkled all round. The worship of Brahmā, Viṣṇu, Śiva, Īśa and of their miraculous missiles shall be performed in due order. Then for the sake of incense and lamp, fire shall be taken out by the expert devotee.

51-52. The devotee shall collect the materials of worship, ghee etc., think of the seat of the lord and the goddess, invoke them in the fire and perform the rites until the

289. On the Saṁskāras Garbhādhāna, Puṁsavana, Sīmantonnayana, Jātakarma, Nāma-karaṇa, Caula and Upanayana (verses 42, 46, 47) see 'Hindu Saṁskāras'

Pūrṇāhuti. Or the devotee following the Śaivite conduct of life shall perform the rites in fire as prescribed in his scriptural code dedicating the same to Śiva. There is no other injunction there.

53-54. The ashes from Śivāgni shall be collected and preserved. Similarly the ashes of Agnihotra rite or from the fire connected with the celebration of marriage. The fire shall be ripe, pure and sweet-smelling. The dung shall be of the cow, tawny in colour. It is commendable if collected as it falls from the cow before it reaches the ground.

55. If he collects the dung that has already fallen on the ground the upper and the lower portions shall be eschewed. The dung shall not be too watery nor too solidified nor dried up. It shall not emit foul smell.

56-58. It shall be made into balls and the balls shall be consigned to Śivāgni or other types of fires repeating the basic mantra. The portions over-burnt or under-burnt shall be eschewed and the white ashes shall be gathered and ground into powder. It shall be preserved in receptacles made of metals, wood, clay or stone or any other material. The receptacle of water shall be pure. It shall be kept in a pure auspicious, even place and guarded like valuable wealth.

59. It shall not be handed to any undeserving person. It shall not be kept or thrown in any unholy place. If the hands or limbs are dirty it shall not be touched. It shall not be neglected nor shall one jump over it.

60. Hence after taking the ashes it shall be utilised with the mantras on occasions previously mentioned and not otherwise. It shall not be given to others.

61. The ashes shall be collected before the ritualistic dismissal of the lord. After the rite of the ritualistic dismissal it becomes Caṇḍabhasma.

62. After the rites in the fire have been concluded he shall perform the oblation rite according to the injunctions in the Śaivite scriptures or as mentioned in his own Sūtra.

63. Then after conceiving the seat of Vidyā on the well-smeared Maṇḍala he shall instal the sheath of Vidyā and worship the same with flowers etc. in due order.

64. In front of the seat of Vidyā, the seat of the

preceptor too shall be conceived. After assigning the seat there, he shall worship the preceptor with flowers etc.

65. Thereafter the venerable persons shall be worshipped and the hungry shall be fed. The devotee shall take the wholesome food at leisure, comfortably.

66-67. What has been offered as Naivedya or what is left over he shall partake of, with full faith and not out of covetousness. It shall be for the purity of the Ātman. Out of covetousness he shall not partake of what is offered to Caṇḍa. The injunctions about scents, garlands etc. are the same. But the expert devotee shall not have the conception "I am Śiva".

68. After taking meals he shall perform Ācamana and meditate upon Śiva in the heart repeating the basic mantra. He shall spend the leisure thereafter in discussing Śaivite philosophy and legends.

69. At night he shall perform worship and then make out bed for Śiva and Śivā.

70. He shall offer mentally or physically various food-stuffs, garments, unguents flower-garlands, etc. all performed in a charming way.

71. The devotee shall go to bed at the feet of the lord and the goddess. The householder shall sleep there with his wife. Others shall sleep alone.

72-73. He shall wake up before dawn and utter the first Mātrā. After bowing mentally to the lord accompanied by Ambā and his Gaṇas he shall attend to his morning duties. After washing himself he shall awaken the lord and the goddess by the divine sounds of conch and other instruments.

74. He shall perform the worship of Śiva and Śivā by means of fresh blown fragrant flowers and begin the rites as mentioned before.

CHAPTER TWENTYEIGHT

(The compulsory and optional rites)

Upamanyu said:—

1. Now I shall explain the procedure of rites under certain conditions to be performed by those who follow the Śaivite conduct of life in the manner prescribed in the Śaivite scriptures.

2-3. The great worship shall be performed every month in both the fortnights on the eighth and fourteenth days and on the Full-moon and the New-moon days. It must be performed particularly at the tropical and equinoctial transit of the sun and during the eclipses, according to his capacity.

4. Every month he shall observe fast for a day and prepare Brahmakūrca. He shall perform the ablution of Śiva thereby and drink the residue.

5. The atonement for the murder of a brahmin and other great sins is the drinking of Brahmakūrca.[290] There is no better remedy.

6. In the month of Dec-Jan. when the moon is in the asterism Puṣya he shall perform the rite of Nīrājana to the lord. In the month of Jan-February in the Maghā star he shall make the charitable gifts of ghee and woollen blanket.

7. In the month of Feb-March in the star Uttarā-Phālgunī he shall start the great festival. In the month of March-April on the full-moon day and Citrā star, he shall perform the Swing-festival duly.

8. In the month of April-May on the full-moon day with the star Viśākhā he shall make the great temple of flowers. In the month of May June on the star Mūlā he shall offer a pot of cold water.

9-10. In the month of June-July on the star Uttarā-ṣādhā the rite of investiture with sacred thread shall be performed. In the month of July-August the mystic diagrams shall be arranged. In the month of Aug-September in the star

290. It is a kind of penance in the observance of which the five products (pañcagavya) of the cow are eaten.

Pūrvāṣāḍhā the swimming festival of the lord shall be performed.

11. In the month of Sep-October on the full moon day he shall make charitable gifts of milk pudding and cooked rice with grains recently harvested. On the star Śatabhiṣak he shall perform the rites of fire too with the same.

12. In the month of Octo-November when the moon is in conjunction with the star Kṛttikā he shall light a thousand lamps. In the month of Nov-December on the Ārdrā star he shall perform the ablution of Śiva with ghee.

13. Those who are unable to perform the rites on the respective occasions shall perform the festival in the big hall of the temple or perform worship or more.

14-16. On occasions when commendable rites shall be performed, when the mind is afflicted and dejected, when the conduct of life has become defiled, when bad dreams occur, when wicked men are seen, when inauspicious portents occur or when afflicted by great ailments, the devotee shall perform ceremonial ablutions, worships, Japas, meditations, sacrifices and other rites and offer charitable gifts suitably along with Puraścaraṇa. When the series of Śiva-fire is broken it shall be revived.

17. Śiva bestows salvation on the person who performs his rites thus, perpetually and assiduously, even in a single birth.

18. He who performs in succession the compulsory and optional rites attains the divine and primordial region of lord Śiva.

19-21. The man enjoys great pleasures there for millions and millions of Kalpas. After some time, falling from there he occupies the regions of Umā, Kumāra, Viṣṇu, Brahmā, Rudra and enjoys the pleasures there as mentioned. Again he goes up and transcends the five regions. Securing knowledge of Śiva he attains Śiva's city.

22. A devotee who performs half the number of holy rites has this upward and downward journey twice and thereafter secures knowledge and attains Śiva's Sāyujya.

23-26. A devotee who performs one-fourth of the

number of holy rites goes beyond the two worlds, to the end of the universe and the unmanifest above, and reaches the Pauruṣa and Raudra regions of Śiva. After enjoying the pleasures there in diverse ways for thousands of Yugas when the merit is exhausted he reaches the earth and is born in a great and noble family. There also due to the previous impressions, he will eschew brutish activities and be engaged in Śaivite holy rites. Meditating well due to the holy rites he will attain Śiva's city.

27-28. After enjoying extensive pleasures he will attain the region of Vidyeśvaras. After enjoying the vast pleasures along with Vidyeśvaras he will return for once either within or outside the universe. Thereafter he will secure the perfect knowledge of Śiva and the great devotion. After attaining identity with Śiva he does not return again.

29-30. A person who is devoted to Śiva even as the others are devoted to sensual objects shall be liberated whether he performs or does not perform the Śaivite holy rites. He returns once, twice, or thrice but ultimately does not return.

31-32. He becomes an emperor and is invested with the right in the Śaivite ritual. If one desires welfare one shall seek refuge in Śiva and resort to his holy rites. But we do not compel anyone through any means.

33-35. Neither importunities nor over-discussions are appealing. The Śaivite rites appeal to some others by virtue of the merits they bestow and the previous impressions they invoke if the cause of worldliness in their case is not competent to help. Hence, if one longs for the welfare of the Ātman, one shall ponder over all these things in accordance with his nature and engage himself in the Śaivite holy rites.

CHAPTER TWENTYNINE

(*Description of Kāmya rites*)

Lord Kṛṣṇa said :—

1. O holy lord, the compulsory and optional rites of those who depend on him, as mentioned by Śiva, have been heard by me from your mouth itself which is to be as much respected as the Vedas.

2. Now I wish to hear if there is any Kāmya rite for those who are authorized in Śaivite rites. It behoves you to mention it.

Upamanyu said:—

3-5. Some rites yield benefit here itself. Some yield benefit hereafter. Both of them are of five types. Some rites are in the form of activities, some in the form of penance, some in the form of Japas, some in the form of meditation, some in the form of all these. Those in the form of activities are the rites of Homa and worship.

6. The rites can be fruitful only for those who have all Śaktis. Śakti is the behest of Śiva the great Ātman.

7. Hence only the brahmin who upholds the behest shall perform the Kāmya rites. Now I shall mention the Kāmya rites yielding benefit here and hereafter.

8-10. The internal rites shall be performed by the followers of Śiva and the external by the followers of Maheśvara. In fact the followers of Śiva and of Maheśvara are not different even as Śiva and Maheśvara are not different. Men engaged in the sacrifice of knowledge are the followers of Śiva and seek refuge in him. Those who are engaged in the sacrifice of activities are the followers of Maheśvara. Śaivas shall perform internal and the Māheśvaras external rites.

11-13. In the rite which is going to be mentioned the procedure is not different. The ground shall be tested through smell, colour and taste. It shall be desirable. A canopy shall be spread above. The ground shall be well-scrubbed and smeared to appear like the surface of a mirror. Along the path, as seen in the sacred scriptures he shall consecrate the eastern sector at first. The Maṇḍala shall be one Hasta or two Hastas in width.

14. An eight-petalled pure lotus along wtth its pericarp shall be drawn by means of gold dust, gem dust etc. gathered according to availability.

15-18. It shall have five Āvaraṇas and shall be very splendid. The Siddhis shall be conceived in the petals. The Rudras along with Śaktis shall be conceived in the filaments. The eight deities Vāma etc. shall be conceived in the petals beginning with the eastern one; Vairāgya in the pericarp, the nine Śaktis in the seeds, Śaivite holy rite in the bulbous root, knowledge of Śiva in the stalk. Above the pericarp the discs of the fire, the sun and the moon shall be conceived. Beyond that shall be conceived the trio: Śiva, Vidyā and Ātmā. Above all seats Śiva shall be conceived equipped with the flowers of various colours.

19-22. He shall worship Śiva with the five Āvaraṇas accompanied by Ambā. Śiva shall be conceived as pure as the pure crystal, delighted and having cool lustre. He is bedecked with the coronet of matted hair resembling a circle of lightning. He wears the hide of the tiger. His lotus face is slightly smiling. His soles, palms and lips resemble the petals of the red lotus. He is richly endowed with all characteristics. He is bedecked in all ornaments, and equipped with excellent weapons. He has divine scents and unguents. He has five faces and ten arms. The sector of the moon is his crest.

23. His eastern face is gentle, having the lustre of the rising sun. It has three lotus eyes and the rising moon for its crest.

24-27. The southern face has the charming lustre of the blue cloud. The brows are crooked and the face is terrible with three red and circular eyes. It is terrible with the curved fangs. None dare offend it. His lips throb. The northern face is like a coral, bedecked with blue forelocks. It has charming movements. It has three eyes and the moon bedecks its crest. The western face has three brilliant eyes and the lustre of the full moon. It also wears the digit of the moon. It is gentle and charming with smiles. The fifth face is crystal-like with the shining digit of the moon. It is very gentle and looks splendid with the three shining eyes.

28-30. In his right side he shines with the trident, axe, thunderbolt, sword and fire. In his left side he shines brilliantly with the serpent, arrow, bell, noose and goad. The nivṛttikalā envelops him upto the knee, the pratiṣṭhākalā to the navel, the Vidyākalā to the neck and the Śāntākalā to the forehead. Above that he is enveloped by the great Śāntyatītakalā. Thus pervading the five pathways he has the five Kalās constituting his body.

31-37. The lord has Īśāna as his coronet. He is the eternal one named Puruṣa. Aghora constitutes his heart, Vāmadeva his private parts and Sadyojāta his legs. His form consists of thirtyeight Kalās. The lord consists of the Varṇas, letters. He is identical with the five Brahmans. He is of the Oṁkāra form. He is endowed with the Śakti of Haṁsa Ātman. His lap is enveloped by the Icchāśakti. His right side is flanked by Jñāna Śakti and the left by Kriyāśakti. Sadāśiva in the form Vidyā shall be conceived as identical with the trio of Tattvas. The Mūrti shall be conceived with the basic mantra and everything shall be combined into one unit. Until the Arghya he shall be worshipped duly with the basic mantra. Śiva shall be invoked along with the great Śakti, in the embodied form. The lord devoid of Sat and Asat shall be invoked and worshipped with the five articles of worship.

38-40. He shall be worshipped with the five brahmans and six ancillaries. With Mātṛkās repeating the Praṇava, he shall worship Śiva in the company of Śakti, in the quiet form repeating the mantras. Or he shall worship the lord only with the Śiva mantra. Then he shall begin the Pañcāvaraṇa Pūjā after offering Pādya etc. upto Mukhavāsa. But the rite of Prasthāpana (bidding the deity farewell) shall not be performed.

CHAPTER THIRTY

(*The Kāmya rites of the followers of Śiva*)

Upamanyu said:—

1. There at the outset he shall worship lords Heramba and Ṣaṇmukha on either side, the right and the left in order, of Śiva and Śivā.

2. Then in the first Āvaraṇa he shall worship the five Brahmans beginning with Īśāna and ending with Sadyojāta along with their Śaktis all round.

3. The six limbs—the heart etc. of Śiva and Śivā shall be worshipped from the south-east.

4. Afterwards he may or may not worship the eight Rudras-Vāma etc. along with their Śaktis all round in order, from the east onwards.

5. Thus, O Kṛṣṇa, the first Āvaraṇa has been mentioned to you. Now listen to the second Āvaraṇa with faith.

6. He shall worship Ananta in the eastern petal and his Śakti to his left. In the southern petal he shall worship Sūkṣma and his Śakti.

7. Then in the western petal he shall worship lord Śiva along with his Śakti. Similarly in the northern petal he shall worship Ekanetra and his Śakti.

8. Afterwards he shall worship Ekarudra and his Śakti in the north-eastern petal. He shall worship Trimūrti and his Śakti in the South-eastern petal.

9. He shall worship Śrīkaṇṭha and his Śakti towards his left in the south-western petal. Similarly he shall worship Śikhaṇḍīśa and his Śakti in the north-western petal.

10. In the second Āvaraṇa the Cakravartins, in the third Āvaraṇa the Aṣṭamūrtis shall be worshipped along with their Śaktis.

11-12. They shall be worshipped in the eight quarters from the east onwards in order. The eight Mūrtis[291] in order are Bhava, Śarva, Īśāna Rudra, Paśupati, Ugra, Bhīma

291. For details see ŚRS. Ch. 2. The eight forms shall be distinguished from the eight names mentioned in the Vāyavīya (I. 32. 23).

and Mahādeva. Afterwards the eleven Mūrtis, Mahādeva etc. shall be worshipped along with their Śaktis.

13-15. The eleven Mūrtis are : Mahādeva, Śiva, Rudra, Śaṅkara, Nīlalohita, Īśāna, Vijaya, Bhīma, Devadeva, Bhavodbhava and Kapardīśa. The first eight shall be worshipped in the south-eastern quarter onwards. Devadeva shall be worshipped in the eastern petel. Bhavodbhava shall be worshipped either in the north-east or in the south-east. Kapālīśa shall be worshipped in their middle.

16-18. In the same Āvaraṇa he shall worship the lordly bull in the east, Nandin in the south, Mahākāla in the north, Śāstṛ in the south-eastern petal or in the petal to the south of the goddess. He shall worship Gaṇeśa in the south-western petal and Ṣaṇmukha in the western petal. He shall worship Jyeṣṭhā in the north-western petal, Gaurī in the north and Caṇḍa in the north-east. He shall worship Munīndra between Śāstṛ and Nandīśa.

19. He shall worship Piṅgala to the north of Mahākāla. Then he shall worship Bhṛṅgīśvara in the middle of Śāstra and Mātṛ group.

20. He shall worship Vīrabhadra in between the Mātṛs and Vighneśa. He shall worship goddess Sarasvatī in between Skanda and Vighneśa.

21. Srī is to be worshipped at the feet of Śiva in between Jyeṣṭhā and Kumāra. He shall worship Mahāmoṭī in between Jyeṣṭhā and Gaṇāmbā.

22. He shall worship goddess Durgā in between Gaṇāmbā and Caṇḍa. In the same Āvaraṇa he shall worship the host of Śiva's attendants.

23. He shall perform the Japa after due meditation with mental purity, of the female friends of Śivā along with the Śaktis of Rudra, Pramatha and Bhūta.

24. When the third Āvaraṇa has been worshipped thus he shall worship the fourth Āvaraṇa outside it after meditation.

25. The sun shall be worshipped in the eastern, Brahmā in the southern, Rudra in the western and Viṣṇu in the northern petal.

26. There are separate Āvaraṇas to all the four lords.

His six limbs shall be worshipped at the outset along with the Śaktis, Dīptā etc.

27. They are Dīptā, Sūkṣmā, Jayā, Bhadrā, Vibhūti, Vimalā, Amoghā and Vidyutā. These shall be worshipped all round form the east onwards.

28. The four shall be worshipped in the second Āvaraṇa in order from the east to the north and their Śaktis afterwards.

29-30. Āditya, Bhāskara, Bhānu, Ravi, Arka, Brahmā, Rudra and Viṣṇu these are the extensions of Vivasvat in the east and stationed more so in the south. Bodhinī is in the west and Āpyāyinī in the north.

31. He shall worship in the second Āvaraṇa, Uṣā, Prabhā, Prājñā and Sandhyā after fixing them in Īśāna etc.

32-33. In the third Āvaraṇa he shall worship Soma (moon) Aṅgāraka (Mars), Budha (Mercury) most excellent among the intelligent, Bṛhaspati (Jupiter) of extensive intellect, Bhārgava (Venus), the storehouse of splendour, Śanaiścara (Saturn), Rāhu and Ketu the smoke-coloured and terrible.

34. Or he shall worship the twelve Ādityas in the second Āvaraṇa and the twelve Rāśis (signs of Zodiac) in the third Āvaraṇa.

35-36. Externally he shall worship the groups of seven, sages, gods, Gandharvas, serpents, Apsaras, Grāmaṇīs (leaders), Yakṣas, Yātudhānas, horses, and the seven Vālakhilyas in the form of Chandas.

37. After worshipping the sun in the third Āvaraṇa he shall worship Brahmā along with the three Āvaraṇas.

38. He shall worship Hiraṇyagarbha in the east, Virāṭ in the south, Kāla in the west and Puruṣa in the north.

39-40. Hiraṇyagarbha is the first Brahmā resembling the lotus, Kāla has the lustre of Jāti and collyrium. Puruṣa resembles the crystal. He has three Guṇas : sattva, rajas and tamas. The four are stationed in order in the first Āvaraṇa.

41. Sanat, Sanaka, Sananda and Sanātana shall be

worshipped in the second Āvaraṇa all round beginning with the east.

42. He shall then worship the Prajāpatis in the third Āvaraṇa. The first eight shall be worshipped in the east and the remaining three in order from the east onwards.

43-44. The following are the famous Prajāpatis: Dakṣa, Ruci, Bhṛgu, Marīci, Aṅgiras, Pulastya, Pulaha, Kratu, Atri, Kaśyapa ahd Vasiṣṭha. Their wives too shall be worshipped along with them.

45-46. They are Prasūti, Ākūti, Khyāti, Sambhūti, Dhṛti, Smṛti, Kṣamā, Sannati, Anasūyā, Aditi and Arundhatī. These chaste ladies are ever engaged in the worship of Śiva. Endowed with glory and prosperity they are very pleasing to look at.

47. He shall worship the four Vedas in the first, the Itihāsas and Purāṇas in the second Āvaraṇa.

48. The entire Vedic lore beginning with law codes shall be worshipped in the third Āvaraṇa.

49. The Vedas shall be worshipped beginning with the east. The other texts shall also be worshipped just as one pleases. They are divided into four or eight and their worship performed all round.

50. After worshipping Brahmā endowed with the three Āvaraṇas, in this manner in the south, he shall worship Rudra in the west along with the Āvaraṇas.

51-52. The five Brahmans and the six limbs are his first Āvaraṇa, The second Āvaraṇa consists of Vidyeśvara. There is difference in regard to the third Āvaraṇa : His four forms shall be worshipped beginning with the east.

53-54. The lord is possessed of three Guṇas. As Śiva he shall be worshipped in the east. The Rājasic creator Brahmā shall be worshipped as Bhava in the south. The Tāmasic Agni shall be worshipped as Hara in the west. The Sāttvic bestower of happiness, Viṣṇu shall be worshipped as Mṛḍa in the north.

55. After worshipping Śiva the lord of twentysix principles thus to the west of Śiva, he shall worship Vaikuṇṭha in the northern side.

56-58. In the first Āvaraṇa he shall worship Vāsudeva in the east, Aniruddha in the south, Pradyumna in the west,

Saṁkarṣaṇa in the north. Or the last two can be worshipped inversely. Such are the first and second Āvaraṇas. Matsya (fish), Kūrma (Tortoise), Varāha (Boar) Narasiṁha (man-lion), Vāmana (Dwarf) any of the (three) Rāmas, Kṛṣṇa and the horse-faced Kalki shall be worshipped.[292]

59-61. In the third Āvaraṇa, he shall worship the Cakra in the east, the unthwartable missile Nārāyaṇa in the south, Pāñcajanya in the west and the bow Śārṅga in the north. Thus he shall worship the great Hari—Viśva himself after making an idol of Mahāviṣṇu, Sadāviṣṇu, by means of the three Āvaraṇas. After worshipping the four forms of Viṣṇu thus in the form of a circle of four, their Śaktis too shall be worshipped.

62. He shall worship Prabhā in the south-east, Sarasvatī in the south-west, Gaṇāmbikā in the north-west and Lakṣmī in the north-east.

63. After performing the worship of the sun and other forms as well as their Śaktis, he shall worship the lords of the worlds in the same Āvaraṇa.

64. He shall worship Indra, Agni, Yama, Nirṛti, Varuṇa, Vāyu, Soma, Kubera ahd Īśāna thereafter.

65. After worshipping the fourth Āvaraṇa in accordance with the injunctions he shall worship the weapons of Maheśa externally.

66-69. He shall worship the glorious trident in the north-east, thunderbolt in the east, axe in the South-east and the arrow in the south, the sword in the south-west, the noose in the west, the goad in the north-west, the Pināka in the north, the Kṣetrapāla in the west. After worshipping the fifth Āvaraṇa thus externally he shall worship the great bull in the east along with the mothers of the gods of the Āvaraṇas, either externally or in the fifth Āvaraṇa.

70-72. Then the different types of gods shall be wor-

292. In the Āvaraṇa-worship Śiva is the principal deity to be worshipped. The attendant deities of different regions—celestial, atmospheric, ethereal or nether, along with the incarnations of Viṣṇu—Matsya etc. are also worshipped, Buddha is conspicuous by absence. The worship of the deities of heterogeneous traits indicates the cosmopolitan and proselytizing nature of this purāṇa.

shipped all round. The heaven-walkers, sages, Siddhas, Daityas, Yakṣas, Rākṣasas, Ananta and other leading serpents, and those of the different families, Dākinīs, goblins spirits, ghosts Bhairava leaders, different residents of the nether worlds, the rivers, oceans, mountains, forests and the lakes shall be worshipped.

73-76. The animals, birds, trees, worms and other insignificant creatures, men of different forms, deer of the insignificant types, the worlds within the universe, the crores of universes, the innumerable external seed-germs, their worlds, along with their rulers, Rudras stationed in the ten quarters supporting the universe, in fact everything fashioned out of the Guṇas or Māyā or originating from the Śakti shall be worshipped generally considering their presence on either side of Śiva and Śivā. They shall be in the form of Cit and Acit whatever that can be expressed in words.

77. They shall be thought of as having their palms joined in reverence, smiling in their faces and glancing devoutly at the lord and the goddess always.

78. After performing the Āvaraṇa Pūjā thus, he shall worship the lord again for quietening distraction and perplexity and utter the five-syllabled mantra.

79-80. He shall then offer to Śiva and Śivā as Naivedya the sweet and charming Mahācaru, nectarlike and accompanied by side dishes and vegetables. The Naivedya prepared fiom thirtytwo Āḍhaka measures of grains is commendable and that prepared with less than one Āḍhaka measure is the meanest one. After collecting and preparing the Naivedya to the extent of one's affluencc he shall offer it with faith.

81. After offering water for drinking, pickles, Tāmbūla and performing the rite of Nīrājana he shall conclude the remaining rites of worship.

82. Articles intended for the enjoyment of pleasures shall be excellent ones. The devotee shall not be stingy in spending money for this if he is fairly well to do.

83. Good men say that the Kāmya rites of the stingy and the stubborn, the indifferent and the defaulter in some items do not yield the benefits.

84. Hence if he wishes for the achievement of proper benefits he shall perform the Kāmya rites attending to all the items scrupulously and avoiding indifference.

85. After concluding worship thus and bowing to the lord and the goddess he shall concentrate his mind with devotion and repeat eulogical hymns.

86. After the eulogy he shall perform the Japa of the five-syllabled mantra not less than hundred and eight times. An eager devotee shall perform the Japa more than a thousand times.

87. After performing the worship of Vidyā and of the preceptor he shall perform the members assembled in the proper order in accordance with prosperity and purity.

88. Then he shall perform the rite of ritualistic bidding of farewell to the lord along with Āvaraṇas. He shall give the Maṇḍala to the preceptor along with the articles used in the rite.

89. He can give them to the devotees of Śiva or hand them over to the temple of Śiva.

90. Or he shall worship the lord in the Śiva-fire with the seven articles of sacrifice after duly worshipping the Āvaraṇa deities.

91. This rite is Yogeśvara. Nowhere in the world is there a Yoga superior to this.

92. A benefit of this world or the next unattainable through this does not exist anywhere.

93. We cannot fix like this—"This is the fruit thereof, this is not the fruit." This rite is the excellent means of benefits by way of welfare.

94. This can be said that whatever is solicited is obtained as fruit from this as from the wish-yielding precious stone.[293]

95. Still none shall perform this rite for trivial benefits. A man praying for a small help from a great man demeans himself.

96. If the rite is performed surely the desired fruit

293. It is a fabulous gem that yields the possessor his desires. It is also a mantra that confers the desired fruit.

shall be achieved. Whatever rite is performed, let it be performed with the lord as aim.

97. Hence, an expert man shall perform this rite for the conquests of his enemy or death even if those fruits are not to be secured from any one else whether those fruits are seen or unseen.

98. When great sins are committed, when there is a terror of great epidemics, famine or any other calamity, this rite shall be performed for the pacification of the evil.

99. Of what avail is much talk ? The lord has said that this is the spiritual missile to be used by the devotees of Śiva, to ward off great mishaps.

100. Hence, a person performing this rite with the conviction that there is no greater protection for the Ātman enjoys the benefit.

101. He who reads the hymn with purity of body and mind attains an eighth of the benefit desired.

102. If any one thinks into the hymn, observes fast on the full moon and the new moon days and recites it on those days or on the eighth or fourteenth day, he shall derive half the benefit.

103. He who thinks over the meaning, observes rites on Parvaṇ and other days and performs the Japa of this stotra for a month derives full benefit.

CHAPTER THIRTYONE

(*The Hymn of lord Śiva*)

Upamanyu said :—

1. O Kṛṣṇa, I shall tell you the hymn whereby this holy rite of Yogeśvara is concluded along the path of five Āvaraṇas.

2. Be victorious, O Śiva, the sole lord of the universe, naturally charming one, of the nature of eternal knowledge. You are the principle beyond the region of words and minds O lord, who have transcended the confused universe.

3. O lord, of a naturally pure physical body, O lord of charming activities. O lord, having a great Śakti on a par with yourself, O ocean of pure attributes.

4. O one endowed with infinite splendour, O one of incomparable physical body, the support, and of unarguable greatness, be victorious O one of undisturbed auspiciousness.

5. O Unsullied one, O one having no other support, O one rising up without cause and of incessantly great bliss, be victorious, O cause of extreme delight.

6. Be victorious, O one of excessively great prosperity. O receptacle of excessive mercy, O the sole possession of the free, O one of unequalled affluence.

7. O lord who have enveloped the universe, O one not enveloped by any one, O one standing superior to all, O one to whom there is no one at all who is superior.

8. Be victorious, O wonderful one, who are by no means insignificant. O unwounded one: O unchanging one. O immeasurable one, O one uninfluenced by Māyā, O one having no emotions, O one devoid of dirt, be victorious.

9. O one of great arms, O one of great essence, O one of great attributes, O one of great narratives, O one of great strength, O one of great Māyā, O one of great taste, O one of great chariot.

10. Obeisance to the great lord, the great cause, the quiescent one, more auspicious than any one else.

11-13. The entire universe including the gods and Asuras is subservient into you. Hence who is competent to transgress the behest ordained by you? This devotee is solely dependent on you. Hence, O sir, bless me and bestow on me what I have prayed for.

14. Be victorious, O goddess, the mother of the universe identical with the universe, and of unlimited prosperity. Be victorious, O goddess of incomparable beautiful person.

15. Be victorious, O goddess transcending speech and mind annihilating the darkness of ignorance, devoid of birth and old age, O one superior to that which is superior to Kāla.

16. Be victorious, O goddess stationed in many rites,

O beloved of the lord of the universe, O goddess, worthy of being propitiated by all the gods, O goddess who multiply the universe.

17. Be victorious, O goddess endowed with divine and auspicious body of auspicious light, O one of auspicious conduct. Be victorious, O goddess, bestowing auspiciousness.

18. Obeisance to the goddess possessed of great and auspicious attributes. The universe born from you merges into you alone.

19-21. Without you even the lord is not competent to bestow the benefits. O goddess of the gods, ever since birth this person has sought refuge in you. Hence, please fulfil the desire of this devotee of yours. Sadāśiva, of five faces, ten arms, resembling the pure crystal, having the physical body constituted by the letters, the five Brahmans and the Kalās, the lord who is both Sakala and Niṣkala, who is endowed with devotion to Śiva and who is beyond the Śānti Kalā, has been worshipped by me with devotion. May he bestow on me what is prayed for by me.

22. May the Icchā Śakti named Śivā seated on the lap of Sadāśiva, the mother of all the worlds, grant me what I desire.

23-26. Lords Heramba and Ṣaṇmukha are the beloved sons of Śiva and Śivā. Their accomplishments are auspicious. They are omniscient. They imbibe the nectar of knowledge. Being content they are mutually affectionate. They are perpetually honoured by Śiva and Śivā. They are always respected and revered by Brahmā and other gods. They are always ready to protect the worlds. Out of their will they take incarnations with their many different parts. They have been always worshipped thus by me on either side of Siva and Śivā. May they grant me what I have prayed for with due deference for their behest.

27-29. May the lord grant me what I have prayed for—the lord who resembles the pure crystal, who is called Īśāna, Sadāśiva, the great Ātman, who is quiescent, who occupies the firmament transcending the Śāntikalā, who is the final Bīja of the five-syllabled mantra equipped with five Kalās and has been worshipped by me in the first Āvaraṇa along with Śakti.

30-32. May the lord grant me what I have prayed for—the lord who is ancient, who is named Puruṣa, who resembles the rising sun, who is identified with the eastern face of Śiva Parameṣṭhin, who is in the form of Śānti stationed in the wind, who is engaged in worshipping the feet of Śiva, who is the first among Śiva-Bījas, who has four Kalās and who has been worshipped by me with devotion in the east along with Śakti.

33-35. May the holy middle Brahman grant me what I have prayed for—he who is named Aghora resembling collyrium, who has a terrible physical body, who is identified with the southern face of the lord, who is engaged in the worship of Śiva's feet, who abides in the Vidyā region and is stationed in the middle of fire, who is the second among Śiva's Bījas, who has eight Kalās and has been worshipped along with Śakti to the south of Śiva.

36-38. May the holy Brahman grant me what I have prayed for—he who is Vāma, who has an excellent dress resembling saffron powder, who is identified with the northern face of Śiva and who is well established in Pratiṣṭhā, who is stationed in the middle of the zone of water. He is engaged in worshipping the lord. He is the fourth one among Śiva-Bījas. He has thirteen Kalās. He has been worshipped along with Śakti to the north of the lord.

39-41. May the great Brahman grant me what I have prayed for—he who is named Sadya having gentle characteristics, who is as white as the conch, Kunda flower and the full moon. He is the western face of Śiva that is engaged in worshipping Śiva's feet, who is established in the Nivṛtti region and is stationed in the earth, who is the third one among Śiva-Bījas and is endowed with eight Kalās, and who has been worshipped along with Śakti to the west of the lord.

42. May the two heart-forms of Śiva and Śivā purified by Śiva grant my desire at the behest of the two—Śiva and Śivā.

43. May the two tuft-forms of Śiva and Śivā, depending on Śiva, grant my desire after honouring the behest of the two.

44. May the two coats of mail of Śiva and Śivā purified by Śiva grant my desire at the behest of the two.

45. May the two eye-forms of Śiva and Śivā dependent on Śiva grant my desire at the behest of the two.

46. May the missile forms of Śiva and Śivā always engaged and devoted to the worship of the pair grant my desire at their behest.

47-48. Let these deities Vāma, Jyeṣṭha, Rudra, Kāla, Vikaraṇa, Balavikaraṇa, Balapramathana and Sarvabhūtadamana grant me what I desire, at the behest of the two.

49-50. May the eight deities Ananta, Sūkṣma, Śiva, Ekanetra, Ekarudra, Trimūrti, Śrīkaṇṭha and Śikhaṇḍaka and their Śaktis, worshipped in the second Āvaraṇa grant my desire at the behest of the two.

51-52. May the eight Mūrtis Bhava and others and their Śaktis as well as the eleven Mūrtis Mahādeva and others accompanied by their Śaktis, all stationed in the third Āvaraṇa confer the desired benefit after honouring the behest of Śiva and Śivā.

53-57. The king of Bulls, of great splendour, thundering like the great cloud, who is comparable to the peaks of Meru, Mandara, Kailāsa and the Himavat, whose hump is huge in size like the white peaks of clouds and who shines with a tail like the great lord of Serpents, whose face, horns and feet are red in colour, whose eyes are almost red, whose limbs are plump and lifted up, who shines with a charming gait, who has all praiseworthy characteristics, who is glorious, who has glittering gemset ornaments, who is a favourite of Śiva, who is devoted to Śivā, who makes up the banner and vehicle of Śiva and Śivā, who has purified his body by touching their feet with it, who is the king of cows, who is glorious, and is possessed of the excellent and glorious trident as his weapon, may grant my desire at the behest of the two.

58-61. Nandīśvara of great splendour, the son of Pārvatī is worshipped and revered every day by the gods including

Nārāyaṇa. He is stationed at the door of the harem of Śiva along with his attendants. He has the lustre of the lord; he is the suppressor of all Asuras. He is crowned as the president of all Śaivite rites. He is a favourite of Śiva. He is fondly devoted to Śivā. He has the excellent weapon of the glorious trident. He is attached to those who depend on Śiva. They too are attached to him. May he grant my desire at the behest of the two.

62. Mahākāla of great arms is like another Mahādeva unto those who seek refuge in him. May he protect us always.

63. He is a favourite of Śiva and is fondly attached to Śivā. He is their perpetual worshipper. May he grant my desire at the behest of the two.

64. The chastiser is the knower of the meaning and truth of all Scriptures. He is another body of Viṣṇu. He is his son in the form of great delusion. He is fond of honey, meat and wine. May he grant my desire at the behest of the two.

65-66. May the seven mothers—Brahmāṇī, Māheśī, Kaumārī, Vaiṣṇavī, Vārāhī, Māhendrī and Cāmuṇḍā of fierce valour, mothers of all the worlds, grant my desire at the behest of the two.

67-69. He has the face of the elephant in rut. He is the son of Gaṅgā, Umā and Śiva. The firmament is his body ; the quarters his arms ; the moon, the sun and the fire his eyes. He is worshipped by the elephants of the quarters, Airāvata and others. The ichor of Śaivite knowledge comes out of him. He wards the obstacles of gods. He causes obstacles to the Asuras and others. He is sanctified by Śiva. May he grant my desire at the behest of the two.

70-74. Ṣaṇmukha is born of Śiva. He holds Śakti and thunderbolt. He is the son of fire. He is also the son of Gaṅgā, Gaṇāmbā and Kṛttikās. He is surrounded by Viśākha, Śākha and Naigameya. He is the conqueror of Indra and the demon Tāraka. He is the Generalissimo of Indra's armies. He pierced the important mountains Meru and others with his splendour. He resembles molten gold. He has eyes resembling petals of lotuses. He is Kumāra and the model for all tender beings. He is the favourite of Śiva and fondly attached to Śivā. He is a perpetual worshipper of Siva's feet. May he grant my desire at the behest of the two.

75. Jyeṣṭhā, the excellent deity granting boons, is always engaged in worshipping them. May she grant my desire at the behest of the two.

76-79. The goddess is saluted by the three worlds in the form of Ulkā (meteor, comet). She is requested by Brahmā to multiply the creation through Śivā. She came out from the middle of the eyebrows of Śivā who divided herself into Dākṣāyaṇī, Satī, Menā, Haimavatī, Umā. She is the mother of Kauśikī, Bhadrakālī, Aparṇā and Pāṭalā. She is Rudrāṇī the beloved of Rudra. She is always engaged in worshipping Śiva. May she grant my desire at the behest of the two.

80. Caṇḍa is the lord of all the Gaṇas who is born of the face of Śiva. May he grant my desire at the behest of Śiva and Śivā.

81. May Piṅgala the chief of Gaṇas, the prosperous one, fondly attached to Śivā and a favourite of Śiva, grant my desire at the behest of the two.

82. May the chief Gaṇa Bhṛṅgīśa who is interested in propitiating Śiva grant my desire at the behest of Śiva.

83-85. Vīrabhadra is of great splendour. He resembles snow, Kunda flower and the moon. He is the beloved of Bhadrakālī. He is the perpetual protector of mothers. He removed the head of Yajña and of Dakṣa of wicked soul, he pared the limbs of Viṣṇu, Indra, Yama and other gods. He is a follower of Śiva. He is a glorious executor of Śiva's behests. May he grant my desire at the behest of Śiva.

86. Sarasvatī born of the lotus-like speech of Maheśa is interested in worshipping Śiva and Śivā. May she grant my desire.

87. Lakṣmī is stationed in the chest of Viṣṇu. She is engaged in worshipping Śiva and Śivā. At the very bidding of Śiva and Śivā, may she grant my desire.

88. Mahāmoṭī is engaged in worshipping the feet of Mahādevī. At her very bidding may she grant my desire.

89-90. Kauśikī is the daughter of Pārvatī. She rides on a lion. She is the great Māyā, the slumber of Viṣṇu. She is the suppressor of the demon Mahiṣa. She destroyed Śumbha and Niśumbha. She is fond of wine and meat. May she grant my desire duly honouring at the behest of her mother.

91-95. Rudras have the lustre of Rudra. Pramathas are famous for their prowess. The Bhūtas have great virility. They have the lustre of Mahādeva. They are perpetual Yogins. They are uncomparable and devoid of conflicting pairs of defaults. They are free from dangers. They are accompanied by their Śaktis and followers. They are bowed to by the world. They are competent to create and annihilate the worlds. They are mutually loving and accommodating. They are very affectionate and respectful to one another. They are favourites of Śiva and are marked by his traits. They are gentle, terrible and mixture of both. They are in the midway between the two. They are ugly, good-featured and multifeatured. May they grant my desire at the behest of the two.

96-97. The group of the friends of the goddess has all the characteristics of the goddess. They are accompanied by the daughters of Rudras and Śaktis many in number. They have been worshipped in the third Āvaraṇa of Śiva with great devotion. Let them grant my desire at the behest of the two.

98-101. The sun is the Mūrti with illuminated disc of Maheśa. He is Nirguṇa, Guṇasaṅkīrṇa, Guṇakevala, and Avikārātmaka. The first one is single with general variations. He is of extraordinary activity in creation, sustenance and annihilation. Thus he is divided into three, four or five ways. He is worshipped in the fourth Āvaraṇa of Śiva along with the followers. He is a favourite of Siva and fondly attached to Śivā. He is engaged in worshipping the feet of Śiva. May he grant my desire at the behest of the two.[294]

102-105. The eight Mūrtis of the sun viz. Āditya, Bhāskara, Bhānu, Ravi, Arka, Brahmā, Rudra, and Viṣṇu, the eight Śaktis Dīptā[295] etc., the six Aṅgas of the sun-god, the

294. The verses 99 to 102 are repeated. See Verses 110 to 113.

295. The Śaktis– Dīptā, Sūkṣmā, Jayā etc., eight in number (Cp. Vāyavīya S. II. 30. 27) are the female guardian deities of the quarters and sub-quarters from the east onwards.

Śaktis viz. Vistarā, Sutarā, Bodhinī, Āpyāyinī, Uṣā, Prabhā, Prājñā and Sandhyā and the planets beginning with Soma and ending with Ketu purified by Śiva—may these urged by the behest of Śiva and Śivā grant me everything auspicious.

106-112. May the twelve Ādityas, and the twelve Śaktis, sages, Gandharvas, serpents, Apsaras, Grāmaṇīs, Yakṣas Rākṣasas, Asuras, the seven sets of seven, the seven horses identical with the Vedas and Vālakhilya and others, the worshippers of Śiva's feet, grant me everything at the behest of Śiva and Śivā. Brahmā the chief of the universe, a form of the lord of gods, having sixtyfour attributes and achievements, and established in the principle of Buddhi, shall be worshipped in the fourth Āvaraṇa of Śiva. He is a favourite of Śiva, fondly attached to Śivā and is engaged in worshipping the feet of Śiva. May he grant my desire at the behest of the two.

113-115. Hiraṇyagarbha the lord of the worlds, the Virāṭ, Kāla, Puruṣa, Sanat, Sanaka, Sananda, Sanātana, the Prajāpatis, the sons of Brahmā, Dakṣa and others, eleven in number with their wives, Dharma and Saṁkalpa—all these are engrossed in their devotion to Śiva being subservient to the behests of Śiva. May these grant my desire.

116-117. May the four Vedas, the Itihāsas, Purāṇas, Dharma-Śāstras accompanied by the Vedic lore, although mutually disagreeing but based on the nature of Śiva, grant my desire at the behest of Śiva and Śivā.

118-123. Then the great lord Rudra, the important form of lord Śivā, is the lord of the zone of Fire and possesses all Aiśvaryas. He is enriched with the identity with Śiva. He is devoid as well as possessed of attributes. He is Sāttvic, Rājasic and Tāmasic. Basically he is not prone to aberrations. Then outwardly he assumes aberrations. He is of extraordinary activity apart from the activity of creation etc. He cut off the head of Brahmā. He is his father as well as his son. He is the progenitor and son of Viṣṇu to whom he controls. He is the enlightener of both. The lord blesses them for ever. Rudra is stationed within and without the cosmos. He is the lord of the worlds. He is fond of Śiva to whom he is fondly attached. He is engaged in the worship of Siva. May he grant my desire at the behest of Śiva.

124-125. His six ancillaries Brahman etc. and the eight deities ending with Vidyeśa, the four different Mūrtis devoted to Śiva, with Śiva as their cause, Śiva, Bhava, Hara and Mṛḍa —may these grant my desire at the behest of Śiva.

126-133. Viṣṇu is another form of the great lord Śiva himself. He is the lord of the principle of water. He is stationed in the region of the unmanifest. He is Nirguṇa. He is predominantly Sāttvic as well as possessed of single Guna. He does not identify himself with the created things. He has the three general aberrations. He is of extraordinary activity apart form that of creation. He compares with Brahmā though he is born of the right part of Śiva. He is created by the first Brahmā and he is his creator too. Viṣṇu abides within and without the universe. He is the lord of the worlds. With his discus he destroys Asuras. He is the younger brother of Indra. He has manifested himself in ten forms under the curse of Bhṛgu. He incarnated on the earth at his will for removing the burden of the Earth. His strength is immeasurable and incomprehensible. He is the wielder of Māyā. He fascinates the universe with his Māyā in the form of Mahāviṣṇu and Sadāviṣṇu. He is worshipped by the devotees of Viṣṇu in the seat of the three Mūrtis. He is a favourite of Śiva and is fondly attached to him. He is engaged in the worship of his feet. May he grant me what is auspicious at the behest of Śiva.

134-136. The four Mūrtis of Viṣṇu, viz Vāsudeva, Aniruddha, Pradyumna, and Saṁkarṣaṇa, the ten Avataras viz—the fish, tortoise, boar, man-lion, dwarf, Rāma trio, Kṛṣṇa and the horse-faced Kalki, his discus Pāñcajanya and the bow Śārṅga—may these grant my desire at the behest of the two.[296]

137. May Prabhā, Sarasvatī, Gaurī, and Lakṣmī sanctified by Śiva grant my desire at the behest of the two.

138-139. May Indra, Agni, Yama, Nirṛti, Varuṇa,

296. The Verse is repeated. See Vāyavīya S. 30. 58.

Vāyu, Soma, Kubera and Īśāna the wielder of the trident grant my desire at the behest of Śiva and Śivā. These are engaged in the worship of Śiva and have sanctified by their pious feelings to him.

140-141. May the divine weapons of the lord and the goddess—viz—the trident, thunderbolt, axe, arrow, sword, noose, goad and the excellent weapon Pināka protect me always at behest of the two.

142-143. May the bull, the powerful son of Kāmadhenu, rivalling with the submarine fire Vaḍavā, surrounded by five mother-cows[297] who has attained the state being the vehicle of the lord and the goddess, grant my desire, at the behest of the two.

144. The five mother-cows stationed in Śiva's region are Nandā, Sunandā, Surabhi, Suśīlā and Sumanās.

145. They are engaged in devotion to Śiva and are engrossed in his worship. May these grant my desire at the behest of the two.

146-150. Kṣetrapāla of great splendour resembling the blue cloud with his face terrible due to the curved fangs, refulgent with throbbing red lips, with red hairs lifted up, with the crooked, eyebrows, three circular red eyes, with the moon and the serpents as ornaments, being in nude form holds the trident noose, sword and the skull in his hands, of terrible aspect, surrounded by Bhairavas, Siddhas and Yoginīs, is seated in every temple. He is the protector of the good. Bowing to lord Śiva is his great interest. He is purified by pious feelings towards Śiva. He protects those who seek refuge in him particularly as his own sons. May he grant my desire at the behest of the two.

151. May the four deities Tālajaṅgha and others worshipped in the first Āvaraṇa protect me at the behest of Śiva and Śivā.

152. May Bhairava and others who surround him all round bless me at the behest of the two.

153-155. Nārada and other sages who are worshipped even by the gods, the Sādhyas, serpents, gods who reside in

297. For the names of the mother-cows, see below verse 144.

Janaloka, the residents of Maharloka who have been deposed from authority, the seven sages and others along with the Gaṇas moving about in aeroplanes—all these engaged in the worship of Śiva and subservient to his bidding may grant my desire at the behest of the two.

156 163. The four types of gods beginning with Gandharvas and ending with the Piśācas, Siddhas, Vidyādharas and others who move about in the sky, the Asuras and Rākṣasas who reside in the netherworlds, Ananta and other leading serpents, Vainateya and other birds, Kuṣmāṇḍas, Pretas, Vetālas, Grahas and Bhūtas, Ḍākinīs, Yoginīs, Śākinīs and evil witches, temples, parks, houses, holy centres, mansions continents, oceans, rivers, lakes, sumeru and other mountains, forests, animals, birds, trees, germs, worms, deer, the worlds, overlords of the worlds, seeds of life along with their Āvaraṇas, ten quarters, elephants of the quarters, letters, words, mantras, Tattvas along with their lords, Rudras who support the cosmos and other Rudras and their Śaktis whatever is seen, heard or inferred in this world—may all these grant my desire at the behest of the two.

164-167. The great lore of Śiva capable of releasing the individual soul from the fivefold bondage is different from Paśuvidyā. The scripture of Śaivite virtue and the Dharma, the Purāṇa of Śiva approved of by Śrutis, and the Śaivite scriptures Kāmikā and others of four types honoured by Śiva and Śivā and worshipped by me may all these make this holy rite accomplished well and fruitful.

168-169. May the early preceptors from Śveta to Nakulīśa along with their disciples, the preceptors born as members of their families, especially my preceptors, both Śaivas and Māheśvaras engrossed in Śiva's knowledge and holy rites, permit this holy rite to be fruitful and well accomplished.

170-172. May the lay brahmins, Kṣatriyas., those who are experts in the knowledge of the Vedas and the ancillaries together with their tenets in the lines of Śaivite virtue, those who are well-versed in all sacred scriptures, the followers of Sāṁkhya, Vaiśeṣika, Nyāya and other systems of philosophy, the followers of the sun, Brahma, Rudra and Viṣṇu and all other good men particularly those who are wedded to Śaivite discipline—permit this holy rite which is the instrument for achieving my purpose.

173-174. The followers of Śiva who adhere to the philosophical path, those who perform the Pāśupata rites those who observe the holy rites and the Śaivite holy men such as Kapālikas—all these are adherents and executors of Śiva's behests. They shall be worshipped by me at the behest of Śiva. May these bless me. Let them praise the successful holy rite.

175. Those who adhere to the path of knowledge according to the southerners, those who follow the southern cult and the northern cult abide by me without mutual clash since I wish and seek the welfare through the mantras.

176. May the atheists, tenacious rogues, ungrateful and Tāmasic heretics and great sinners be far away from me.

177. Of what avail is the long eulogy? Let all the faithful bless me. Let all good men pronounce everything auspicious.

178. Obeisance to Śiva accompanied by Śivā. Obeisance to you the primordial cause accompanied by your son. Obeisance to you encircled by the universe in the form of five Āvaraṇas.

179. After saying this he shall prostrate before Śiva and Śivā and perform the Japa of the five-syllabled mantra not less than hundred and eight times.

180. Similarly he shall perform the Japa of Śakti mantra, dedicate it to Śiva and crave forgiveness. He shall thus conclude the remaining rites of worship.

181. This holiest of holy hymns is pleasant and agreeable to Śiva and Śivā. It yields all desires. It is the sole means for the achievement of worldly pleasures and salvation.

182. He who repeats this everyday or listens to this with mental purity shakes off sins and attains Śivasāyujya soon.

183-184. Slayers of cows, ungrateful wretches, murderers of heroes, those who slay children in the womb, murderers of those who seek refuge, those who kill friends and those who confide in them, those who commit wicked sins such as matricide, patricide.—all these are released from their sins on repeating this hymn.[298]

185. When bad dreams and evil portents occur indicating terror and danger this hymn shall be repeated. Then those dangers do not befall.

186 The man who regularly performs the Japa of this hymn obtains longevity, health, prosperity and everything else desired.

187. The benefit thus mentioned is of the mere Japa of the hymn without worshipping. It is impossible to count the benefit if the Japa of the hymn is performed along with worship.

188. Let the accruing of the benefit stand alone. When this Japa is repeated the lord on hearing this stands in the heaven along with the goddess.

189. Hence after worshipping the lord and Umā in the heaven the devotee shall stand with palms joined in reverence and repeat the hymn.

CHAPTER THIRTYTWO

(The rites for achieving worldly benefits)

Upamanyu said :—

1. O Kṛṣṇa, what has been mentioned to you is the site which yields benefit here and hereafter. It is a great synthesis of physical rites, penance, Japas and meditation.

2. Now I shall mention that great rite of worship, Homa, Japa, meditation, penance and charitable gifts, which yields benefits here itself to men who follow Siva.

3. The devotee expert in the meaning of mantras shall at the outset practise mantras since the rites of visible benefits here itself are not fruitful otherwise.

298. This is another instance of the proselytizing attempt of the Purāṇic Ācāryas to entice the laity to their fold.

4. A learned and sensible devotee, even after the mantra has been achieved, shall not haphazardly perform any rite the fruit whereof has been thwarted by some unseen powerful obstacle.

5. Atonement is possible for that obstacle. Hence he shall perform that atonement after testing it at the outset by means of omens.

6. He who due to delusion performs the rite yielding the benefit here itself does not attain the fruit thereof and becomes the laughing stock.

7. Without faith and devotion no one shall perform the rite intended to yield direct benefit. He becomes an unbeliever and an unbeliever does not attain fruit.

8. It is not the fault of the lord if the rite does not yield the fruit since it is found to yield fruit here itself for those who perform the rite exactly as ordained.

9. An aspirant who has mastered the mantras overcoming the obstacles and who performs the rite with full confidence and conviction attains the fruit.

10. Or, for the attainment of the benefit let him be scrupulously celibate, eating only the Haviṣya, milk-pudding or fruits.

11. He shall not even think of, much less physically do, such prohibited actions as violence. He shall be pure always with clear dress and smear the body with Bhasma always.

12-17. After observing the rules of conduct, the devotee shall on an auspicious and favourable day with the characteristics mentioned before, smear the ground with cowdung in a spot bedecked with garlands of flowers and draw the auspicious lotus shining with its own refulgence. It shall be of molten gold with eight petals and filaments, with the pericarp in the middle set with all gems. It shall be not less than a Hasta in width and must have a stalk befitting its size. He shall conceive Animā etc. in the bulbous root made of gold, in accordance with the injunctions. He shall instal the phallic idol with its pedestal, made of gems, gold or crystal with the requisite characteristics. He shall invoke the eternal lord accompanied by Ambā and the Gaṇas. Śiva's form as Maheśvara shall also be conceived in the idol

18-19. It shall have four arms and four faces. It shall be bedecked in all ornaments. It shall wear the tiger's hide with the smiling face and the gestures of granting boons and of protection to the devotee. Other hands shall hold the deer and the axe. Or if the conceiver desires he can conceive of the Mūrti as having eight arms.

20. Then the right hand holds the trident, axe, sword and the thunderbolt. The left hands hold the noose, goad, iron club and the serpent.

21. The Mūrti shall have the lustre of the rising sun. It shall have three eyes in every face. The face towards the east is gentle and has the refulgence befitting its size and features.

22. The southern face resembles the blue cloud and has a terrific appearance. The northern face has the lustre of coral and is bedecked with dark forelocks.

23. The western face is gentle with the lustre of the full moon. Seated on his lap is the great Śakti of Maheśvara

24-25. She is famous as Mahālakṣmī dark coloured and wholly charming. After conceiving the Mūrti thus and unifying it into a whole he shall invoke the embodied lord and worship him. For the purpose of ablution he shall arrange for Pañcagavya prepared from a tawny cow.

26-27. There shall be Pañcāmṛta and particularly the full seeds. He shall prepare the Maṇḍala ahead decorated with gem-dust. The water-pot of Īśāna shall be put in the pericarp. The water-pots of Sadyojāta shall be placed around, afterwards.[299]

28-30. Eight pots of Vidyeśa shall be filled with the waters of holy centres and threads shall be tied round them. Sacred articles of worship shall be dropped therein with due incantations in accordance with the injunctions. They shall be completely covered into the silken cloth with the mantras. When the proper time arrives he shall perform the ablution of the lord with Pañcagavya.

299 On the consecrated water-jars see Vāyavīya S. 17. 16-17.

31-33. Waters dropped from the Darbha grass, golden and gemset vessels, scented and flowery waters purified with the mantras shall be taken from the vessels and Maheśvara shall be bathed. Scents and flowers shall be offered, lights shown and the worship performed. The unguent shall be not less than a Pala by weight and the maximum shall be eleven Palas.

34-36. Auspicious and charming flowers of good colour and fragrance blue and other lilies, plenty of Bilva leaves, red lotuses and white lotuses if available shall be used. The incense shall be offered with the black Aguru. The gum-resin shall be used with the camphor and ghee. The ghee used for lamps shall be of the milk of tawny cows. The five Brahmans, the six Aṅgas and the Āvaraṇas shall be worshipped.

37. The Naivedya shall be made of Caru prepared in ghee and milk with jaggery. The water shall be rendered fragrant with the Pāṭala flowers, lilies and lotuses.

38. Well-consecrated Tāmbūla along with five fragrant spices shall be offered.[300] The ornaments offered shall be made in gold and set with gems.

39. Freshly woven cloths of various colours and of fine fabric attractive to the sight shall be offered with songs and instrumental music.

40. The maximum number of times for Japa is hundred thousand. According to the benefit desired the number of worship varies from one to three.

41. The number of sacrifices is not less than ten for every article and the maximum is hundred. In such rites as Māraṇa and Uccāṭana Śiva shall be conceived terrific in form.

42. When quiescent or nourishing rites are being performed, Śiva shall be thought of as gentle in the phallicimage in the Śiva-fire and in other idols as well.

43. In Māraṇa and other rites the Śruk and Śruva shall be made of iron. In all other rites such as quiescent these shall be made of gold.

300. On the Pañcasaugandhika, see P. 2006 note.

44-46. In the rite of Mṛtyuñjaya the Homa is performed with Dūrvā mixed with ghee and cow's milk, or honey or with Caru along with ghee, or milk alone. For the rites intended to quell ailments to attain prosperity and subdue poverty, gingelly seeds, ghee, milk or lotus-flowers shall be used. Persons seeking to bring persons under control shall perform Homa with Jātī flowers and ghee.

47. A Brahmin shall perform the rite of Ākarṣaṇa with ghee and Karavīra flowers, Uccāṭana with oil and Stambhana with honey.

48. Stambhana rite can be performed with mustard also; Pātana with garlic; Tāḍana with the blood of mule, camel or of both.

49. Māraṇa and Uccāṭana shall be performed with Rohi and gingelly seeds. Vidveṣaṇa rite shall be performed with the oil of Lāṅgala.

50-52. Bandhana rites and the rite of paralysing of a vast army shall be performed with the seeds of Rohi. In Ābhicārika rites the articles of Homa shall be used with the red mustard and the Homa shall be performed with oils extracted from manually operated machines. It can also be performed with seeds of cotton in combination with Kaṭukī and husk. In Ābhicārika rites the devotee shall perform Homa with mustard seeds mixed with oil. Milk yields the subdual of fevers and is conducive to good fortune.

53. Homa offered with honey, ghee, curds, milk and rice-grains or with Caru grants all desires.

54. Quiescent, nourishing, Vaśya and Ākarṣaṇa rites shall be performed with the seven articles of worship sacrificial twigs etc.

55. Vaśya, Ākarṣaṇa and Śrīpada (glorious position) rites shall be performed with the leaves of Bilva for Havana. It yields conquest over the enemies.

56. In quiescent rites the twigs of Palāśa, Khadira etc. shall be used. In rites of cruelty the twigs of Karavīra and Arka shall be used. Twigs of thorny trees shall be used in the rite of war.

57. A quiet man shall perform the quiescent and

nourishing rites particularly. A ruthless man with angry mind shall perform Abhicarika rites.

58. When the harassment is unbearable and condition is pitiable, when there is no other remedy, only then shall one perform the Ābhicārika rite against desperadoes.

59. No virtuous man, occupying honourable position or otherwise shall perform the Ābhicārika rite against the ruler of his country.

60. Even if he happens to be a desperado one shall not perform Ābhicārika rite against a person who has sought refuge in Śiva, mentally, verbally or physically.

61. A man performing Ābhicārika rite against the ruler of his country whether he be a devotee of Śiva or not, shall have a fall immediately.

62. If he wishes for his own happinness he shall not perform Ābhicārika rite against the protector of his country or against any devotee of Śiva.

63. If he performs the rite of Māraṇa etc. against any other person he shall perform expiatory rites after due repentence.

64. Whether the devotee is rich or poor he shall worship the lord in a Bāṇa or selfborn or Ārṣaka or a Vaidika liṅga.

65. If liṅgas of gold and gems are not available or if he is unable to possess them he shall perform the worship mentally or with substitute articles.

66. If a devotee can perform worship in some part he too derives the benefit of that part in accordance with his ability.

67. If the benefit is not seen even if the rite is performed, it shall be repeated twice or thrice. By all means the benefit will be received.

68. Whatever material is used in worship, gold, gem and other articles shall be handed to the preceptor apart form the Daksiṇā offered separately.

69. If the preceptor does not wish to receive, the entire gift shall be given to Śiva or the devotees of Śiva. It shall not be given to any other.

70-71. If any one performs the rite himself without

the help of a preceptor the procedure shall be the same. He shall not appropriate the gift to himself. If he appropriates the articles of worship for himself out of greed under delusion he will not attain his desire.

72. The liṅga used for worship may be taken by himself or given to others. If he takes that himself he shall worship it everyday or cause it to be worshipped on his behalf.

73. If he performs the rite as ordained he cannot but have the benefit. What other inducement for worship shall there be?

74-75. Still I shall mention about the excellent achievement through the rite. Even if he is attacked by the enemy or tormented by ailments, even if he falls into the jaws of death he will be freed without danger. Even the worst miserly fellow will become worthy of respect. The poor will become Kuvera,[301] god of wealth.

76. The ugly man will become beautiful, the aged will become young. The enemy will turn a friend, the opponent will grow subordinate.

77-79. The nectar that may have turned into poison shall become nectar again. The ground may turn into ocean and ocean into ground; the ditch into a mountain and the mountain into a ditch; fire into a lotus lake and the lotus lake into fire; the park into a forest and the forest into a garden; the animal into a lion and the lion into an animal.

80. Women will run after him voluntarily. Prosperity will behave like a chaste lady and will not leave him. The goddess of speech will be his slave girl, fame a prostitute.

81. The intelligence will roam about as it pleases. His mind will be pure like a diamond. His strength will be like a violent gust of wind or like an elephant in rut.

82. His activities on the side of the enemies will be paralysed in their effort. The friends of enemies will become their enemies.

83. The enemies along with their kinsmen will be no better than corpses though physically alive. Though faced

301. Vaiśravaṇa is the patronymic name of Kuvera, son of Viśravas.

with mishaps he will be freed from them and become immortal.

84. Even if he takes unwholesome food it will act as aphrodisiac. Even if he indulges in sexual intercourse everyday it will give him fresh thrills.

85. Everything hitherto inaccessible to him will become accessible like the myrobalan in the palm. Even Siddhis aṇimā etc. will become available at his will.

86. Of what use is much talk ? When this rite is performed there remains nothing unattainable.

CHAPTER THIRTYTHREE

(Rites for deriving benefits hereafter)

Upamanyu said:—

1. Now I shall mention the rite for the benefits attainable solely after death. There is nothing like this rite in the three worlds.

2-6. The rite is attended with the excellence of merits. It has been performed by all the gods, particularly by Brahmā, Viṣṇu, Rudra, Indra, the guardians of the quarters, the nine planets—sun-god and others, by Viśvāmitra, Vasiṣṭha and other sages who know Brahman, by Śveta, Agastya, Dadhīca and others, by us seeking refuge in Śiva, by Nandīśvara, Mahākāla, Bhṛṅgīśa and other Gaṇeśvaras, by the Daityas residing in the nether worlds, by Śeṣa and other serpents, by Siddhas, Yakṣas, Gandharvas, Rākṣasas, Bhūtas, Piśācas and practically by every one who has attained his respective position. It is by means of this rite that the gods have attained their godhood.

7. Brahmā attained his Brahmāhood, Viṣṇu his Viṣṇuhood, Rudra his Rudrahood and Indra his Indrahood. It is by means of this rite that Gaṇeśa attained his Gaṇeśahood.

8-10. The liṅga shall be bathed with white sandal water. Therein Śiva and Śivā shall be worshipped with full-blown white lotuses and bowed to. He shall make a lotus-seat very charming and endowed with all characteristics by means of gold-dust and gem-dust in accordance with one's affluence. In the midst of the filaments a small liṅga shall be placed. It shall be of the size of the thumb, but charming, auspicious and rendered fragrant with all scents. It shall be placed to the south and worshipped with Bilva leaves.

11-12. To the south he shall apply Aguru. To the west he shall apply red arsenic. To the north he shall apply sandal and to the east he shall apply yellow orpiment. He shall then worship with charming fragrant flowers of various colours.

13. The black Aguru shall be used for incense and fumigation along with Guggulu. Fine cloths bright in colours shall be offered.

14. Milk-pudding mixed with ghee, and lamps with ghee for burning shall be offered. After offering everything with repetitions of mantras he shall circumambulate.

15. After bowing with devotion to the lord of the gods he shall eulogise the lord and crave forgiveness. Naivedya consisting of all offerings shall be offered to the Liṅga.

16-17. It shall be dedicated to Śiva with his mantras. The devotee shall seek refuge in Dakṣiṇāmūrti. He who performs the worship with the auspicious five scents shall be freed from all sins. He shall be honoured in Śiva's region. This holy Vrata of Śiva liṅga is the most excellent, a great secret.

18. This has been mentioned to you since you are a great devotee. This shall not be given to any one and everyone. It shall be given to devotees of Śiva as mentioned by Śiva formerly.

CHAPTER THIRTYFOUR

(*Delusion of Viṣṇu and Brahmā*)

Upamanyu said :—

1. The achievement of benefit that has been mentioned here from the Nitya, Naimittika and Kāmya rites can entirely be secured immediately by installing the phallic and the bodily image of Śiva.

2. The world is in the form of Liṅga. Everything is founded on Liṅga. Hence if the Liṅga is installed, everything is installed.

3. It is only by resorting to the installation of the Liṅga that Brahmā, Viṣṇu, Rudra or other deities maintain their splendour.

4. What more reason can be advanced for the installation of Liṅga than that Liṅga of Viśveśvara has been installed by Śiva too?

5. Hence by all means one shall instal the phallic or the bodily image of Śiva for his welfare here and hereafter.

Śrī Kṛṣṇa said :—

6. What is a Liṅga? How is lord Śiva a Liṅgin? How did he have the status of a Liṅga? Why is he worshipped in it?

Upamanyu said :—

7. The unmanifest is called the Liṅga. It is the source of attributes as well as that wherein the universe merges and dissolves. It has neither beginning nor end. It is the material cause of the universe.

8. It is the Māyā, the Mūlaprakṛti as extensive as the firmament. This universe including the mobile and immobile beings is born of that.

9. The universe is of three types: the impure, pure and the pure-impure. From the Liṅga are born Śiva, Maheśa, Rudra, Viṣṇu and Brahmā.

10. The Bhūtas with the sense-organs merge into this at the bidding of Śiva. He is Liṅgin since he commands the Liṅga.

11-12. Since the Liṅga can do nothing by itself without being commanded by Śiva, since the dissolution of the universe born of it is only within it, this constitutes the state of being Liṅga in Śiva and not due to any other reason. The Liṅga is the body of Śiva and Śivā because it is presided over by them.

13. Hence Śiva is worshipped therein for ever along with Śivā. The goddess is the pedestal of the Liṅga and Liṅga is lord Śiva himself.

14. By the worship of Liṅga alone, Śiva and Śivā are worshipped. Their having the Liṅga for their body is not the ultimate reality.

15-16. Since they are pure it is their body only in a secondary sense. That is the great Śakti of Śiva the great Ātman. Śakti at the behest of Śiva gives birth to mobile and immobile beings. One cannot describe the glory of the Liṅga, even in hundreds of years, by which Brahmā and Viṣṇu were deluded at the outset.

17-19. Formerly when the universe was in the state of dissolution, Viṣṇu lying on his couch in the waters went into deep slumber. He lay comfortably asleep. Brahmā the grandfather of the worlds casually went there. He saw the lotus-eyed Viṣṇu sleeping undisturbedly. Deluded by the Māyā of Śiva, Brahmā said to Viṣṇu.

20-21. "Who are you? Tell me". Thus saying he hit Viṣṇu angrily and wakened him. Struck by the blow of his hand Viṣṇu woke up in a trice and got up from his bed. He saw Brahmā there. Viṣṇu though infuriated within addressed him politely.

22-25. "O dear son, whence have you come? Why are you agitated? Tell me." On hearing the words of Viṣṇu, indicative of his lordly attitude Brahmā felt irritated due to his Rājasic qualities and spoke again. "Why do you address me as "dear son" like a preceptor calling his disciple? Don't you know that I am the lord. This universe is my creation. After dividing myself into three, I create, protect and annihilate. There is none in the universe who has created me." When thus addressed Viṣṇu said to Brahmā.

26-30. "I am the primordial creator of this universe,

the protector and the annihilator. You too, O sir, were born of me formerly. At my unthwartable bidding you divided yourself into three and began creation. You create the three worlds, protect, dissolve and re-create it. You forget Viṣṇu the lord of the universe free from ailments. You insult even me, your father. It is not your fault. You have been deluded by my Māyā. Due to my favour this delusion of yours will disappear ere long. O Brahmā, listen to the truth. I am the lord of all gods. I am the creator, sustainer and annihilator. There is no other lord equal to me."

31. A verbal dispute between Brahmā and Viṣṇu arose thus. Thereafter a terrible fight ensued causing horripilation.

32-36. Due to Rājasic quality they fought and hit each other with fists. In order to dispel their arrogance and to enlighten them, the wonderful Liṅga of the lord appeared in between them. It had thousands of flames. It was incomprehensible and incomparable. It did not increase or decrease. It had no beginning, no middle, no end. Brahmā and Viṣṇu were enchanted by thousands of flames. Ceasing from their fight they began to think "What is this?" When they could not understand the reality they attempted to survey its beginning and end.

37. Brahmā took the form of a swan with wings all round and went up assiduously with the speed of the mind or wind.

38. Viṣṇu, the Ātman of the universe, assumed the form of a Boar resembling a mass of collyrium and went downwards.

39. Thus hastening down for a thousand years he did not have even a glimpse of the root of Liṅga.

40. Meanwhile, Brahmā too was going up to know his top. But unable to see the end he became exhausted and fell down.

41. Similarly the weary Viṣṇu with dejected mind due to the great distress quickly rose up from below.

42. When they met each other again they were completely perplexed and stared at each other with a smile of shame. Deluded by the Māyā of Siva they did not know what to do or what not to do.

43. They stood in front, at the back and on either side of it and bowed. They began to think "Of what nature is this ?"

CHAPTER THIRTYFIVE

(The delusion of Viṣṇu and Brahmā)

Upamanyu said:—

1. Then there manifested the single-syllabled Brahman in the characteristic way o a word with its sound 'Om'. It expressed the Brahman.

2. That too was incomprehensible to Brahmā and Viṣṇu because their minds had been screened with Rajas and Tamas.

3. Then that syllable divided itself into four, the three Mātrās—A, U, Ma and half the Mātrā thereafter.

4. The letter 'a' attached itself to the southern side of the blazing Liṅga, the letter "u" to the north and the letter "ma" to its middle.

5-6. The half a Mātrā sound was heard on the head of the Liṅga. Even when the great syllable Praṇava was divided, the two gods did not understand the purpose of division. The unmanifest Praṇava then underwent the change into the Veda.

7. There the letter "a" became the Ṛgveda, the letter "u" the Yajurveda, the letter "ma" the Sāmaveda and the Nāda the Atharvaveda.

8-10. The Ṛgveda established half of itself succinctly. Thus Brahmā possessed of the Rajas, the first among the deities in rites also, the creator of the worlds and the principles as well as the unchanging Ātman; Nivṛtti in the path of Kalā and Sadyojāta in the five Brahmans, the lower portion in the parts of Liṅga and the source in the three reasons. It established the sixtyfour Guṇas and Aiśvarya of the cosmic intellect Aṇimā etc. Thus with the ten topics the universe was pervaded by the Ṛgveda.

11-13. Then the Yajurveda established itself in the ten ways : Sattva among the attributes, Viṣṇu the first among the deities in the rites also, sustenance in the worlds and the firmament, Vidyā in the three principles, Pratiṣṭhā in the paths of Kalā and Vāmadeva in the five Brahmans, the parts of Liṅga and Yoni in the three causes. The Prākṛta was established in accordance with the Aiśvarya. Hence the universe is of the form of the Yajurveda.

14-16. Similarly the Sāmaveda established itself in ten ways. It established Tamas and Rudra the first among the deities in the rites, annihilation in the three worlds and the excellent Śiva in the Tattvas, Aghora in the five Brahmans and Vidyā among the Kalās, the upper seat in the parts of the Liṅga and the source in the three causes. So also the Aiśvarya of the Puruṣa. Thus the universe is pervaded by the Sāman.

17-20. Then the Atharvaveda established itself thus. It was devoid of Guṇas. It placed Maheśvara, Sadāśiva as the first among the deities. Though the great Ātman, Śiva is devoid of activities. It established Sadāśiva for the purpose of activities. It created pure blessing whereby the creatures are liberated. Above the worlds, where the words recede along with the mind are the Unmanā worlds over which is the divine Somaloka where the lord stays with Umā.

21-22. He who reaches above there in the Unmanā world does not return. Śānti and Śāntyatītā are all-pervasive among the Kalās. Among the five Brahmans it is Puruṣa and Īśāna. There is the head of the Liṅga, the most excellent among the parts, where the sole Niṣkala Śiva shall be invoked and propitiated.

23-33. Among the Tattvas it is the greater Tattva than Bindu, Nāda and Śakti. It is greater than the greatest and in reality a non-Tattva. It transcends the three causes. It is beyond Māyā the cause of agitation. It is beyond Ananta, the Śuddhavidyā, Maheśvara, Sadāśiva the great lord of all lores. It is beyond the lord who has mantras for his body, who is accompanied by all Śaktis, who has five faces and ten arms and who is both Sakala and Niṣkala. Beyond even that, beyond the Bindu, the half moon, the moon, the great Nāda, the lord of Suṣumṇā, the lord of Brahmarandhra beyond that, beyond Śakti and beyond the principle of Śiva the great cause there is lord Śiva who has no cause. He is the creator of causes, the subject and object of meditation and stationed in the middle of the great sky above the great Ātman. Equipped with prosperity and glory he is the lord of all. He has no overlord. He is beyond Aiśvarya due to Māyā, beyond humanity, beyond the big and small, beyond what is to be discarded, what is not to be discarded, beyond Śuddhavidyā, Unmanā, and the Aiśvarya of Unmanā. He is great and devoid of beginning, limitless and independent, stable and unsurpassable. Thus with ten such characteristics Atharvaveda is very weighty and so the universe is pervaded by it.

34-42. Ṛgveda said again—"The state of wakefulness is being mentioned by me whereby I perpetually express the Ātmatattva". Yajurveda said—"The state of dream is being mentioned by me because the Vidyā that has transformed itself into objects of enjoyments is to be known through me." Sāmaveda said:—"What is called sound slumber is being mentioned wholly by me through Śiva that is my meaning and Tāmasic in form. Atharvaveda said :--"What is called the fourth stage and what is beyond the fourth is expressed by me." The three which are of the nature of the path are termed Śiva, Vidyā, Ātman. Their state of three attributes is attainable through the Vedas and shall be purified by him who wishes for Śiva's region. What is called Turīya, beyond the path is the greatest region of salvation. That which is beyond it is the purifier of this path because of its attributeless state. The Nāda is the measurer of both. The end of Nāda has me for its Ātman. Hence the supreme lord is the chief in view of freedom from my topics. Whatever object is there whether compounded or separated, they call as the meaning of Praṇava in view of the association of the Guṇas. Therefore, this single-syllabled Brahman is the expression of all meanings.

43. Therefore, at the outset Śiva creates the universe saying "Om". Śiva is Praṇava and Praṇava is Śiva.

44-46. That is because there is not much of difference

between that which is expressed and the expression. Rudra is devoid of thought. The words along with the mind recede without reaching him. He is that which is expressed by the single-syllabled Om. Letter "a" expresses Brahmā, the letter "u" Viṣṇu, the letter "ma" expresses Śiva.

47-50. The deity Brahmātman is born of the right limb of Maheśa. Viṣṇu came out of the left. So he is termed Vidyā. Nīlarudra came out of the heart of Śiva and is called Śiva. Brahmā is the activiser of creation, Viṣṇu the enchanter maintains sustenance. Rudra who controls both is the initiator of annihilation. The three are the causes of the universe. Śiva, the source of the three, is the great cause.

51. The Liṅga stood in between you two in order to enlighten you when you became mutually inimical due to your Rājasic quality and could not understand this meaning.

52-53. Thus they call me "Om". What was thus mentioned by the Atharva was repeated by the Ṛgveda, Yajurveda, Sāmaveda and thousands of their Śākhās. Even when the Vedas themselves declared thus clearly through their own mouths it was not comprehended by the two who thought it were a dream.

54. In order to enlighten them and to remove their ignorance the statement of the Vedas was inscribed in the Liṅga too.

55. On seeing that inscribed in the Liṅga due to the favour of Śiva the deities were pacified and enlightened.

56-61. On realising the mode of evolution and dissolution, the nature of the six pathways and the splendour beyond the Puruṣa possessing brilliance, the Brahman than whom there is nothing greater, Niṣkala Śiva Īśvara, who is the perpetual lord of this universe consisting of Paśu and Pāśa who has no fear from any quarter, who is stable without increase or decrease who pervades within and without who has neither inside nor outside, who is unsurpassable, who is different from all the worlds, who is indefinable, incomprehensible, inexpressible, who is essentially in the form of brilliance, who is quite delighted and ever rising, who is the abode of auspiciousness and who is accompanied by a similar Śakti, Brahmā and Viṣṇu joined the palms in reverence above their heads and spoke thus in fright to the lord.

Brahmā said :—

62. Whether I am ignorant or not, O lord, I was created by you at the beginning. Whose fault is it that I have been under such a delusion?

63. Let my ignorance alone. O lord, when you are near who can fearlessly talk about his duty or that of others.

64. O lord of gods, our mutual wrangle too is splendidly auspicious since it has yielded us the benefit of paying our homage to the feet of the lord.

Viṣṇu said :—

65. O lord, I do not have the power of eulogising you in the manner befitting your greatness. On the other hand if the devotees keep quiet in front of the lord it is merely a transgression of virtue.

66. What is proper to be achieved is the relevant point now. Without knowing anything I have blurted out something for which I pray to be excused.

67. That you were the primordial cause we forgot due to your Māyā. I am deluded, puffed up and have hence been chastised by you.

68. Of what avail is this submission? O lord, I am extremely afraid because I have endeavoured to determine your size when in fact you cannot be gauged.

69. O Śiva, they call you a great lord, the destroyer of the distress of the frightened. I entreat you to forgive my transgression thus.

70. When thus implored lord Śiva became highly delighted. He blessed the two deities and spoke to them smilingly.

Lord Śiva said:—

71. Dear Brahmā, dear Viṣṇu, you had been deluded by my Māyā. You were proud of your lordship and became mutually inimical.

72. You did not cease even when the wrangle turned into an actual fight. Therefore the creative activity of you both, the cause of the universe, was broken in the middle.

73-74. In order to turn you back from your mutual

dissention arising from ignorance and arrogance and to dispel your delusion and pride I indulged in this sport of manifesting myself in the phallic idol. Hence eschew a recurrence of your dispute and forget the shame. Devoid of mutual rivalry you shall resume your respective duties.

75-77. Formerly at my command the compendiums on knowledge were given to you in order to proclaim your causal nature. The jewel of Mantras consisting of five syllables has been imparted to you. But you forgot all this. I shall give you everything as before together with my behest since without that you cannot create or sustain.

78-80. After telling Viṣṇu and Brahmā thus, the lord gave them the principal mantra along with the Jñānasaṁhitā. After obtaining the divine order of the lord, the jewel of Mantra pregnant with meaning, and the Kalās, they prostrated at the feet of the lord. They stood without fear. They were overpowered by joy.

81-83. In the meantime there was a great wonder. As if by magic the Liṅga of the god became invisible. Due to the sudden snapping of love they lamented and cried loudly, saying to each other 'O what a false thing has befallen us, Pondering over the unimaginable prowess of Śiva they became free from pain.

84. Becoming great friends once again and embracing each other the leading deities returned to their duties in the universe.

85. Ever since that Indra and other gods, Asuras, sages, men, serpents as well as women instal Liṅgas in accordance with the injunctions and worship him in the Liṅga.

CHAPTER THIRTYSIX

(*Installation of Śiva*)

Śrī Kṛṣṇa said :—

1. O lord, I wish to hear the rules governing the installation of the phallic and the embodied image of Śiva.

Upamanyu said :—

2. On a day in the bright half of the month not unfavourable to him, the devotee shall make the Liṅga of the proper size in the manner prescribed in the Śaivite scriptures.

3. Selecting an auspicious spot he shall test the ground. He shall perform the ten forms of service.

4. But before the actual performance of this service Vināyaka shall be worshipped. After purifying the spot and other rites he shall take the Liṅga to the ablution chamber.

5. With a gold rod dipped into the solution of saffron he shall draw the characteristic signs in the prescribed manner.

6. He shall purify the Liṅga along with its axle or nave with a solution of eight or five types of clay as well as with Pañcagavya.

7. After worshipping the Liṅga along with its pedestal he shall take it to the water-receptacle and keep the Liṅga immersed in water.

8-14. In a well-constructed shed for the immersion of Liṅga, pure and well-embellished with festoons and screens all round, surrounded by garlands of Darbha grass, an inner shed for the seat shall be arranged in the middle. The seat may be metallic or wooden in the shape of a lotus. On the eight quarters the representations of the eight elephants of the quarters shall be made. Eight pots shall be kept for the eight quardians of the guarters. Eight auspicious things shall be kept ready. The guardians of the quarters shall be duly worshipped. Subhadra, Vibhadra, Sunanda and Vinanda the gatekeepers of the lord shall be worshipped in the four quarters. The Liṅga shall be bathed and worshipped with the pedestal. It shall be tied with two cloths and bunches of Kuśa grass. It shall be brought to the Pīṭha and laid over it immersed in water. The head of the Liṅga shall be put to the east and the threads shall be put below, the nave to the west of it. The Liṅga shall be kept in water for one, three or five nights.

15. Thereafter the liṅga shall be worshipped after due ceremonies as before. After worship it shall be carried along the path of festivities to the place of rest.

16. A resting place shall be made in the middle of the Maṇḍala. After bathing the liṅga with pure water he shall worship it.

17. A mystical lotus-diagram shall be drawn in the north-east on a spot of ground well-smeared. The water vessel of Śiva shall be purified. Śiva shall be invoked and worshipped.

18. In the middle of the altar he shall make a diagram of white lotus in accordance with injunctions and to the west of it he shall draw the lotus of Caṇḍikā.

19. The bed shall be made of silken cloth or other cloth fresh from the loom, before being washed or of flowers or Darbha grass. After making it up he shall put golden flower in it.

20-22. The Liṅga shall be brought there with the songs and music vocal and instrumental. It shall be wrapped in two red cloths and a bunch of Kuśa grass along with the nave and laid down as before. A lotus shall be drawn in front and in its petals he shall place the water-pots of Vidyeśa and the vessel Vardhanī of Śiva. The excellent brahmins shall perform Homa all round the three lotuses.

23-25. Beginning with the east, the eight Mūrtis shall be placed all round or only the four Mūrtis Brahmā and others in the four quarters. The conductors of the Homa shall possess good mastery of the Vedas. They shall be accompanied by those who can repeat the mantras well. The preceptor shall perform the main Homa either in the north-east or in the west. He shall use all the seven materials in order. The other brahmins shall perform half or one-fourth of the number of sacrifices that the preceptor performs.

26-28. Or the preceptor alone shall perform the main sacrifice. He shall perform the Pūrṇāhuti and then another set of hundred and eight Homas with ghee. He shall place his hand ritualistically on the top of the Liṅga repeating the basic mantra. After each Homa he shall touch both the Liṅga and the pedestal. On the whole a hundred or a fifty or twentyfive Homas shall be performed with the seven materials of worship. He shall perform the Pūrnāhuti and give Dakṣiṇā.

29. The priest and the sculptor shall be given half or one-fourth of what the preceptor is given and half of that shall be given to the other brahmins in accordance with one's capacity.

30-32. Then either an image of the bull made of gold or a bunch of Kuśa grass shall be placed in the pit. Brahmaśilā shall be purified with water and clay, also with Pañcagavya, with pure water. It shall be placed in the pit after smearing it with sandal. Repeating the names of the nine Śaktis, the rite of Karanyāsa shall be performed. Then in accordance with the injunctions prescribed in Śaivite scriptures he shall strew the minerals—Haritāla and others along with scents, seeds and medicinal herbs.

33-35. The Liṅga shall be installed on the Brahmaśilā and dripped in the exudations of trees. To the east and the north the aloe wood shall be placed repeating the basic mantra. Repeating the basic mantra of Śakti the nave shall be joined to the articles of fixation and joining. The place shall be purified. Arghya shall be given and flowers offered. Thereafter the screen shall be drawn all round.

36. The ablution and other rites of the Liṅga shall be performed in a befitting manner. After taking it away from the place of rest the Kalaśas shall be placed in order.

37-39. The great worship begins with the worship of the ten water-jars. In the water inside the Śivakumbha, the thumb and the ring-finger shall be jointly inserted with the Śiva mantras. Water thus taken shall be sprinkled. The knower of mantra shall touch the north-east side of the Liṅga. He shall perform the Nyāsas of Śakti, Vidyā and Vidyeśas in order at the root of the Liṅga. He shall perform the ablution of the Liṅga with auspicious water.

40. The nave and the Liṅga shall be bathed with the

water of Vardhanī and Vidyeśa Kalaśas. The seats, supports etc. shall be arranged.

41. After performing the Nyāsa rite of the five Kalās he shall meditate on the blazing Liṅga. Facing the east or north with palms joined in reverence he shall invoke Śiva and Śivā.

42-44. He shall conceive the lord arriving with the goddess, seated on the lordly bull or in an aerial chariot. He shall be conceived as fully bedecked in shining ornaments. He is surrounded on all sides by Brahmā, Viṣṇu, Maheśa, sun-god, Indra, other gods and the dānavas with their body drenched in the tears of delight with palms joined in reverence above the heads. They are eulogising, dancing and bowing. Then with the five services the worship shall be concluded.

45. There is no further rite after the five reverential services. The installation of idols is wholly identical with that of the Liṅga.

46. At the rite of Lakṣaṇoddhāra the eyes shall be shut. The immersion shall be performed with the idols placed prone on the bed.

47. The installation of the idol with the rites for the temple is better than without those rites. If the idols are immersed in the water of the vessel the mantras shall be repeated touching the chest.

48-49. Affluent people shall first build the temple and then perform the installation. If the devotee is not affluent he shall perform the installation of the phallic or the embodied image and shall afterwards build the Śiva temple in accordance with his capacity. Now I shall mention the mode of worship at the house and the excellent installation rite.

50-53. The idol shall be small in size but endowed with all traits. In the northern transit of the sun (Jan-July) on an auspicious day in the bright half of the month, the altar shall be made in an auspicious spot. He shall draw the diagram of the lotus in as before. The idol shall be purified with water and clay as before. An auspicious seat shall be kept in the north. Covering the Liṅga with flowers he shall place it on the seat. Flowers and leaves shall be strewn and the vessel placed in the middle. Four vessels shall be placed all round. In those five vessels the five Brahmans are ritualistically fixed. After worship Mudrās shall be shown and the Rakṣā mantra repeated.

54-55. After placing the flower on its top it shall be sprinkled with the water from the Prokṣaṇī vessel. Again it shall be worshipped along with the proclamation of victory. With the water from the vessels of the four deities from Īśāna to Vidyā he shall bathe the Liṅga with the basic mantra.

56. The rite of the Nyāsa of the five Kalās shall be performed and the worship too as before. The devotee shall worship the lord and the goddess there everyday.

57. Or only one vessel shall be placed with the basic mantra and everything fixed therein. Every other rite shall be performed as before.

58. Too much unclean Liṅga shall at first be purified and reinstalled. Unclean Liṅgas shall be sprinkled with holy water. Slightly unclean Liṅgas too shall be worshipped.

59. Bāṇa Liṅgas may be installed at will, for they have been already consecrated by Śiva himself.

60-61. Such other Liṅgas may also be installed. In regard to a Svayambhū, a divine or a sage Liṅga the same is the procedure. If there is no pedestal, a pedestal shall be assigned and the rite of Prokṣaṇa performed.

62. Burnt, weakened or partially broken Liṅga shall be thrown in a pond or a river. That which can be joined shall be joined and installed.

63. The lord shall be dismissed ritualistically from the idol that is mutilated, after due worship but retained in the heart.

64. If the worship is in default for one day it shall be doubled, if in default for two days, great worship shall be performed. Samprokṣaṇa rite shall be performed thereafter.

65. If there is default in worship for about a month, or for more days, some advocate reinstallation. But others say that the Samprokṣaṇa rite alone is enough.

66-67. Samprokṣaṇa rite is as follows:—The lord is ritualistically dismissed from the Liṅga as before, bathed with clay of eight or five types, water, Pañcagavya and purified with water from Darbha grass and sprinkled with water from the Prokṣaṇī vessel, one hundred and eight times with the basic mantra.

68. Holding flowers and Darbha, the hand shall be placed on the top of the Liṅga five times and the basic mantra shall be repeated hundred and eight times.

69. Beginning from the head and ending with the pedestal, the Liṅga shall be touched repeating the basic mantra. The great worship shall be performed after invoking the lord as before.

70. If an installed Liṅga is not available, he shall worship the lord in a place sacred to Śiva, or in water, fire, the sun or the sky.

CHAPTER THIRTYSEVEN

(*The Goal of Yoga*)

Śrī Kṛṣṇa said :—

1. Everything mentioned succinctly by your holiness with regard to knowledge, rites and activities, after taking out the essence, has been heard by me. It is as sacred as the Vedas.

2. Now I wish to hear about Yoga which is very difficult to achieve along with its authorisation, ancillaries, injunctions and purpose.

3-4. If death were to overtake before, it can be averted without resorting to the practices of penance, by taking recourse to Yoga whereby the man avoids becoming a self-killer. Hence it behoves you to mention factually the different types of Yoga and their relative importance, cause, time and procedure.

Upamanyu said:—

5. O Kṛṣṇa, the question has been pertinently put by you

who understand the meaning of all questions. Hence I shall mention everything in order. Listen attentively.

6-7. All other activities are restrained and the mind kept steady in Śiva. This is succinctly called Yoga. It is of five types : Mantrayoga, Sparśayoga, Bhāvayoga, Abhāvayoga and Mahāyoga which is greater than everything.

8. The concentration of the mind without disturbances, on the expressed meaning of the mantra along with the practice of the mantra is mantrayoga.

9. Coupled with Prāṇāyāma the same is called sparśayoga. Without the contact of Mantra, it is Bhāvayoga.

10. Wherein the universe with all its parts is meditated upon it is called Abhāvayoga since in that the existent object is not seen.

11. Wherein the nature of Śiva is contemplated without any conditioning or restricting factor, the concentration of the mind on Śiva is called Mahāyoga.

12. In this Yoga only he is authorised whose mind is detached from the perceived and Veda-ordained objects of pleasure.

13. The mind is detached only on perceiving the defects in the objects and in the attributes of the lord, perpetually.

14-15. In brief the Yoga is of eight or six ancillaries. The eight ancillaries are Yama, Niyama, Āsana Prāṇāyāma, Pratyāhārā, Dhāraṇa, Dhyānā and Samādhi as mentioned by the wise.

16. The six Aṅgas are in brief Āsana, Prāṇasaṁrodha, Pratyāhāra, Dhāraṇā, Dhyāna and Samādhi.

17-18. The definitions of all these separately have been mentioned in Śivaśāstra and other Śaivite scriptures, especially Kāmikā etc. They are mentioned in Yogaśāstras and Purāṇas also. Yama is the observance of restraints such as non-violence, non-stealing, abstention from sexual intercourse and non-acceptance of monetary gifts. The five constitute the subdivisions of Yama.

19. Niyama is the positive curb or restraint with the following five subdivisions—purity, contentment, penance, japa and attentiveness.

20. Āsana is the Yogic pose and is of eight types such

as Svastika, Padma, Ardhendu, Vīra, Yoga, Prasādhita, Paryaṅka and Yatheṣṭa.

21. Prāṇa is the vital breath in the body. Āyāma is checking. Hence Prāṇāyāma means checking or restraining the breath. It is of three forms—Recaka, Pūraka and Kumbhaka.

22. One of the nostrils is pressed with the finger and the air from the belly is let out through the other. This is Recaka (Exhaling).

23. Then through the other nostril the external air is inhaled and the body is filled up like the bellows. It is Pūraka (Inhaling).

24. He does not breathe out the internal or breathe in the external air. He remains steady like the filled-up jar. It is called Kumbhaka (Retention).

25. The three, Recaka etc. shall not be done hurriedly or slowly. The practiser of Yoga shall adopt them gradually with restraint.

26. The practice of Recaka shall begin with the purification of the veins and conclude with its voluntary exit as mentioned in the Yogānuśāsana.

27. Prāṇāyāma is one of the four varieties in view of the time-units, Kanyaka etc.

28. Kanyaka is without Udghāta (strokes). Its duration is twelve Mātrās. Madhyama has two strokes, its duration is twentyfour Mātrās.

29. Uttama has three strokes and its duration is thirty-six Mātrās. Uttara is the Prāṇāyāma that causes perspiration and trembling of the body.

30. The yogin has experiences—the thrill of bliss, horripilation and shedding of tears. He may prattle. There may be vertigo and senselessness.

31. Mātrā is the unit of time required for the snapping of the fingers after moving them round the knees neither speedily nor slowly.

32. The duration of Prāṇāyāma shall be increased in accordance with the Mātrās and strokes. The veins shall be necessarily purified.

33. The Prāṇāyāma is again twofold : Agarbha and

Sagarbha. Restraining the breath without meditation and Japa is called Agarbha Prāṇāyāma. If they too are included it is called Sagarbha.

34. The Sagarbha Prāṇāyāma is hundred times more efficacious than the Agarbha. Yogins practise Sagarbha Prāṇāyāma.

35-36. The vital breaths of the body can be conquered through the mastery over Prāṇa. The vital breaths are Prāṇa, Apāna, Samāna, Udāna, Vyāna, Nāga, Kūrma, Kṛkara, Devadatta and Dhanañjaya.[302] That which causes the movement is called Prāṇa.

37. Apāna is the vital air that takes the food lower down. Vyāna is diffused through the limbs and it develops them.

38. Udāna is the vital air that affects the vulnerable points in the body among the limbs. The vital air that spreads equally is called Samāna.

39. The vital air Nāga is for the activity of belching. Kūrma is for the activity of closing the eyes; the vital air Kṛkara is the activity of sneezing and the vital air Devadatta is the activity of yawning.

40. Dhanañjaya is the vital air that circulates through the body. It does not leave off even the dead body. Gradually practised, Prāṇāyāma is very efficacious.

41. It burns off all defects. It preserves the body of practisers. When the Prāṇa is mastered the symptoms are manifest.

42-44. Urine, phlegm and faeces are reduced in quantity. Ability to eat much and to breathe slowly, lightness of the body, ability to walk fast, enthusiasm, clearness of voice and tone, destruction of ailments, strength, brilliance, comeliness of features, courage, intelligence, youthfulness, firmness and all round pleasure these are the symptoms. All forms of

302. The vital airs of the body, Prāna, Apāna and others, ten in number, play a distinct role in the general yogic exercises. The practices of these airs constitute an important feature of Śivayoga too. The present context describes the various processes in regulating the function of vital airs as a part of Śivayoga.

austerities, expiations, sacrifices, charitable gifts, holy rites do not merit even a sixteenth part of the benefit of Prāṇāyāma.

45-47. The total withdrawal of the sense-organs operating in their respective objects is called Pratyāhāra. The sense-organs are the mind etc. They are capable of according heaven and hell. When restrained they yield heaven, when let loose they are hellish. Hence the intelligent man who seeks happiness shall have recourse to perfect knowledge and detachment, and lift up his soul through his own soul after carefully restraining the horses of his sense-organs.

48-50. In brief, what is called Dhāraṇā is the fixation of the mind in a spot. The spot is Śiva alone and nothing else. The Dhāraṇā shall take place when the mind is established in the spot for a stipulated duration and when it does not swerve from the target. The initial stability of the mind is generated through Dhāraṇā. Hence one shall endow the mind with fortitude by the practice of Dhāraṇā.

51-56. The root 'Dhyai' means to contemplate. Frequent contemplation of Śiva with an unconfounded mind is called Dhyāna. It is a series of visions in the mind that is fixed on the object of meditation to the exclusion of other visions. Eschewing everything else, Śiva, the cause of auspiciousness, the great lord of the gods, shall be meditated upon. Thus concludes the Atharvaveda. Similarly the great goddess Śivā shall be meditated upon. In the Vedas Śiva and Śivā are mentioned as pervading all living beings. In the Smṛtis and Śāstras they are mentioned as present everywhere and awakened always. They are omniscient. They shall always be meditated upon in different forms. There are two benefits accruing from meditation, the first one being freedom from other visions and the second one the acquisition of Siddhis, Aṇimā etc.

57. The knower of Yoga shall practise Yoga with the knowledge of four things—the meditator, the meditation, the object of meditation and the benefit of meditation.

58. The meditator shall be a man who is endowed with knowledge and detachment, who is faithful, patient, who is free from ego and who is always enthusiastic.

59. A person who is tired of Japa shall begin meditation. A person who is tired of meditation shall begin Japa. A person who practises Japa and Dhyāna acquires Yoga quickly.

60. Dhāraṇā extends upto the twelve-petalled lotus of the heart. Dhyāna is the fixation of the Dhāraṇā in the twelve-petalled lotus. When Dhyāna extends to the twelve-petalled lotus it is called Samādhi.

61. Samādhi is the final state of Yoga. Through Samādhi, the lustre of intellect begins to function.

62. In Samādhi, the vision is steady like the calm ocean, the form vanishes but the vision persists.

63. Fixing the mind in the object of meditation he shall see it steadily. The Yogin thus like the fire extinguished is absorbed in Samādhi.

64. He neither hears nor smells nor prattles nor sees nor feels the touch. The mind does not think.

65. Nor does he identify with anything external. Nor is it bound like the inanimate log of wood. A person whose Ātman has thus merged into Śiva is called Samādhistha.

66. Just as the lamp in a windless spot never flickers so also is the Yogin who is Samādhistha, An intelligent man shall not swerve. He shall be steady.

67. All his obstacles and hindrances perish gradually if the Yogin practises the excellent Yoga.

CHAPTER THIRTYEIGHT

(Obstacles in the path of Yoga)

Upamanyu said:—

1-2. There are ten obstacles in the path of those who practise Yoga :—Idleness, acute ailments, blunder, doubtfulness about the spot, unsteady mind, lack of faith, illusions, miseries, dejectedness and indulgence in sensual objects.

3. Idleness affects the body and the mind. Ailments are caused by the imbalance of the Dhātus. They are also due to the defective previous Karmans.

4. Blunder is the non-contemplation of the means of Yoga. Doubtfulness is the double perception—"this or this?"

5. Unsteadiness is the inability to stabilise the mind. Lack of faith connotes absence of piety in the path of Yoga.

6-7. Illusion is misconception. Misery is of three types. That due to ignorance is spiritual misery. The misery that affects the body due to previous actions is the corporal misery. Thunderbolt, missiles, poisons are the miseries caused by divine intercession.

8. Dejectedness is the agitation due to the frustration of desires. Indulgence in diverse sensual objects is the overfondness for them.

9. When the obstacles subside and the Yogin is absorbed in Yoga the signs begin to appear. They are divine indications of the imminent success.

10. The Upasargas are—Pratibhā, Śravaṇa, Vārtā, Darśana, Āsvāda and Vedanā. They are the Siddhis at the expense of Yoga.

11. The correct perception of objects whether they be subtle, hidden by other objects, or of bygone days, or situated far off, or not yet born is called Pratibhā.

12. Śravaṇa is the ability to hear all sounds without any strain. Vārtā is the knowledge of everything concerning all embodied beings.

13. Darśana is the ability to see all divine objects without difficulty. Similarly, Āsvāda is the ability to taste divine delicacies.

14-15. Vedanā is the ability to know the divine touch and the divine smell. All the lords of the worlds beginning with Brahmā stand before him and give him many gems and jewels. Words naturally sweet and eloquent function through his mouth.

16. The divine potions, aphrodisiacs and divine medicines are offered to him by celestial damsels who pay him their homage.

17. Though this is only a fraction of the Siddhis of

Yoga, when this is done he will have confidencc in salvation: "This has been seen by me. In the same manner salvation too shall occur."

18-19. The Yogic Siddhi pertaining to the earth named 'Paiśāca Pada' consists of eight types of powers, viz., leanness, bulkiness, infancy, old age, youthfulness, the ability to assume different forms and the ability to collect sweet-smelling scents without any earthly part.

20-23. The `wonderful Yogic Siddhi pertaining to water consists of sixteen powers, viz:—he can stay under water, he can come out of the earth, at his will he can drink up even the ocean and be none the worse for it, wherever he wishes he can let water spring up or he can hold water in the palm of his hand. Whatever he wishes to eat he can transform into juicy substance, he can assume these forms, he can have the body free from cuts and wounds. Over and above these powers he can have the eight powers of the Yogins.

24-25. The Yogic Siddhi called Taijasa consists of twenty-four types of powers viz:—the ability to create fire from the body, absence of fear of being scorched by the fire, the ability to burn the universe without difficulty, placing of fire in water or in the palms, re-create things burnt in fire, cook food in the mouth, create bodies with the fire and wind and above all these are the sixteen powers of the Āpya Yogins.

26-28. The wise know that the Yogic Siddhi called Māruta consists of thirtytwo types of powers viz:—the speed of the mind, the ability to enter the bodies of living beings, to hold weighty things like mountains etc. without difficulty, weightiness, weightlessness, holding the wind within the palms, ability to shake even the earth with the tip of the finger, to produce bodies with the wind and apart from these the twenty-four powers of the Taijasa Yogins.

29-31. The Yogic Siddhi called Aindra pertaining to the ether consists of forty powers:—Shadowlessness, absence of the sense-organs, ability to walk over the ether, to have the sense-objects at will, to transgress the ether, to instil the ether into the body, to solidify ether, having no body and over and above these the thirtytwo powers of the Māruta Yogins.

32-34. Ability to acquire whatever is desired, to wander as he pleases, to attack all, to see all the hidden secrets of others, to create bodies according to the task, to bring others under control, to appear pleasing, and to see the world, these powers along with those of the Aindra Yogins constitute the cāndramasa type of yogin. The powers are mainly mental and the number of powers is fortyeight.

35-36. Ability to cut, to strike, to bind and to release, seizure of all living beings under the influence of worldly existence, ability to delight all, mastery over death and time these are the special powers of the Prājāpatya Yogins. These powers along with those of Cāndramasa Yogins are fiftysix in number.

37-39. Creation by mere conception, protection, and annihilation, ability to exercise authority, to make minds function, dissimilarity with all, creation of a separate universe doing auspicious and inauspicious things—these powers along with the Prājāpatya powers, altogether numbering sixtyfour, constitute the powers of the Yogin of the Brāhma type.

40. This Aiśvarya functions through intellect. The power greater than and beyond this is the Prākṛta Aiśvarya called Vaiṣṇava. The sustenance of the universe is his alone. Only Brahmā can explain that region wholly and not others.

41. Beyond that is the region of Puruṣa which functions the attributes and then the region of Gaṇeśa and then the region of Īśvara. This can be understood by Viṣṇu a little and cannot be understood by others.

42. All the Siddhis due to knowledge and the Upasargas shall be checked assiduously by means of great detachment.

43. The great Aiśvarya that affords protection and is coveted by all cannot by acquired if the mind is attached to false appearances, forms and attributes.

44. Hence he who abandons the attributes and the pleasures of the gods, Asuras and kings, considering them as worthless as blades of grass acquires the greatest Yogic power.

45. Or the sage with Yogic powers shall move about with a desire to bless the universe. He can then enjoy the pleasures at his will and attain salvation.

46-52. Now I shall explain the practice of Yoga. Listen attentively. The time and the spot shall be auspicious; it may be the temple of Śiva and or other clean place; it shall be a secluded spot devoid of people, creatures, noises and other disturbances. It shall be well-scrubbed and smeared. It shall be rendered fragrant with scents and incense. Flowers shall be strewn. There shall be canopies etc. above. The place shall be abounding in Kuśa grass, flowers, sacrificial twigs, water, fruits, roots, etc. It shall not be near fire or water-receptacles. There shall not be too many dry leaves. The place shall not be infested by flies, mosquitoes, serpents and beasts of prey. There shall not be harmful beasts or wicked men instilling terror. It shall not be the cremation ground, monastery, anthill, dilapidated house, meeting-place of highways, banks and shores of rivers and oceans nor should it be the middle of streets. It shall not be a park in disrepair nor a dilapidated cowshed. It shall not be displeasing nor repulsive. It shall not have been defiled by vomited material or undigested foul smell or faeces and urine. The Yogin shall not practise when he has vomiting or when he suffers from diarrhoea, when he has taken too much of food, or when he has exhausted himself. If he is too hungry or too thirsty or too much worried he shall not practise Yoga. If he is engaged in any of the tasks set by his preceptor he shall not practise Yoga.

53-54. He shall have proper food and activity. He shall be sober in recreation and rest. Both his sleep and wakefulness shall be of the normal proper nature. He shall eschew all tiresomeness. The seat shall be soft, pleasant, sufficiently wide, level and pure. He shall practise one of the poses Padmaka, Svastika and others.

55-60. He shall pay homage to all those venerable persons who reside with his preceptors. He shall keep his head and chest erect. The head shall be lifted up a little. The teeth should not gnash one another. The tongue should be kept well within the teeth and motionless. The scrotum and the penis shall be well guarded by the soles and heels of the feet. The arms shall be placed sideways above the thighs without any strain. The back of the right hand shall be kept over the left palm. The back shall be gradually straightened and the chest shall be projected forward. The eyes shall be fixed at the tip of the nose. He shall not look at any other quarter. The vital breath shall be retained. He shall be as motionless as a stone. He shall meditate on Śiva along with the goddess within his own body, in the seat of the lotus of his heart. He shall worship by meditational sacrifice.

61-63. He shall remember the lord at the root or tip of the nose, or in the umbilicus, or neck, or in the palate or the gullet or in the middle of the eyebrows or at the nostrils or in the forehead or on the head. After conceiving a suitable seat to Śiva and Śivā he shall remember Śiva with or without Āvaraṇa in the two-petalled, or twelve-petalled lotus in accordance with injunction. Or it may be in the ten-petalled six-cornered or four-cornered lotus.

64-66. The lotus shall be conceived in the middle of the eye-brows as having two petals and as brilliant as lightning. To the south and north of the lotus in the middle of the eyebrow two leaves shall be conceived with the colour of lightning ending with letters. The leaves of the sixteen-petalled lotus are the sixteen vowels. They shall be conceived beginning from the petal to the east and proceeding in order.

67-69. The twelve letters beginning with 'Ka' and ending with 'Ṭha' are the leaves. The lotus of the colour of the sun, which is meditated inside the heart and which is of the colour of the cow's milk has ten letters from "Da" to "Pha" for its petals. The letters upto the letter "La" (i.e Ba, Bha, Ma, Ya, Ra and La) constitute the six petals of the lotus with petals facing down and having the colour of the smokeless burning coal. The letters from "Va" to "Sa" constitute the petals of the lotus at the Mūlādhāra, having the colour of gold.

70. He shall meditate on the lord and the goddess in any of these lotuses according to his taste. The mind shall be steady.

71-73. He shall conceive him in any of the following forms—of the size of the thumb, pure, brilliant and illuminating all round, of the form of pure lamp, endowed with its Śakti completely, of the size of the digit of the moon, of the form of the star, the awn of Nīvāra grain and the stalk of the lotus, of the circular shape of the Kadamba, of the form of the dewdrop. He shall contemplate on him as the lord of different Tattvas of the earth and others of which the meditator wishes the mastery.

74-75. The Mūrtis beginning with Brahmā and ending with Sadāśiva, the eight Mūrtis beginning with Bhava, the gross Mūrtis of Śiva prescribed in the Śaivite scriptures, the terrible, the quiet or the mixture of both shall be meditated upon by the sages without the desire for fruits, and by the experts in meditation.

76-78. If the terrible forms of the lord are meditated upon they shall dispel sins and ailments. If the mixtures of the form are contemplated upon, the effect is often delayed. If the calm and the gentle form is contemplated upon, the effect is neither immediate nor delayed. But the special benefit in the gentle form is salvation, peace and intellect. The Siddhis are achieved gradually. There is no doubt about this.

CHAPTER THIRTYNINE

(*The Śaivite Yoga*)

Upamanyu said :—

1. Some Yogins perform meditation with the full conviction that Siddhis are immediately acquired by those who remember the lord.

2. In order to steady the mind some perform meditation on the gross form. The mind that is fixed on the gross form becomes stable in the subtle form.

3. When Śiva is directly meditated upon, Siddhis are achieved. Even when the other forms are meditated upon the devotee shall think of the form of Śiva also.

4. He shall observe the steadiness of the mind and frequently meditate. This meditation, they say, has at the outset a specific object. Thereafter it becomes devoid of any specific object.

5. Philosophers say that there is no Nirviṣaya meditation. They hold that a series of intellectual vision is called meditation.

6-9. But the intellectual vision by itself without an object shall also function. Therefore the fact is—the Saviṣaya meditation is on the lord who is conceived as brilliant as the sun. The meditation on the subtle form is Nirviṣaya. Saviṣaya meditation has a definite form in view. Meditation of the formless is the Nirviṣaya meditation. The two are called Nirbīja and Sabīja also. Hence the practiser shall at the outset perform the Saviṣaya or Sabīja meditation and in the end perform Nirbīja or Nirviṣaya meditation.

10-13. The benefits derived from Prāṇayāma are Śānti, Praśānti, Dīpti and Prasāda. When adversities subside it is called Śānti. Praśānti is the destruction of ignorance both external and internal. The external and internal illumination is called Dīpti. The normal and the healthy state of the intellect is called Prasāda. When the intellect is in healthy normal state the internal and external sense-organs too acquire healthy and normal state.

14-18. The meditator shall perform meditation after realising the four : viz. the meditator, meditation, the object of meditation and the benefits of meditation. The meditator as defined by good men shall be richly endowed with knowledge and detachment. His mind shall never be excited. He shall have faith and his Ātman shall remain delighted. The root Dhyai means to contemplate. Frequent contemplation on Śiva with even a little practice of Yoga shall quell sins of the person who meditates on the lord with faith and unexcited mind.

19. The object of meditation on the form of intellectual visions is Dhyeya and that is Śiva himself accompanied by Śivā.

20. The experience of salvation and the perfect Aṇimā etc. is the direct fruit of meditation on Śiva.

21. Man shall eschew everything and be engaged in meditation since he will be having both happiness and salvation from the practice of meditation.

22. Knowledge cannot be attained without meditation. A non-yogin cannot have meditation. The ocean of worldly existence is crossed by the person who has both meditation and knowledge.

23. The clear and single-centred knowledge devoid of all conditioning factors can be achieved only by a Yogin who regularly practises Yoga.

24. The minds of only those whose sins have been entirely quelled become inclined towards knowledge and meditation. Those whose intellects have been defiled by sins find it wholly inaccessible.

25. Just as the blazing fire burns both the dry and the wet twigs, so also the fire of meditation burns in a trice both the auspicious and the inauspicious Karmans.

26. Just as even a modicum of light dispels darkness so also even the slightest practice of Yoga destroys great sins.

27. There is no limit to the benefits acquired by one who meditates on the lord with faith even for a moment.

28. No holy centre is so efficacious as meditation; no penance, no sacrifice is equal to it. Hence one shall perform meditation strenuously.

29. Yogins do not resort to holy centres full of waters nor to deities made of stone or clay because they have belief only in their Ātmans.

30. Just as the gross form of the lord fashioned out of clay or wood is observed by the non-yogins so also his subtle form can be perceived by the Yogins.

31. Just as in the Royal household, the interior officials not the workers outside are the favourites of kings so also those who are engaged in inner meditation are the favourites of lord Śiva and not those who perform holy rites.

32. Just as the exterior workers do not enjoy the pleasures in the royal palace, the same is the case with the Karmins.

33. If a person in his attempt for knowledge and

Yoga were to die in the middle he shall go to Rudraloka even due to his mere endeavour for yoga.

34. He enjoys happiness here and is reborn in the family of a Yogin. Attaining knowledge and Yoga or the path of knowledge he transcends the worldly existence.

35. Even by performing sacrifices, that goal is not obtained which a man with the desire for the knowledge of Yoga attains.

36. The fruit derivable by worshipping a crore of brahmins can be attained by giving alms alone to a Śiva Yogin.

37. By giving cooked rice to him the benefits of sacrifices, Agnihotras, charitable gifts and pilgrimages can be secured.

38. Those who disparage Śivayogins under delusion undergo sufferings in hells along with those who listen, till the dissolution of the world.

39-42. Only when there is some listener, does a person disparage the Yogin. Hence the listener too is a sinner. Those who worship Śivayogins attain pleasures here and salvation hereafter. Hence, Śivayogins shall be honoured and revered by those who seek worldly pleasures, giving them asylum, food stuffs and drinks, beds and blankets. The Yogic virtue cannot be smashed by the iron clubs of sins. It is very strong and shall be considered to possess adamantine fibres. Yogins are not smeared by sins like the lotus leaf not affected by water.

43. Even the land where the sage engaged in Śivayoga resides is hallowed and sacred, let alone Śivayogin himself.

44. Hence a shrewd and efficient man shall eschew all activities and practise Śivayoga in order to quell miseries.

45. A Yogin who has achieved the fruits of Yoga may sport about after enjoying the pleasures as he wishes or shall remain here performing the requisite services.

46. Or let him consider worldly pleasures worthless and eschew them. Due to detachment let him abandon rites and be liberated.

47. Or seeing evil portents and realising death as imminent the Yogin engaged in the practice of Yoga shall resort to a Śaivite holy centre or temple.[303]

48. If he has courage enough he shall abandon his life there voluntarily even without ailments.

49-50. He who voluntarily forsakes his life as prescribed in Śaivite scriptures, by observing fast, or by consigning his body to Śiva-fire, or by plunging into Śaivite holy rivers, shall immediately be liberated.

51. Even if he is afflicted by ailments and dies after resorting to Śaivite holy centres he shall be liberated.

52. Since voluntary death by means of fasts etc. is sought with a mind full of confidence and devotion, they say that this death is commendable.

53. After killing a person engaged in disparaging Śiva or being afflicted himself, if a devotee eschews his life, not ordinarily possible to forsake, he is not reborn.

54. He who dies after fighting being incapable of killing a disparager of Śiva shall be liberated with the members of his family for twentyone generations.

55. No man treading the path of salvation is equal to one who eschews his life for Śiva or for a devotee of Śiva.

56-57. Hence his liberation from the worldly sphere becomes speedier. If a Śivayogin dies after resorting to one of the means cited before or after attaining the purity of the six pathways, obsequies shall not be performed as they are done for the layman.

58-60. His descendants shall not observe post-mortem pollution. His body shall be buried under ground or burnt in fire, or cast off in Śaivite holy waters or left abandoned like a log of wood or a clod of clay. Or if at all some post-mortem holy rite has to be performed let it be some auspicious rite. The descendant shall propitiate devotees. Only a devotee

303. As detailed in the purāṇas, the regions sacred to Śiva (Śivakṣetras) are spread over the vast expanse of Indian territory. The Purāṇas place these in all directions, mostly on the rivers, sea-coasts, forests or hills

of Śiva shall inherit his wealth. If his children are not initiated in Śaivite cult the wealth shall be handed over to Śiva. No child shall take it.

CHAPTER FORTY

(*Journey of the sages of Naimiṣa*)

Sūta said :—

1. After explaining to the sages, who honoured and exalted him, the path of knowledge that had been previously imparted by the sage Upamanyu of restrained senses to Śrī Kṛṣṇa, Vāyu vanished in the air at sunset.

2. The next day in the morning the sages of Naimiṣa set out to perform the holy rite of ablution at the end of their Sattra.

3. Then at the behest of Brahmā the delighted goddess Sarasvatī herself flowed as an auspicious river of sweet water.

4. On seeing her the sages were delighted in their minds. They concluded the Sattra they had begun and plunged into the river.

5. After performing the rite of Tarpaṇa to the gods with her auspicious waters they remembered the previous events and went to Vārāṇasī.

6. There they saw the holy river Gaṅgā descending from the Himālayan ridges and flowing to the south. They took their bath there and went along the bank.

7-9. After reaching Vārāṇasī they rejoiced much. They plunged into the north-flowing waters of the Gaṅgā. They visited Avimukteśvara[304] and worshipped it. They were about to start when they saw a brilliant splendour in the sky that resembled a crore of suns. Its spreading lustre pervaded all the quarters.

304. Avimukteśvara, the celebrated phallic emblem of Śiva, is placed in the holy city of Vārāṇasī.

10. Then the Siddhas and sages who had performed Pāśupata rites with their bodies covered with Bhasma came there in hundreds and merged into that splendour.

11. When those noble saints merged in it, the splendour suddenly vanished. It was highly mysterious.

12. On seeing that great mystery the sages from Naimiṣa could not know what it was. They went to the forest Brahmavana.[305]

13-15. Even before they arrived there, the wind-god, the purifier of the worlds, had mentioned to Brahmā the creator of the worlds and the source of the Vedas how he visited the sages of Naimiṣa, what he talked to them, how they were inclined to Śiva, his attendants and Śivā and how they had concluded their Sattra of long duration. When permitted by Brahmā, the wind-god left for his own city.

16-17. Brahmā was comfortably seated in his abode acting as an umpire when Tumburu and Nārada had their mutual rivalry in regard to their musical performance. He was taking a keen interest in their performance while Gandharvas and Apsaras waited on him.

18. That being inopportune time the sages were stopped at the threshold by the gate-keepers and they sat outside the palace of Brahmā towards a side.

19-21. Nārada was pronounced equal to Tumburu[306] in musical skill. Permitted by Brahmā to act in collaboration with him he eschewed mutual rivalry and quarrel and contracted friendship with Tumburu. With him and the other Gandharvas and Apsaras, he started from the palace of Brahmā like the sun coming out of the clouds, in order to sing and play on his Vīṇā before lord Nakulīśvara.

22. On seeing Nārada the sages bowed to him and asked him whether that time was suitable to see the lord.

23. Saying "Yes, this is the proper time, come this way in", the gatekeeper went away in hurry on another mission.

305. Not identified.

306. Tumburu is well known as the first-rate musician among the Gandharvas.

24. The gatekeepers intimated to Brahmā and the party entered the abode.

25. After entering, the party prostrated to the lord from distance. Or being permitted by Brahmā, the party stood there respectfully.

26-30. The lotus-seated lord enquired after their health and said—"I have had your news from Vāyu. But tell me when the wind-god had vanished how did you proceed" Thereupon the sages related everything:—their journey to Vārāṇasī after their sacrificial ablution, their visiting the Liṅgas, their worship of Avimukteśvara, the appearance of the mass of splendour in the sky, the merging of the sages therein, the disappearance of the splendour and their desire to understand the reality thereof. All this they submitted to Brahmā with reverence.

31-32. On hearing what was mentioned by the sages the four-faced creator of the universe shook his head and spoke in a majestic tone—"A great Siddhi in the next world awaits you all."

33. The lord has been propitiated by you through the protracted Sattra. The fact that the lord is delighted has been indicated.

34. The refulgence in the air seen by you in Vārāṇasī is the splendour of Maheśvara Liṅga.

35. The sages who were merged therein are those who had performed the Pāśupata rites in accordance with the Vedic injunctions. They have become liberated. Their sins have been washed in view of their stable piety.

36. Just as they achieved salvation by means of Pāśupata rite, so also, ere long, you too will achieve liberation. This fact is indicated by the splendour seen by you.

37. Fortunately your time has come up now. You go to the southern summit of Meru resorted to by the gods.

38. There my son the sage Sanatkumāra is waiting for Nandin, the lord of the Bhūtas.

39-40. Formerly, on seeing Lord Śiva, Sanatkumāra did not pay homage due to his ignorance or arrogance of being a Yogin or carelessness or lack of humility. Due to this offence Nandin was infuriated and he made him a camel.

41-42. I bewailed this for a long time. I worshipped the lord and the goddess and craved forgiveness. With great difficulty I atoned for his wickedness. Sanatkumāra was restored to his previous form.

43-45. Lord Śiva smiled and spoke to the chief of Gaṇas. This sage was arrogant and he insulted me. Hence O sinless one, explain my true nature to him. The eldest son of Brahmā who took me for a fool is given to you as your disciple. He will be the protagonist of my knowledge. He will perform your coronation as the presiding deity of virtue.

46. Thus addressed, the leader of the Bhūtas was pleased to accept the behest.

47. Sanatkumāra is performing penance on the Meru at my behest for the propitiation of the Gaṇa.

48. He shall be seen by you all before the lord of the Gaṇas meets him. Ere long, Nandin will come there to delight him.

49. After bidding thus the Viśvayogin sent the sages to Kumāraśikhara,[307] the southern peak of Meru.

CHAPTER FORTYONE

(*Instruction of Vyāsa*)

Sūta said :—

1. There is a lake known as Skandasaras[308] as vast as the ocean. It has nectar-like sweet cool water, deep, clean and light.

2. Crystal slabs are neatly fixed all around. The place abounds in blooming flowers in the seasons throughout.

307. Not identified. According to the context this hill can be placed to the south of mount Meru.

308. Not identified.

3. Lilies, lotuses and other aquatic plants resemble the stars. The waves are like clouds. The sky itself appears to have come to the earth.

4. The steps that lead to it consist of blue stones and are beautiful. People can ascend and descend comfortably. Through these the lake brightens all the eight quarters.

5-8. The sons of sages take water and flowers from it for the worship of the deities. They wear white sacred threads, white loin-cloth and bark garments. Some get into it for taking bath. Some come up from it after taking bath. Some have matted hair. Some have tufts. Some have shaven heads. They are embellished with Tripuṇḍras. Some have grave or helpless or smiling faces. They have various vessels Ghaṭas, Kalaśas, Kamaṇḍalus, Karakas or lotus-çups for taking water.

9-11. Some stand on rocks submerged in water as if avoiding contact with the low-born people. They observe good conduct and their bodies are grey with Bhasma. They plunge into the water here and there. On the rock are seen the remnants of worship—gingelly seeds, raw rice-grains, flowers, Darbhas, Pavitras These indicate that the brahmins who come here for bath perform worship and Tarpaṇas to the gods, sages and the manes.

12-14. At places people perform worship on dry banks after performing Arghya to the sun as indicated by the scattered oblations and flowers. At places leaders of elephant herds are merging in and emerging out of water. At places the deer, the hind and the horses have come to quench thirst. At places peacocks and elephants are drinking water. At places oxen and hostile bulls are butting against the banks.

15-17. In some places the sound of the Kāraṇḍava is heard. In some places there is the chirping sound of the Sārasa. In some places the ruddy goose cackles. In some places the bees hum. The lake appears to be holding a loving conversation perpetually with the birds and animals living on the trees and taking bath therein or drinking its water. Through the cooing sound of the cuckoos lying hidden on the trees on its banks it appears to invite all those who are oppressed by the sun.

18-20. On the northern bank of the lake under the Kalpa tree, on a platform of adamantine rock, the sages from Naimiṣa saw Sanatkumāra seated on a soft deer-skin. He had just woken up from his trance. He was being worshipped by the sages and the leading Yogins. On seeing him they bowed to him and stood in reverence.

21. On being asked they told him the purpose of their visit. The tumultuous sound of Dundubhi was heard in the heaven immediately.

22-25. At the same time an aerial chariot brilliant as the sun was visible. All round, it was surrounded by leading Gaṇas, numerous and countless. It was thronged by the celestial damsels and surrounded by Rudra girls. Sounds of Mṛdaṅga, lute and flute were heard. It had canopies set with gems of various colours. It shone with strings of pearls. It was encircled by sages, Siddhas, Gandharvas, Yakṣas, Cāraṇas, Kinnaras dancing, or playing on instruments. A banner marked by the sign of a heroic bull was fluttering from a post set with corals. The aerial chariot had a gabled front.

26-33. In the middle of the aerial chariot the son of Brahmā accompanied by the sages saw the son of Śilāda seated in a divine throne with Suyaśā, brilliant as the goddess Lakṣmī. On either side there was a chowrie. He sat under a royal umbrella with a gemset handle, resembling the pure moon. He had three eyes. Even by his gestures he reminded one of the lord. He appeared like the untransgressable behest of the creator. He was one who blessed all. He stood directly in front of Śiva. He held an excellent trident. As the commander of the Gaṇas he looked like another Viśveśvara. He could curb and bless the rulers of the universe. He had four arms, a splendid body embellished with the digit of the moon. A serpent adorned his neck and the moon his head. He was the embodied form of Aiśvarya. He appeared like active efficiency. It seemed that the very salvation or the omniscient lord had come there. On seeing him the son of Brahmā was highly delighted. He stood up with palms joined in reverence. He seemed to dedicate himself to him.

34-36. In the meantime when the aerial chariot reached

the ground, Sanatkumāra prostrated. After eulogising him he informed him of the arrival of the sages—"These are the sages of six families who had performed the Sattra of long duration in Naimiṣa. At the bidding of Brahmā they have come here to have a sight of you, O lord. On hearing these words of the son of Brahmā, Nandin cut off their Pāśas by his mere glance immediately. He imparted to them the Śaivite virtue and the perfect knowledge of Śiva Yoga. Then he returned to the lord.

37. Everything was imparted by Sanatkumāra to Vyāsa my direct preceptor who imparted the same to me and now I succinctly mention this to you.

38. This excellent gem of Śivapurāṇa should not be mentioned to those who do not know the Vedas, nor should it be imparted to a disciple who is not a devotee of Śiva nor to an atheist. If it is imparted to these out of delusion it yields hell.

39. If it is imparted, accepted, read or heard along the stipulated path accompanied by service it yields happiness, the three aims of life—Dharma, Artha, and Kāma and in the end, liberation invariably.

40. You and I have helped each other through this path. I have realised my desire. I shall go now. Let everything be auspicious to you always.

41. Then Sūta blessed them and left. The righteous sages fixed their abode permanently at the outskirts of Vārāṇasī after performing the sattra at Prayāga when they perceived that everything was being defiled by the advent of the Kali age.

42. Then the sages performed the Pāśupata rites with the desire to get released from the bondage. They attained enlightenment. They learnt modes of Samādhi and achieved the greatest Bliss.

Vyāsa said :—

43. This wholesome Śivapurāṇa is concluded now. It shall be read and heard assiduously.

44. It shall not be mentioned to an atheist nor to one lacking in faith nor to a stubborn rogue nor to one who is not a devotee of Śiva nor to a religious hypocrite.

45. On hearing this once, the sins are reduced to ashes. A non-devotee attains devotion and a devotee attains more devotion.

46. If it is heard again a further devotion is achieved. If it is heard again salvation is the result. Therefore it shall be heard over and again by those who desire salvation.

47. If one aims at some big benefit one shall read or hear this Purāṇa five times with a pious mind. He is sure to achieve the desired result.

48. Kṣatriyas of yore, excellent brahmins and Vaiśyas repeated it seven times and attained the vision of Śiva.

49. If a man with devotion hears it, he enjoys all pleasures here and secures liberation hereafter.

50. Śivapurāṇa is a great favourite of Śiva. It yields worldly pleasures and liberation. It increases devotion and it is on a par with the Vedas.

51. May Śiva with his Gaṇas, sons and Ambā bestow blessings upon those who explain or listen to this Purāṇa.

---o---

INDEX